SEMICONDUCTORS & ELECTRONIC COMMUNICATIONS MADE EASY

No. 1435
$15.95

SEMICONDUCTORS & ELECTRONIC COMMUNICATIONS MADE EASY

BY VICTOR F. VELEY

TAB BOOKS Inc.

BLUE RIDGE SUMMIT, PA. 17214

FIRST EDITION

FIRST PRINTING

Copyright © 1982 by TAB BOOKS Inc.

Printed in the United States of America

Reproduction or publication of the content in any manner, without express permission of the publisher, is prohibited. No liability is assumed with respect to the use of the information herein.

Library of Congress Cataloging in Publication Data

Veley, Victor F.
    Semiconductors & electronic communications made
easy.

    Includes index.
    1. Electronics. 2. Semiconductors. 3. Telecommuni-
cation. 4. Radar. 5. Sonar. I. Title.
TK7816.V44   621.38   81-18225
ISBN 0-8306-0052-3   AACR2
ISBN 0-8306-1435-4 (pbk.)

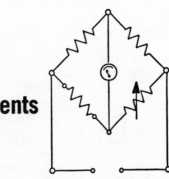

Contents

Preface

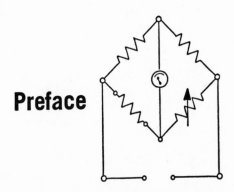

This book is a direct follow-up to my *AD/DC Electricity and Electronics Made Easy* (TAB book No. 1233). The subjects covered in this book are *solid-state devices* and *communications*. The same format has been used in both books. Of particular interest is the unusually detailed description of *Smith chart* applications, which are fully illustrated with numerous examples. Also included is a chapter on sonar which is a subject that is too often neglected.

The purpose of this book is threefold. First it should prove to be a valuable reference for the technician in the field. Each chapter is organized into a number of sections; in each, one or more important concepts are introduced and relevant equations are given. The concepts and the equations are then used in a number of comprehensive examples, which are accompanied by detailed solutions. Finally, at the end of each chapter, is a summary of the more important equations.

The second purpose is to assist college students in the more advanced semesters of electronics technology. This reference manual will be a valuable supplement to any other textbook which the student is using. In addition, the examples chosen are unusually comprehensive and should provide the student with a better understanding the principles involved. In virtually every example only standard practical values are used.

Finally if this book is read in conjunction with *AC/DC Electricity and Electronics Made Easy* and *Practical Electronics Math* (TAB book No. 1136), these books will form the basis of an electronics library that will also provide all the information necessary to obtain the FCC Commercial Radiotelephone License with Radar Endorsement.

I wish to acknowledge a great debt to my wife, Joyce, for typing the manuscript and for making this work possible.

Chapter 1
Power Supplies

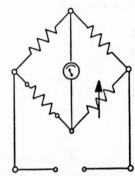

The modern power rectifier device is the silicon diode which basically uses a pn junction to provide the "one-way" action. The p-type material is produced by doping pure silicon with an acceptor or a trivalent impurity such as indium, gallium or boron; the n-type silicon is created by doping with a donor or pentavalent impurity of arsenic, antimony or phosphorus. Although both n-type and p-type are electrically neutral, the majority charge carriers in the n-type and p-type materials are, respectively, negative electrons and positive holes.

THE SILICON DIODE

When the pn junction is formed there is a movement of the majority carriers across the junction. At room temperature this creates an internal potential barrier of about 0.7 V across a depletion region, which is in the immediate vicinity of the junction and is devoid of majority carriers. In order to forward bias the junction, it is necessary to correct the positive terminal of a voltage source to the p region and the negative terminal to the n region (Fig. 1-1A). However, the applied bias must exceed the 0.7 V internal potential before appreciable forward current will flow (Fig. 1-1B).

For a general purpose silicon diode, with the p region as the anode and the n region as the cathode, a forward voltage, V_F, of about 1 V will correspond to a forward current, I_F, of several hundred milliamperes. The small voltage drop across the conducting silicon diode is its real advantage compared with other rectifier devices, since even with high forward currents, the power dissipation will be low. The approximate equation for the forward biased diode is:

1

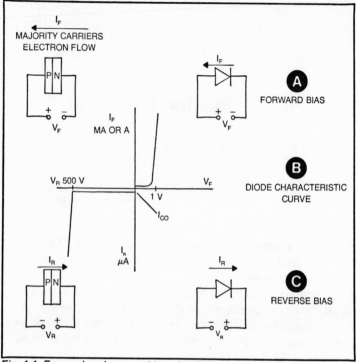

Fig. 1-1. Forward and reverse bias of a diode.

$$I_F = \frac{V_F - 0.7}{R_B}$$ **Equation 1-1**

where R_B is the bulk resistance of the semiconductor material from which the diode is made.

To create a reverse bias (Fig. 1-1C), the positive terminal of a voltage source is connected to the n region (cathode) and the negative terminal to the p region (anode). If only the majority carriers were involved there would be zero reverse current; however thermal energy creates minority carriers (electrons in the p region and holes in the n region) and there is a small reverse current, I_{co}, whose value rises rapidly and saturates at about 1 μA. However, the saturated value of I_{co} depends on the diode's temperature and will approximately double for every 10° Celsius rise. Typically a reverse voltage, V_R, of about 250 V to 500 V may be applied with only a small reverse current, I_R. However, with excessive reverse voltage there is a break-down point at which there is a rapidly increasing flow of reverse current; this action is the principle behind the zener diode which is used for voltage regulation purposes. In the rectifier circuits of this chapter it is assumed that only silicon diodes are used; however the 0.7 V drop and the bulk resistance will be ignored.

Example 1-1

For a particular silicon diode V_F if 0.9 V and the bulk resistance is 0.5 Ω. What is the corresponding value of I_F?

Solution

Forward current, $I_F = \dfrac{V_F - 0.7 \text{ V}}{0.5 \text{ }\Omega}$

$= \dfrac{0.2 \text{ V}}{0.5 \text{ }\Omega} = 400 \text{ mA}$

THE HALF-WAVE RECTIFIER CIRCUIT

In Fig. 1-2 the capacitor C is included as part of the low pass filter which reduces the output ripple voltage to an acceptable level. Under no-load conditions, C charges to the peak value of the secondary voltage so that the dc output voltage between X and Y is 1.414× E_s which must not be greater than the capacitor voltage rating. If Y is grounded, X will carry a positive potential but if X is grounded, the potential of Y will be negative.

At the peak of the negative half cycle of the secondary voltage, the highest value of reverse voltage appears across the diode with the anode being driven negative to the cathode. Under no-load conditions, this highest value of reverse voltage is equal to twice the peak value of the secondary voltage or 2.828 E_s, which must not exceed the diodes's dc blocking voltage (maximum reverse voltage which will not cause breakdown).

Under loaded conditions, the diode current charges C rapidly during part of one half cycle of the secondary voltage and when the diode cuts off, C discharges relatively slowly through the load (the time constant of the diode current charging path is much shorter than that of the discharge path through the load). The dc output voltage consists of a mean steady level together with a ripple component which possesses a complex waveform but whose fundamental frequency is equal to the line frequency applied to the primary of the power transformer.

The ripple percentage in the output voltage is:

$$\frac{\text{rms value of the fundamental ripple component}}{\text{dc output voltage}} \times 100\%$$

Equation 1-2

Example 1-2

In Fig. 1-3 what is the potential at the point X under open-circuit load conditions and the required voltage rating for the capacitor, C? Under open-circuit load conditions what is the highest value of the reverse voltage across the diode? Under loaded conditions what is the frequency of the fundamental ripple component in the output voltage? If the full-load output voltage is 65 V dc, with a peak-to-peak ripple voltage of 3 V, what are the ripple percentage and the percentage of regulation?

Solution

RMS value of the secondary voltage $= 110 \div 2 = 55$ V. The direction of the electron flow through the diode indicates that X will carry a negative with respect to ground. Since the magnitude of the voltage at X is $55 \times 1,414 = 78$ V, rounded off, the required answer is -78 V. Under open-circuit load conditions, the voltage across C is 78 V. The capacitor's voltage rating must therefore exceed 78 V and consequently 110 V dc is a reasonable answer.

The rms value of the fundamental ripple component is: $\frac{3}{2} \times 0.707 = 1.06$ V. Ripple percentage $\frac{1.06}{65} \times 100 = 1.6\%$ rounded off.

$$\text{Percentage regulation} = \frac{E_{NL} - E_{FL}}{E_{FL}} \times 100 = \frac{78 - 65}{65} = 100 = 20\%$$

THE FULL-WAVE RECTIFIER CIRCUIT

Capacitor Input Filter. In the full-wave rectifier circuit of Fig. 1-4, the secondary of the power transformer is center-tapped at the point S and the rectified dc voltage appears between S and the junction of the two cathodes. Using only half of the secondary voltage, the diodes D1, D2 conduct alternately so that the filter input capacitor, C, is charged twice during each cycle of the primary source voltage; consequently the frequency of the fundamental ripple component appearing in the output voltage is equal to twice

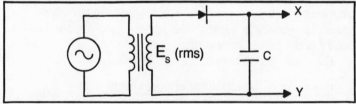

Fig. 1-2. The half-wave rectifier circuit.

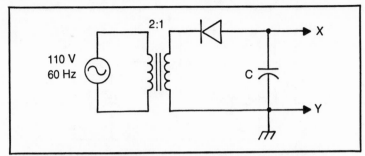

Fig. 1-3. Circuit for Example 1-2.

the line frequency. The components L1 and C1 provide a low pass filter for further attenuation of the ripple voltage. Compared with the half-wave circuit of Fig. 1-2, the full-wave rectifier can provide better regulation and a lower ripple percentage. Under open-circuit load conditions, the dc output voltage is equal to the peak value of one half of the full secondary voltage or:

$$\frac{E_s}{2} \times 1.414 = 0.707\ E_s \qquad \textbf{Equation 1-3A}$$

The highest value of reverse voltage across each diode will be:

$$2 \times \frac{E_s}{2} \times 1.414 = 1.414\ E_s \qquad \textbf{Equation 1-3B}$$

With a load connected to the rectifier, each diode will only conduct during part of one half cycle of the full secondary voltage.

Choke Input Filter. If there are considerable variations in the load, the capacitor input filter will provide poor regulation and it is preferable to use a choke input filter (Fig. 1-5).

With this type of filter, each diode conducts for a complete half cycle. The circuit therefore cannot operate correctly under open-circuit load conditions so that a certain minimum load is provided by

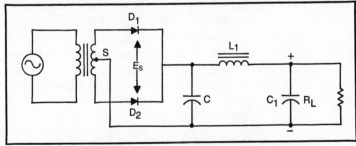

Fig. 1-4. The full-wave rectifier circuit with a capacitor input filter.

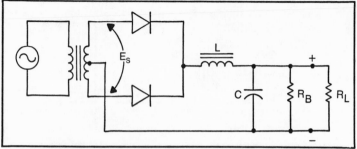

Fig. 1-5. The full-wave rectifier circuit with a choke input filter.

the bleeder resistor, RB, which may also serve as a discharge path for the filter capacitor, C.

If RL is removed so that the only load is provided by the bleeder resistor, the dc output voltage cannot exceed:

$$\frac{2}{\pi} \times \frac{\sqrt{2E_s}}{2} = \frac{\sqrt{2E_s}}{\pi} = 0.45\ E_s \qquad \textbf{Equation 1-3C}$$

Compared with the capacitor input filter, the choke input filter provides better regulation but the obtainable dc output voltage is less for a given secondary voltage and the ripple percentage is higher.

Example 1-3

In Fig. 1-6 what is the potential at X and the highest reverse voltage under no-load (open-circuit) conditions? Under loaded conditions what is the frequency of the fundamental ripple voltage? If the dc output voltage under loaded conditions is 12 V what is the percentage of regulation? If the capacitor input filter is replaced by a choke input filter with its associated bleeder resistor, what is the highest dc output voltage under no-load conditions?

Solution

The direction of the electron flow through the diodes indicates that the potential at X is positive. Since the secondary voltage is 110 ÷ 5 = 22 V rms, the magnitude of the potential is + 15.5 V, rounded off. The highest reverse voltage across each diode is 1.414 E_s = 1.414 × 22 = 31 V, rounded off. In a full-wave rectifier circuit, the frequency of the fundamental ripple voltage is twice the line frequency of the primary source and is therefore 2× 60 = 120 Hz.

Regulation percentage =

$$\frac{(E_{NL} - E_{FL})}{E_{FL}} \times 100 = \frac{(14 - 12)}{12} \times 100 = 17\%$$

When a choke input filter is operating correctly to provide good regulation, the dc output voltage under no-load conditions cannot exceed $0.45 E_s = 0.45 \times 22 = 9.9$ V.

THE BRIDGE RECTIFIER CIRCUIT

Referring to Fig. 1-7, the operation of this circuit is similar to that of the full-wave rectifier discussed earlier. However, the bridge circuit rectifies the full secondary voltage during a portion of each half cycle. Diodes, such as D1 and D3, or D2 and D, in opposite arms of the bridge, conduct simultaneously. The output voltage between X and Y under no-load (open-circuit) conditions is $\sqrt{2} E_s = 1.414 E_s$, which is the peak value of the full secondary voltage. As in the full-wave rectifier circuit, the fundamental ripple frequency is twice the line frequency. The advantages of the bridge rectifier over the full-wave rectifier are the higher dc output voltage available with the same transformer turns ratio and the absence of any center tap on the secondary winding. Furthermore, the maximum reverse voltage across each diode $(1.414 E_s)$ is less than in the case of the full-wave rectifier with the same dc voltage output.

Example 1-4

In Fig. 1-7, the primary source is 110 V, 60 Hz and the transformer has a 4:1 step-down ratio. If Y is grounded, what is the potential at the point X under open-circuit load conditions? Under loaded conditions what is the frequency of the fundamental ripple component?

Solution

The direction of the electron flow indicates that the point X has a negative potential which under open-circuit conditions will be $-1.414 E_s = -1.414 \times 110 / 4 = -39$ V, rounded off. Since the line

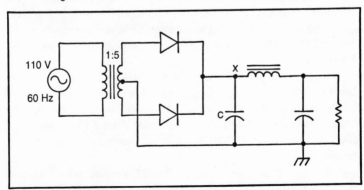

Fig. 1-6. Circuit for Example 1-3.

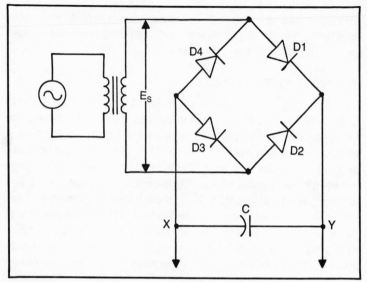

Fig. 1-7. The full-wave bridge rectifier circuit.

frequency of the primary source is 60 Hz, the frequency of the fundamental ripple component will be $2 \times 60 = 120$ Hz.

THE FULL-WAVE DOUBLER CIRCUIT

Referring to Fig. 1-8 and assuming open-circuit load conditions, the diode D1 will charge C1 to the peak value of the secondary voltage, E_s. The diode D2 will charge C2 to the same voltage so that the output dc voltage between X and Y will be $2 \times (1.414 \, E_s) = 2.828$ E_s (the highest reverse voltage across each diode will also be 2.828 E_s). Under loaded conditions, D1 and D2 will conduct during alternate half cycles so that the frequency of the fundamental ripple component will be twice the line frequency of the primary source. Since the capacitors C1, C2 are connected in series relative to the load, this type of doubler circuit does not provide good regulation.

Example 1-5

In Fig. 1-8, the primary voltage is 220 V, 60 Hz and the transformer has a 5:1 step-down ratio. Assuming open-circuit load conditions, what is the output dc voltage between X and Y and the highest reverse voltage across each diode? What is the frequency of the fundamental ripple component under loaded conditions?

Solution

Secondary voltage = $220 \div 5 = 44$ V. The output voltage between X and Y is $2 \times 2.828 \times 44 = 249$ V, rounded off. The highest inverse voltage across each diode under open-circuit load conditions is also 2.828 E_s= 249 V. The frequency of the fundamental ripple component is twice the line frequency of the primary source and is therefore 2× 60 Hz= 120 Hz.

THE HALF-WAVE DOUBLER CIRCUIT (CASCADE DOUBLER CIRCUIT)

Assuming open-circuit load conditions in Fig. 1-9, D1 charges C1 to the peak value of the secondary voltage E_s. On the other half cycle, the combination of the secondary voltage and the voltage across C1 is applied to D2 which conducts and charges C2 to a voltage of 2 × 1.414 E_s = 2.828 E_s which is also the value of the highest reverse voltage across each diode. Under loaded conditions, C2 is only charged once during each cycle of the primary source voltage and therefore the frequency of the fundamental ripple component is equal to the line frequency.

Note that only the capacitor C2 is connected across the load and consequently the regulation of this circuit is superior to that of the full-wave doubler. In addition, the principle of the cascade rectifier may be extended to create triplers, quadruplers, etc.

Example 1-6

In Fig. 1-9, the primary source voltage is 110 V, 60 Hz and the power transformer has a 8:1 step-down ratio. What is the output voltage between X and Y under open-circuit load conditions and the highest reverse voltage across each diode? Under loaded conditions what is the frequency of the fundamental ripple component?

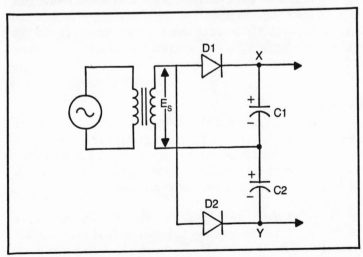

Fig. 1-8. The full-wave doubler circuit.

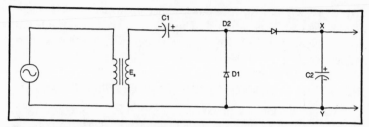

Fig. 1-9. The half-wave or cascade doubler circuit.

Solution

Secondary voltage, $E_s = 110 \div 13.75$ V. The output voltage under open-circuit load conditions is $2.828\ E_s = 2.828 \times 13.75$ V = 39 V, rounded off. The frequency of the fundamental ripple component is equal to the line frequency and is therefore 60 Hz.

THE THREE PHASE HALF-WAVE RECTIFIER CIRCUIT

In Fig. 1-10, each of the secondary phase voltages is half-wave rectified by one of the diodes. The capacitor, C, is then charged by each of the diodes which then conduct in turn. Under open-circuit load conditions, the output voltage across C will be equal to the peak value, E_s, of the secondary phase voltages. The highest inverse voltage under loaded conditions across each diode will be $2 \times 1.414\ E_s = 2.828\ E_s$. Capacitor C will be recharged three times during each cycle of the primary phase voltage creating a lower ripple voltage than that associated with either the full-wave rectifier or the bridge rectifier. The frequency of the fundamental ripple component will be three times the line frequency and this higher ripple frequency is a considerable advantage of three phase rectification since it allows the use of lower value filter components.

Example 1-7

In Fig. 1-10, the primary line voltage is 220 V, 60 Hz and each phase has a step-down transformer ratio of 6:1. Under open-circuit load conditions, what is the potential at the point X and the highest reverse voltage across each diode? Under loaded conditions what is the frequency of the fundamental ripple component?

Solution

Secondary phase voltage = $220 \div 6 = 36.7$ V. The direction of current flow indicates that the potential at X is positive. The potential at X is therefore $+\sqrt{2}\ E_s = +1.414 \times 36.7 = +52$ V, rounded off.

THE THREE PHASE FULL-WAVE RECTIFIER CIRCUIT

In Fig. 1-11, each of the secondary line voltages is full-wave rectified by four of the diodes, acting in a bridge arrangement. Under open-circuit load conditions, C will be charged to the peak value of E_s and therefore the output voltage between X and Y will be $\sqrt{2}\,E_s = 1.414\,E_s$. Under loaded conditions, C will be recharged six times during each cycle of the primary line voltage, and therefore the frequency of the fundamental ripple component will be six times the line frequency. Compared with the three phase half-wave rectifier discussed earlier, the full-wave circuit will have a lower ripple percentage and the higher ripple frequency will allow the use of smaller filter components.

Example 1-8

In Fig. 1-11, the primary line voltage is 220 V, 60 Hz and each phase has a step-down transformer ratio of 5:1. If Y is grounded, what is the potential at X under open-circuit load conditions? Under conditions what is the frequency of the fundamental ripple component?

Solution

Secondary voltage, $E_s = 220 \div 5 = 44$ V. The direction of current flow indicates that the potential at X is positive and therefore equal to $+1.414\,E_s = +1.414 \times 44 = +62$ V, rounded off. The frequency of the fundamental ripple component is six times the line frequency and is therefore $6 \times 60 = 360$ Hz.

THE ZENER DIODE VOLTAGE REGULATOR

The basic zener diode voltage regulator circuit is shown in Fig. 1-12A. Its purpose is to stabilize the value of the load voltage, V_L, against charges in the source voltage, E, and/or changes in the load

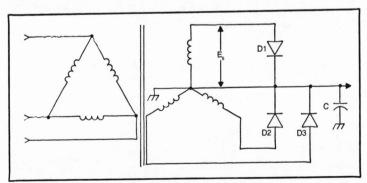

Fig. 1-10. The three phase half-wave rectifier circuit.

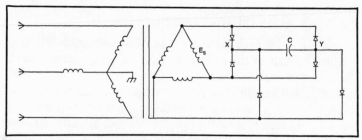

Fig. 1-11. The three phase full-wave rectifier circuit.

current, I_L. The diode operates with reverse bias in the breakdown region (Fig. 1-12B) where to a first approximation the diode's reverse current I_z, is independent of the diode voltage, V_z, which will therefore be equal to the load voltage, V_L. The value of the resistor, R, is such that it allows the diode to operate well within the breakdown region and at the same time regulates the load voltage by dropping the difference between V_z and the unregulated source voltage, E.

Using Kirchhoff's Current-Law,

$$I_R = I_L + I_z \qquad \text{Equation 1-4A}$$

Also:

$$I_L = \frac{F_L}{R_L} = \frac{V_z}{R_L} \qquad \text{Equation 1-4B}$$

and,

$$I_R = \frac{E - V_z}{R} = \frac{E - V_L}{R} \qquad \text{Equation 1-4C}$$

Since the breakdown curve is not completely vertical a second approximation will involve the zener diode's resistance, R_z, which is derived from the slope of the characteristic. Therefore:

$$V_L = V_z + I_z R_z \qquad \text{Equation 1-5}$$

Finally the power dissipation in the zener diode is:

$$P_z = I_z V_z \qquad \text{Equation 1-6}$$

The value of P_z must not exceed the diode's power rating.
Note: A device which has an action similar to that of the zener diode, is the voltage regulator (VR) tube.

Example 1-9

In Fig. 1-12A the zener diode's breakdown voltage is 9 V. If E= 50 V, R=4 kΩ, R_L= 2.5 kΩ, calculate the values I_R, I_z, I_L and P_z. If E changes to 60 V, recalculate the values of I_R, I_z, I_L and P_z. If R_L changes to 5 kΩ, recalculate the values of I_R, I_z, I_L and P_z.

Note: Use the first approximation throughout and neglect any effect of R_z.

Solution

The dropping resistor currents,

$$I_R = \frac{E - V_z}{R} = \frac{50\,V - 9\,V}{4\,k\Omega} = 10.25\,mA$$

The load current, $I_L = \frac{V_z}{R_L} = \frac{9\,V}{2.5\,k\Omega} = 3.6\,mA$

Zener diode current, $I_z = I_R - I_L = 10.25 - 3.6 = 6.65\,mA$

Power dissipation, $P_z = I_z V_z = 6.65\,mA \times 9\,V = 60\,mW$, rounded off.

E= 60 V

$$I_R = \frac{60\,V - 9\,V}{4} = 12.75\,mA$$
$$I_L = 3.6\,mA$$
$$I_z = 12.75 - 3.6 = 9.15\,mA$$
$$P_z = 9.15\,mA \times 9\,V = 82\,mW$$

The diode current has risen by $9.15 - 6.65 = 2.5\,mA$. The increase in the voltage drop across R is $2.5\,mA \times 4\,k\Omega = 10\,V$ which absorbs the charge in the source voltage from 50 V to 60 V.

$R_L \times 5\,k\Omega$

$$I_R = \frac{50\,V - 9\,V}{4\,k\Omega} = 10.25\,mA$$

$$I_L = \frac{9\,V}{5\,k\Omega} = 1.8\,mA$$

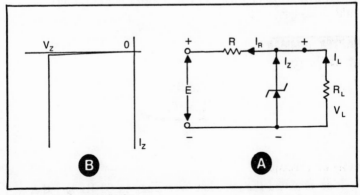

Fig. 1-12. The zener diode.

13

Table 1-1. Comparison of Different Rectifiers.

Type of Rectifier	Fundamental Ripple Frequency	DC Output voltage on no load	Maxium Reverse voltage across each diode
Half-Wave Single Phase	60 Hz	Peak of AC Input	2 × Peak of AC Input
Full-Wave Single Phase	120 Hz	½ × Peak AC input	Peak of AC Input
Bridge Circuit	120 Hz	Peak of AC Input	Peak of AC Input
Half-Wave Voltage Doubler	60 Hz	2 × Peak of AC Input	2 × Peak of AC Input
Full-Wave Voltage Doubler	120 Hz	2 × Peak of AC Input	2 × Peak of AC Input
Three Phase Half-Wave (Wye connected)	180Hz	Peak of Secondary Phase Voltage	2 × Peak of Secondary Phase Voltage
Three Phase Full-Wave (Wye connected)	360 Hz	Peak of Secondary Line Voltage	Peak of Secondary Line Voltage

$$I_Z = 10.25 - 1.8 = 8.45 \text{ mA}$$
$$P_Z = 8.45 \text{ mA} \times 9 \text{ V} = 76 \text{ mW, rounded off.}$$

The decrease of $3.6 - 1.8 = 1.8$ mA in the load current is balanced by an equal increase of $8.45 - 6.65 = 1.8$ mA in the diode current. In this example a zener diode with a power rating of ½ W would be adequate.

CHAPTER SUMMARY

Silicon Diode

Forward Bias:

$$I_F = \frac{R_F - 0.7}{R_B}$$

Rectifier Circuits

It is assumed that the line frequency is 60 Hz and that a capacitor input filter is used. The ac input which is rectified is the full voltage across the secondary of the power transformer. See Table 1-1.

Zener Diode

First Approximation:

$$I_R = I_L + I_Z$$

$$I_L = \frac{V_L}{R_L} = \frac{V_Z}{R_L}$$

$$I_R = \frac{E - V_Z}{R} = \frac{E - V_L}{R}$$

$$P_Z = I_Z V_Z$$

Second Approximation:

$$V_L = V_Z + I_Z R_Z$$

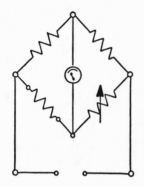

Chapter 2
Bipolar Transistors

Note: Capital letters will be used for dc, quiescent, or no-signal values while lower-case letters will indicate signal conditions.

INTRODUCTION TO BIPOLAR TRANSISTORS

The action of the bipolar transistors involves two sets of charge carriers; these are the positive charge carriers (holes) and the negative charge carriers (electrons). Bipolar transistors are also of two types, pnp and npn, whose symbols are shown in Fig. 2-1. Each of these types possesses three sections which are called the emitter, the base and the collector; the arrow in each symbol indicates the direction of conventional flow (opposite direction to that of electron flow).

COMMON BASE CONFIGURATION

The bipolar transistor may be roughly compared to a triode with the emitter, base, and collector corresponding to the cathode, control grid, and plate. For normal conduction, voltages are applied to the transistor so as to forward-bias the emitter/base junction but reverse-bias the collector/base junction. For the pnp transistor (Fig. 2-1) this requires that the emitter is positive with respect to the base which is in turn positive with respect to the collector; these polarities are reversed for the npn transistor. Some of the methods of producing the correct dc bias voltage for the emitter/base and collector/base junctions are discussed later in this chapter. Under either static or signal conditions, emitter current (I_E), base current (I_B) and collector current (I_C) flow in a bipolar transistor circuit (Fig. 2-1). Applying Kirchhoff's current law:

$$I_E = I_C + I_B, \quad I_C = I_E - I_B, \quad I_B = I_E - I_C \qquad \textbf{Equation 2-1}$$

Under normal operating conditions, I_B is typically less than 5% of either I_E or I_C and I_C is only slightly less than I_E.

As discussed later in Chapter 4, there are three possible vacuum tube circuit configurations: the grounded-grid amplifier, the grounded-cathode amplifier, and the cathode follower. The corresponding transistor configurations are the common-base common-emitter and common-collector (emitter follower) circuits.

Quiescent (No Signal) Conditions in the Common Base Circuit

In the npn circuit of Fig. 2-2, the emitter/base junction is forward-biased by V_{EE}, while the collector/base junction is reverse-biased by V_{CC}. The actual forward bias applied between the emitter and base is only a few tenths of a volt, so that:

$$I_E = \frac{V_{EE} - V_{BE}}{R_E} \qquad \textbf{Equation 2-2}$$

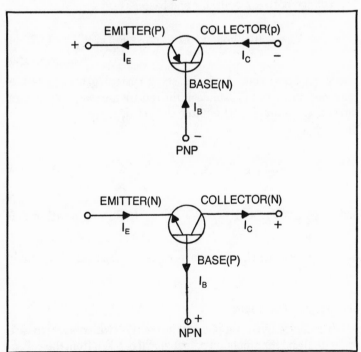

Fig. 2-1. PNP and NPN bipolar transistors. External arrows indicate electron flow.

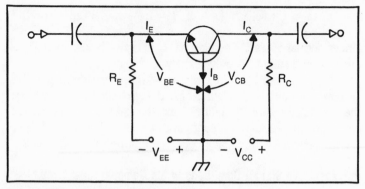

Fig. 2-2. The common base circuit.

or to a first approximation,

$$I_E \approx \frac{V_{EE}}{R_E}$$

Equation 2-3

The voltage between collector and base is:

$$V_{CB} = V_{CC} - (\text{the voltage drop across } R_C) = V_{CC} - I_C R_C$$

Equation 2-4

Under quiescent conditions, the static current gain, α_{dc}, of the common base circuit is defined as the ratio of the (output) collector current, I_C, to the (input) emitter current, I_E.
Thus:

$$\alpha_{dc} = \frac{I_C}{I_E} = \frac{I_E - I_B}{I_E} = 1 - \frac{I_B}{I_E}$$

Equation 2-5

and, $\quad V_{CB} = V_{CC} - I_C R_C = V_{CC} - \alpha_{dc} I_E R_C$ Equation 2-6

Since I_C, is less than I_E, the value of α_{dc} is less than 1 and is typically 0.95 to 0.99.

Small-Signal Conditions

The input signal is applied to the emitter (with respect to base or ground) and the amplified output signal is taken from the collector. As with the grounded-grid circuit, there is no phase change between the input and output signals.

The current gain under signal conditions is measured by the transistor's α which is the ratio of a small change in collector current to the corresponding small change in emitter current.

Therefore:

$$\alpha = \frac{\Delta i_c}{\Delta i_e} \qquad \textbf{Equation 2-7}$$

For a particular transistor, it is common for α_{dc} and α to be practically equal so that the value of α is again in the range of 0.95 to 0.99.

Although the current gain of the common base configuration is less than 1, this circuit can still provide a signal voltage gain (and a power gain) since the input emitter current and the output collector current are associated with different values of input and output resistance. To a first approximation the resistance of the emitter/base circuit consists of the junction resistance r_e, the base spreading resistance and the resistance of the signal source. The output resistance for the circuit of Fig. 2-2 is the collector load, R_c, in parallel with a high resistance which is equal to the reciprocal of the slope belonging to the transistor's V_c/I_c characteristics. This output resistance, R_o, is much higher than the input resistance, R_i, and therefore the voltage gain is:

$$G_v = \frac{i_c R_o}{i_e R_i} = \alpha \frac{R_o}{R_i} \qquad \textbf{Equation 2-8}$$

Compared with the other two configurations, the main disadvantage of the common-base arrangement is the low input resistance presented to the applied signal. Apart from the resistance of the signal source, the principal component of R_i is the emitter/base junction resistance, r_e.

Example 2-1

If, in a common-base circuit, the emitter current changes from 4 mA to 4.15 mA and the corresponding change in collector current is from 3.92 mA to 4.068 mA, what are the values of α and α_{dc} for $I_E = 4$ mA?

Solution

Static current gain, $\alpha_{dc} = \dfrac{I_C}{I_E} = \dfrac{3.92}{4.0} = 0.98$

Change in emitter current, $\Delta i_e = 4.15 - 4.0 = 0.15$ mA
Corresponding change in collector current,
$$\Delta i_c = 4.068 - 3.92 = 0.148 \text{ mA}$$
Then, $\qquad \alpha = \dfrac{\Delta i_c}{\Delta i_e} = \dfrac{0.148}{0.15} = 0.99$, rounded off.

Example 2-2

Assume that the circuit of Fig. 2-2 is being operated under static conditions with $V_{EE} = 12$ V, $R_E = 22$ kΩ, $V_{BE} = 0.7$ V, $V_{CC} = 15$ kΩ, $\alpha_{dc} = 0.97$, $\alpha = 0.98$. Calculate the values of I_E and V_{CB}. If the total input resistance under signal conditions is 1 kΩ and the output resistance is equal to the value of the collector load, what is the value of the voltage gain?

Solution

Voltage drop across R_E is 12 V − 0.7 V= 11.3 V.

Emitter current, $I_E = \dfrac{11.3 \text{ V}}{22 \text{ k}\Omega}$

$= 0.51$ mA, rounded off

Collector current, $I_C = \alpha_{dc} I_E = 0.514 \times 0.97$

Then $V_{CB} = V_{CC} - I_C R_C = 15$ V − (0.514 × 0.97 × 15) = 7.5 V, rounded off.

Voltage gain, $G_V = \alpha \dfrac{R_o}{R_i} = 0.98 \times \dfrac{15 \text{ k}\Omega}{1 \text{ k}\Omega} = 14.7$

THE COMMON EMITTER CIRCUIT

The static current gain, β_{dc}, of the common-emitter circuit (Fig. 2-3) is defined as the ratio of the (output) collector current to the (input) base current.

Therefore:

$$\beta_{dc} = \frac{I_C}{I_B} = \frac{I_C}{I_E - I_C} = \frac{I_C/I_E}{1 - I_C/I_E} = \frac{\alpha_{dc}}{1 - \alpha_{dc}} \quad \text{Equation 2-9}$$

and, $\alpha_{dc} = \dfrac{\beta_{dc}}{1 + \beta_{dc}}$ **Equation 2-10**

The ac β, written simply as β, is often very close to the value of β_{dc} and therefore, to a first approximation, the collector current is β times larger than the base current; this result applies to both direct and alternating currents. β is, however, an unstable quantity and changes both with temperature and the choice of the operating point.

Base current:

$$I_B = \frac{V_{BB} - V_{BE}}{R_B} \approx \frac{V_{BB}}{R_B} \quad \text{Equation 2-11}$$

if the value of V_{BE} (between 0.3 V and 0.7 V) can be ignored.

$$\text{Collector potential, } V_C = V_{CC} - I_C R_C \qquad \textbf{Equation 2-12}$$

Base Bias

The power supply voltage, V_{BB}, may be eliminated by connecting R_B to the positive terminal of V_{CC} (Fig. 2-4). This arrangement is known as base bias and may be used to establish the dc operating point.

Referring to Fig. 2-4,

$$I_B = \frac{V_{CC} - V_{BE}}{R_B} \approx \frac{V_{CC}}{R_B} \qquad \textbf{Equation 2-13}$$

if V_{BE} can be ignored.

The value of I_B is therefore fixed by the values of V_{CC} and R_B. Since $I_C = \beta_{IB}$ and the value of β may vary widely, the collector current will be unstable and this is the major disadvantage of the base bias arrangement.

Emitter Bias

Emitter bias (Fig. 2-5), is a superior method of establishing the dc operating point; it requires the presence of the emitter resistor, R_E, and the additional power supply, V_{EE}. In a similar way to the common base circuit, it may be shown that:

$$I_E \approx \frac{V_{EE}}{R_E} \qquad \textbf{Equation 2-14}$$

Since this equation does not contain β, the values of I_E and therefore I_C, tend to be independent of any fluctuations in β.
A more exact formula is:

$$I_E = \frac{V_{EE} - V_{BE}}{R_E + \dfrac{R_B}{\beta}} \qquad \textbf{Equation 2-15}$$

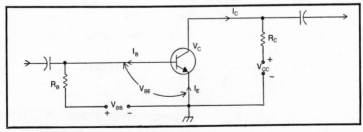

Fig. 2-3. The common emitter circuit.

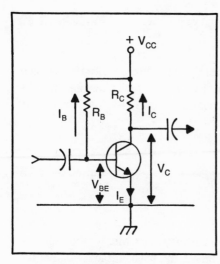

Fig. 2-4. The base bias circuit.

Collector potential, $V_C = V_{CC} - I_C R_C$.

To avoid negative feedback under signal conditions, the resistor R_E must be bypassed by the capacitor C_E.

The emitter bias circuit may be modified to operate from a single power supply (Fig. 2-6). Resistors R_{B1} and R_{B2} provide a voltage divider bias so that the voltage between base and ground is:

$$V_B \approx \frac{V_{CC} R_{B2}}{R_{B1} + R_{B2}}$$ **Equation 2-16**

This result is only approximately true since it ignores the voltage drop across R_{B1} due to the base current. By Kirchhoff's voltage law,

$$V_B = V_{BE} + V_E$$ **Equation 2-17**

If V_{BE} (a few tenths of a volt) is ignored in comparison with V_E, $V_B \approx V_E$ and,

$$I_E = \frac{V_E}{R_E} \approx \frac{V_{CC} R_{B2}}{R_E (R_{B1} + R_{B2})}$$ **Equation 2-18**

I_C which is approximately equal to I_E, will therefore be virtually independent of β.

A more exact result for the collector current is:

$$I_C = \frac{\dfrac{V_{CC} R_{B2}}{R_{B1} + R_{B2}} - V_{BE}}{R_E + \dfrac{R_{B1} R_{B2}}{\beta(R_{B1} + R_{B2})}}$$ **Equation 2-19**

22

Collector potential, $V_C = V_{CC} - I_C R_C$.

Small-Signal Conditions

The input signal is applied to the base relative to ground and the amplified output signal is taken from the collector. As with the grounded-cathode amplifier, the input and output signals are 180° out of phase.

One of the advantages of the common-emitter circuit (as compared with the common-base circuit) is its higher input resistance, R_i, to the signal applied at the base. In the absence of any coupling network to a following stage, the output resistance, R_o, is virtually equal to the collector load, R_C.

$$\text{Voltage gain: } G_v = \frac{i_c R_o}{i_b R_i} = \beta \frac{R_o}{R_i} \quad \textbf{Equation 2-20}$$

The principal component of R_i is a value of resistance equal to βr_e. Therefore, for a common-emitter amplifier, the voltage gain $G_v \approx R_o/r_e$. In the cases of base bias and emitter bias with two supplies, the total input resistance to the stage (as far as the signal is concerned) is approximately equal to the parallel combination of R_B ang βr_e. For the emitter bias circuit with a single supply, the input resistance consists of R_{B1}, R_{B2} and βr_e in parallel.

These results for voltage gain and input resistance with emitter bias are only true if the emitter resistor, R_E, is bypassed by the capacitor C_E. If the emitter resistor is not bypassed, degenerative

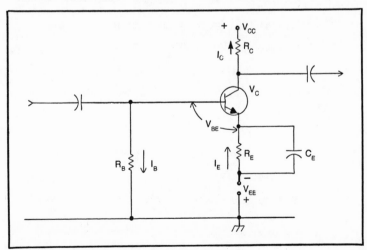

Fig. 2-5. Emitter bias with two supplies.

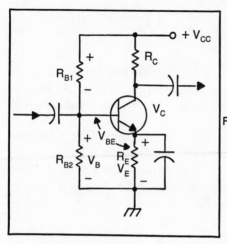

Fig. 2-6. Voltage divider bias.

feedback will occur and the voltage gain will fall to approximately R_C/R_E (provided R_E is large compared with the emitter/base junction resistance, r_e).

Example 2-3

In Fig. 2-7, the value of the base/emitter voltage may be ignored and the transistor's β is 50. What are the values of the base current and the collector potential? If the emitter/base resistance is 40 Ω, what is the circuit's voltage gain?

Solution

Base current, $I_B \approx \dfrac{V_{CC}}{R_B} = \dfrac{15 \text{ V}}{680 \text{ k}\Omega} = \dfrac{15 \text{ V}}{0.68 \text{ M}\Omega} = 22\ \mu\text{A}$, rounded off.

Collector current, $I_C = B_{I_B} = 50 \times 22\ \mu\text{A} = 1.1 \text{ mA}$.

Collector potential, $V_C = -(V_{CC} - I_C R_C) = -(15 - (1.1 \text{ mA} \times 10 \text{ k}\Omega) = (1.1 \text{ mA} \times 10 \text{ k}\Omega) - 15 = -4 \text{ V}$

The output resistance, R_o, consists approximately of R_C and R in parallel.

Therefore:

$$R_o = \frac{10 \times 15}{10 \times 15} = 6 \text{ k}\Omega$$

$$\text{Voltage gain} = \frac{R_o}{r_e} = \frac{6 \text{ k}\Omega}{40\ \Omega} = 150$$

Example 2-4

In Fig. 2-8, the transistor's β is 75 and the base/emitter voltage is 0.7 V. What are the values of the emitter current, the base potential and the collector potential? If the total input resistance under signal conditions is 2.5 kΩ, calculate the peak-to-peak swing of voltage at the collector when a sine wave signal of 1.5 mV rms is applied to the base.

Solution

$$\text{Emitter current,} I_E = \frac{V_{EE} - V_{BE}}{R_E + \frac{R_B}{\beta}} = \frac{12.0 - 0.7}{15 \text{ k}\Omega + \frac{22 \text{ k}\Omega}{75}}$$

$$= 0.73888 \ldots \text{ mA}$$
$$= 0.74 \text{ mA rounded off.}$$

Note that, to a first approximation, $I_E = V_{EE}/R_E = 12 \text{ V}/15 \text{ k}\Omega = 0.75 \text{ mA}$.

The base current, I_B, actually equals I_C/β, but approximately equals:

$$\frac{I_E}{\beta} = \frac{0.74}{75} = 0.01 \text{ mA, rounded off.}$$

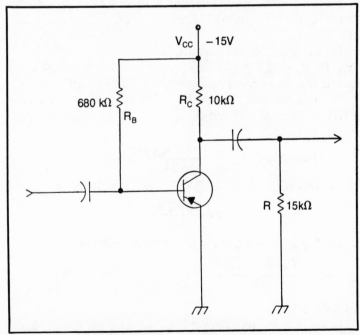

Fig. 2-7. Circuit for Example 2-3.

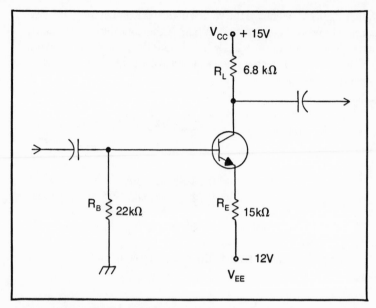

Fig. 2-8. Circuit for Example 2-4.

Since the base current (electron flow) is from top to bottom through R_B, the base potential is approximately $- (0.01 \text{ mA} \times 22 \text{ k}\Omega) = 0.22$ V.

Note that the emitter potential is:
$- V_{EE} + I_e R_E = 12 \text{ V} + (0.73888 \ldots \text{ mA} \times 15 \text{ k}\Omega) = - 0.92$ V.
This confirms the base/emitter voltage of $- 0.22 - (- 0.92) = 0.7$ V

Collector potential, $V_C = + (V_{CC} - I_C R_C) = + 15 - (0.74 \text{ mA} \times 6.8 \text{ k}\Omega) = + 9.97$ V, rounded off.

$$\text{Voltage gain} = \beta \frac{R_o}{R_i} = \frac{75 \times 6.8 \text{ k}\Omega}{2.5 \text{ k}\Omega}$$

The rms value of the signal output at the collector is:

$$1.5 \times \frac{75 \times 6.8}{2.5}$$

which corresponds to a peak-to-peak voltage swing of

$$\frac{1.5 \times 75 \times 6.8 \times 2.828}{2.5} \text{ mV} = 865 \text{ mV, rounded off.}$$

Example 2-5

In Fig. 2-9, the transistor β is 75. Ignoring the voltage drop across the base/emitter junction, what are the values of the emitter

26

current and the collector/emitter voltage? If the emitter/base resistance is 60 Ω, calculate the amplifier's voltage gain.

Solution

Base-to-ground voltage, $V_B \approx \dfrac{V_{CC}R_{B2}}{R_{B1}+R_{B2}} = \dfrac{25 \times 18 \text{ k}\Omega}{33 \text{ k}\Omega + 18 \text{ k}\Omega}$

$= 8.8$ V, rounded off.

Emitter current, $I_E \approx \dfrac{V_B}{R_E} = \dfrac{8.8 \text{ V}}{12 \text{ k}\Omega} = 0.74$ mA, rounded off.

Emitter potential, $V_E \approx V_B = +8.8$ V.

Collector potential, $V_C = V_{CC} - I_C R_C = +25 -(0.74 \times 8.2)$ (assuming that I_c is approximately equal to I_E) $= +18.9$ V, rounded off.

Collector/emitter voltage $= +18.9 - (+8.8) = 10.1$ V.

The output resistance, R_o, of the amplifier is virtually the collector load of 8.2 kΩ. The voltage gain is:

$$\frac{R_o}{r_e} = \frac{8.2 \text{ k}\Omega}{60 \text{ }\Omega} = 140, \text{ rounded off.}$$

THE COMMON COLLECTOR CONFIGURATION

The common-collector circuit is sometimes referred to as the emitter follower and is the transistor equivalent of the cathode

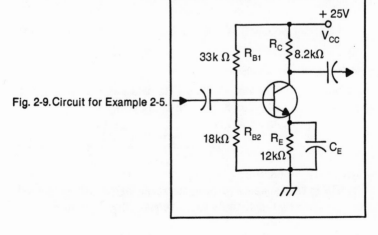

Fig. 2-9. Circuit for Example 2-5.

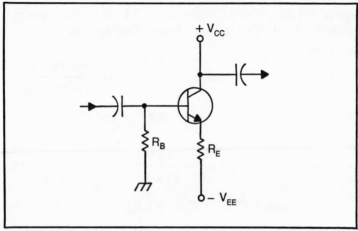

Fig. 2-10. The common collector stage.

follower discussed in Chapter 4. In Fig. 2-10, the emitter resistor R_E is the output load and, in conjunction with V_{EE}, provides the forward bias for the emitter/base junction. The static current gain is defined as the ratio of the (output) emitter current to the (input) base current.

Therefore:

$$\text{Static current gain,} \quad \frac{I_E}{I_B} = \frac{I_C + I_B}{I_B} = \beta + 1 \qquad \textbf{Equation 2-21}$$

$$\text{Emitter current,} \quad I_E = \frac{V_{EE} - V_{BE}}{R_E + \dfrac{R_B}{\beta}} \approx \frac{V_{EE}}{R_E} \qquad \textbf{Equation 2-22}$$

$$\text{Collector potential,} \quad V_C = + V_{CC} \qquad \textbf{Equation 2-23}$$

Small-Signal Conditions

Since R_E is the output load, it is naturally unbypassed and provides negative feedback. Like the cathode follower, the voltage gain is less than unity and is:

$$G_v = \frac{1}{1 + r_e/R_E} \qquad \textbf{Equation 2-24}$$

where r_e is the emitter/base junction resistance.

The input resistance to the signal at the base is high (compared with the other two configurations) and equals $\beta(r_e + R_E) \approx \beta R_E$. Due to the negative feedback action the output resistance is low (as in the cathode follower) and is typically less than 1 kΩ.

Although the common-collector stage has a voltage gain of less than 1, it has a high current gain and is therefore capable of providing a power gain with the input and output signals in phase.

The Darlington Pair

The emitter follower configuration may be used in an arrangement known as a Darlington pair (Fig. 2-11) the purpose of which is to achieve an extremely high effective signal current gain by the direct coupling of two transistors. Assuming that both transistors have the same β, $i_{c_1} = \beta i_{b_1}$ under signal conditions. However $i_{c_1} \approx i_{e_1} \approx i_{b_2}$ and therefore is $i_{e_2} \approx i_{c_2} = \beta i_{b_2} \approx \beta^2 i_{b_1}$. The effective signal current gain of the Darlington pair will be equal to β^2 or $B_1 B_2$ if each transistor has a different β.

The input resistance to the signal at the base of Q1 will be approximately:

$$\beta^2 \times \frac{R_E R_L}{R_E + R_L} \qquad \textbf{Equation 2-25}$$

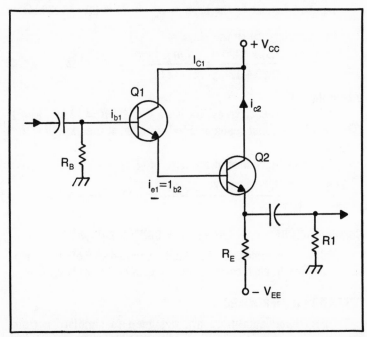

Fig. 2-11. The Darlington pair.

while the input resistance to the entire stage will be the parallel combination of R_B and,

$$\beta^2 \times \frac{R_E R_L}{R_E + R_L}$$

Example 2-6

In Fig. 2-12, the transistor's β is 60. Calculate the values of the static current gain and the emitter current. If the emitter/base resistance is 40 Ω, what is the stage's voltage gain and its input resistance?

Solution

Static current gain $= \beta + 1 = 60 + 1 = 61$

Emitter current, $I_E \approx \dfrac{V_{EE}}{R_E} = \dfrac{25 \text{ V}}{22 \text{ k}\Omega} = 1.14 \text{ mA}$

Voltage gain $= \dfrac{1}{1 + \dfrac{r_e}{R_E}} = \dfrac{1}{1 + \dfrac{40 \, \Omega}{22 \text{ k}\Omega}}$

which is virtually 1.

Input resistance at the base $= B_{R_E} = 60 \times 22 = 1320 \text{ k}\Omega.$

Input resistance to the stage =

$$\frac{120 \times 1320}{1320 + 12} = \frac{120 \times 1320}{1440} = 110 \text{ k}\Omega$$

Example 2-7

In Fig. 2-11, each transistor has a β of 40, $R_E = 15$ kΩ, $R_L = 1$ kΩ. What is the input resistance to the signal at the base of Q1?

Solution

The input resistance at the base of Q_1 is:

$$\beta^2 \times \frac{R_E R_L}{R_E + R_L} = \frac{1600 \times 15 \times 1}{16} = 1500 \text{ k}\Omega = 1.5 \text{ M}\Omega$$

COMPARISON BETWEEN TRANSISTOR CONFIGURATIONS

Table 2-1 summarizes the results obtained so far in this chapter. Note that in each case the power gain is the product, $G_i G_v$.

OPERATIONAL AMPLIFIERS

Operational amplifiers are designed to simulate certain mathematical operations such as addition, subtraction, differentia-

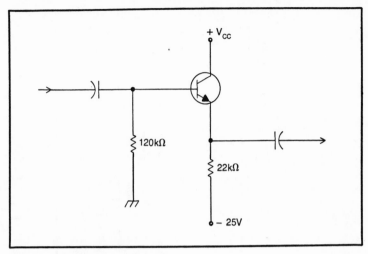

Fig. 2-12. Circuit for Example 2-6.

tion, integration, etc. In Fig. 2-13A the input signal, V_i, is fed through an impedance, Z_i, to a solid state amplifier whose voltage gain is $-A$; the minus sign indicates that the output signal, V_o, is inverted with respect to the input signal (such as would occur with some form of common emitter arrangement). Z_f provides feedback from the output circuit to the input circuit and the combination of Z_f and Z_i may be regarded as a voltage divider between V_o and V_i. Then, provided A is sufficiently large, the voltage gain of the amplifier with feedback is:

$$A = \frac{V_o}{V_i} = - \frac{Z_f}{Z_i} \qquad \textbf{Equation 2-26}$$

The circuit in Fig. 2-13B is a noninverting operational amplifier whose feedback action is similar to that of the inverting type but whose gain is:

$$A = \frac{V_o}{V_i} = 1 + \frac{Z_f}{Z_i} \qquad \textbf{Equation 2-27}$$

Figures 2-14 and 2-15 show operational amplifiers which are capable of performing addition and subtraction; in these cases, Z_f and Z_i are resistors.

In the summing amplifier, the gain for each input signal is $-R_f/R_i$.

Table 2-1. Bipolar Transistor Data.

Configuration	Static Current Gain	Dynamic Current Gain, G_i	Voltage Gain, G_v	Approximate input resistance	Output resistance	Phase Difference Between Input and Output Signals
Common Base	$\alpha_{DC} = \dfrac{I_C}{I_E} = \dfrac{\beta_{DC}}{1+\beta_{DC}}$ Slightly less than 1	$\alpha = \dfrac{\Delta i_c}{\Delta i_e}$ Slightly less than 1	$\dfrac{R_O}{r_e}$	At Emitter r_e Low: 2.5 Ω to 200 Ω	High Several KΩ	0°
Common Emitter	$\beta_{DC} \approx \dfrac{I_C}{I_B} = \dfrac{\alpha_{DC}}{1-\alpha_{DC}}$	$\beta = \dfrac{\Delta i_c}{\Delta i_b}$	$\dfrac{R}{r_e}$	At base r_e Medium: 500 Ω to 2 kΩ	High Several KΩ	180°
Common Collector	$\dfrac{I_E}{I_B} = \beta_{DC} + 1$	$\dfrac{\Delta i_e}{\Delta i_b} = \beta + 1$	Slightly less than 1	At base βR_E High: 20 kΩ to 250 KΩ	Low Less than 1 KΩ	0°

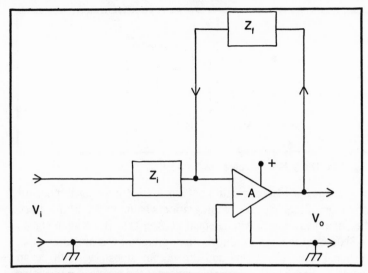

Fig. 2-13A. The inverting operational amplifier.

Output signal,

$$V_o = -R_f \left(\frac{V_{i1}}{R_{i1}} + \frac{V_{i2}}{R_{i2}} + \frac{V_{i3}}{R_{i3}} \right) \quad \textbf{Equation 2-28}$$

By making R_{i1}, R_{i2} and R_{i3} unequal value resistors, this operational amplifier may be used to weight the input signals as well as to sum them.

For the differential amplifier, the output signal is

$$V_o = -\left(\frac{R_f}{R_i} \quad (V_{i1} - V_{i2}) \right) \quad \textbf{Equation 2-29}$$

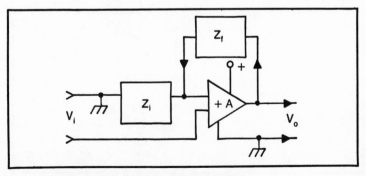

Fig. 2-13B. The noninverting operational amplifier.

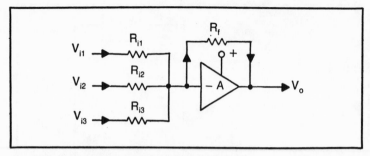

Fig. 2-14. The summing operational amplifier.

In the operational amplifier of Fig. 2-16, Z_f is a capacitor and the amplifier is then capable of integration. Owing to the *Miller effect*, the input capacitance will be equal to $(A + 1)$ C. If the input signal, V_i, is a step voltage as shown, the voltage at the amplifier input terminal will slowly rise and the output signal, V_o, will be an amplified linear fall, which will represent the result of integrating V_i. If C_f is replaced by a suitable inductor L_f, the operational amplifier will be capable of differentiation.

Example 2-8

In Fig. 2-13A, Z_f is a 150 kΩ resistor and Z_i is a 10 kΩ resistor. Assuming that A is large, what is the gain of the operational amplifier?

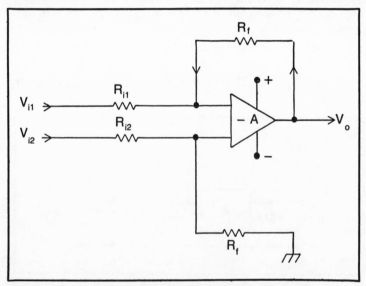

Fig. 2-15. The differential operational amplifier.

Solution

Operational amplifier gain $= -\dfrac{R_f}{R_i} = -\dfrac{150}{10} = -15$

Example 2-9

In Fig. 2-13B, Z_f is a 150 kΩ resistor and Z_i is a 10 kΩ resistor. Assuming that A is large, calculate the gain of the operational amplifier.

Solution

Operational amplifier gain $= 1 + \dfrac{R_f}{R_i} = 1 + \dfrac{150}{10} = +16$

Example 2-10

In Fig. 2-14, V_{i1}, V_{i2}, V_{i3} are step voltages of $+2\,mV$, $+5\,mV$ and $+7\,mV$ respectively, $R_f = 1\,M\Omega$ and R_{i1}, R_{i2}, R_{i3} are each $0.5\,M\Omega$. Determine the value of the output signal.

Solution

Voltage gain for each signal is

$$\frac{R_f}{R_i} = \frac{1\,M\Omega}{0.5\,M\Omega} = 2$$

Output signal, $V_o = -2\,(2 + 5 + 7) = -28\,mV$

Example 2-11

In Fig. 2-15, $R_f = 120$ kΩ and $R_i = 10$ kΩ. V_{i1} and V_{i2} are step voltages of $+15\,mV$ and $+10\,mV$ respectively. What is the value of the output signal.?

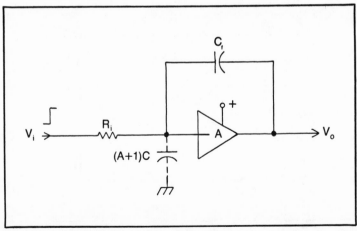

Fig. 2-16. The integrating operational amplifier.

Solution

$$\text{Voltage gain for each signal} = -\frac{R_f}{R_o} = \frac{120 \text{ k}\Omega}{10 \text{ k}\Omega} = -12$$

$$\text{Output signal } V_o = -12 \times (15 - 10) = -60 \text{ mV}$$

RC OSCILLATORS

The multivibrator circuit of Fig. 2-17 consists of two common-emitter stages which are cross-connected for positive feedback. The resultant instability causes the transistors to cut on and off alternately so that approximate square wave voltage outputs appear at the collectors; the base waveforms have a sawtooth appearance.

The Astable Multivibrator

When the transistor Q1 has been driven to the cutoff condition as the result of the positive feedback action, the base potential, e_{b1}, is approximately equal to $-V_{cc}$. Capacitor C2 will then discharge through RB2 and Q2 so that e_{b1} will rise towards V_{cc} with a time constant of approximately C2·RB2. When e_{b1} becomes slightly positive, Q1 will switch on and the positive feedback action will drive Q2 to the cutoff condition. Since e_{b1} approximately reaches its half-way mark in rising from $-V_{cc}$ to a slightly positive potential on its way towards V_{cc}, Q1 is cut off for a time interval of approximately 0.7C2RB2.

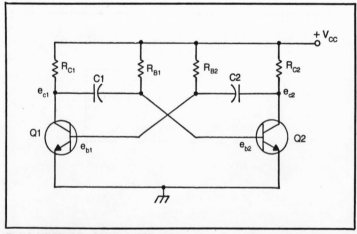

Fig. 2-17. The astable multivibrator.

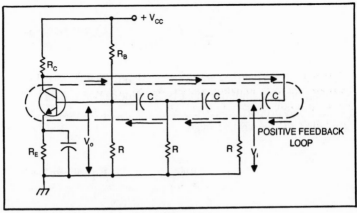

Fig. 2-18. The RC phase shift oscillator.

$$\text{Multivibrator frequency} = \frac{1}{\text{total period}} \qquad \textbf{Equation 2-30}$$

$$= \frac{1}{0.7\,(C1R_{B1} + C2R_{B2})} = \frac{1}{1.4\,CR_B}$$

if the multivibrator is symmetrical with $C1 = C2 = C$ and $R_{B1} = R_{B2} = R_B$

The Phase Shift Oscillator

This type of oscillator (Fig. 2-18) is capable of generating a sine wave which is relatively free of harmonic distortion; its frequency output can range from less than 1 Hz to a few hundred kHz.

The circuit uses the common-emitter configuration so that there is 180° phase change from base to collector; the feedback loop is completed by the RC phase shift network which contains a minimum number of 3 sections (as shown). For the feedback to be positive, the network therefore must provide a further 180° shift (ignoring any effect of the transistor circuitry) and it would appear at first glance that each RC section should contribute a 60° shift. However, this simple approach ignores the shunting effect of one section on another and an exact analysis gives the following results:

Equation 2-31

$$\text{Frequency of oscillation, } f_o = \frac{1}{2\,\pi\,\sqrt{6}\,RC} = \frac{0.159}{\sqrt{6}\,RC} \ \text{Hz}$$

with R measured in ohms and C in farads.
The attenuation factor of the network is:

$$\beta = \frac{V_o}{V_i} = \frac{1}{29} \qquad \textbf{Equation 2-32}$$

and, therefore, if oscillations are to be sustained, the voltage gain of the common-emitter amplifier must be 29. Notice that the formula for f_o is inversely proportional to C (and not $\sqrt{C}$ as in LC oscillator). If a 4-section RC network is used:

$$f_o = \frac{0.7}{2\pi CR} \qquad \textbf{Equation 2-33}$$

and,

$$\text{attenuation factor, } \beta = \frac{1}{18.4} \qquad \textbf{Equation 2-34}$$

The Wien Bridge Oscillator

This oscillator (Fig. 2-19) employs two common-emitter stages so that there is theoretically zero phase shift between a signal voltage on the base of Q1 and the output voltage at the collector of Q2. The feedback loop is completed by the Wien filter consisting of R1R2C1C2, and, therefore, in order for the feedback to be positive, the input voltage to the filter, V_o, and the output voltage from the filter, V_i, must be in phase. This will occur at the frequency of oscillation:

$$f_o = \frac{1}{2\pi\sqrt{R1R2C1C2}} = \frac{1}{2\pi RC} \text{ Hz} \qquad \textbf{Equation 2-35}$$

if R1 = R2 = R ohms and C1 = C2 = C farads.

At the frequency, f_o, the attenuation factor of the filter is:

$$\frac{V_i}{V_o} = \frac{1}{3}$$

Consequently the combined voltage gain of Q1 and Q2 must be equal to 3. This is not practical and, therefore, the oscillator circuit contains negative feedback, provided by R_f and the lamp which form the bridge circuit in conjunction with R1C1R2C2. The combined gain of Q1, Q2 without the negative feedback can then be high but their gain with feedback will equal 3 under stable conditions which will be determined by the operating resistance of the lamp.

38

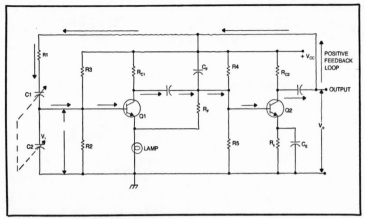

Fig. 2-19. The Wien-bridge oscillator.

Like the RC phase shift oscillator, the Wien bridge circuit is especially suitable for the generation of low frequency sine waves with good stability and a lack of harmonic distortion.

Example 2-12

In Fig. 2-17, $R_{B1} = R_{B2} = 100$ kΩ and C1= C2= 0.01 μF. What is the approximate frequency of the multivibrator?

Solution

Multivibrator frequency, $f_o = \dfrac{1}{1.4\, C\, R_B}$

$$= \frac{1}{1.4 \times 0.01 \times 10^{-6} \times 10^5} \text{ Hz}$$

$$= 714 \text{ Hz, rounded off.}$$

Example 2-13

In Fig. 2-18, $C = 0.01$ μF, $R = 10$ kΩ. Calculate the frequency of oscillation.

Solution

Frequency of oscillation, $f_o = \dfrac{0.159}{\sqrt{6}\, CR} = \dfrac{1.59 \times 10^{-1}}{\sqrt{6} \times 0.01 \times 10^{-6} \times 10^4}$

$$= \frac{1590}{\sqrt{6}} = 650 \text{ Hz rounded off}$$

Example 2-14

In Fig. 2-19, C1 = C2 = 8200 pF, R1= R2= 12 kΩ. Determine the frequency of oscillation.

Solution

Frequency of oscillation, $f_o = \dfrac{0.159}{RC}$

$$= \dfrac{0.159}{12 \times 10^3 \times 8200 \times 10^{-12}}$$

$$= \dfrac{1.59 \times 10^{-1}}{1.2 \times 8.2 \times 10^{-5}}$$

$$= \dfrac{15900}{1.2 \times 8.2} \text{ Hz}$$

$$= 1.62 \text{ kHz, rounded off.}$$

CHAPTER SUMMARY

NPN and PNP Transistors

$$I_E = I_C + I_B$$

Emitter/base junction forward biased; collector/base junction reverse biased. For a comparison between the common base, common emitter and common collector configurations, refer to Table 2-1.

Base Bias

$$I_B = \dfrac{V_{CC} - V_{BE}}{R_B} \approx \dfrac{V_{CC}}{R_B}$$

Emitter Bias
Two supplies

$$I_E = \dfrac{V_{EE} - V_{BE}}{R_E + R_B} \approx \dfrac{V_{EE}}{R_E}$$

Single supply (voltage divider bias)

$$V_B = V_{BE} + V_E \approx \dfrac{V_{CC} R_{B2}}{R_{B1} + R_{B2}}$$

$$I_E = \frac{V_E}{R_E} \approx \frac{V_{CC} R_{B2}}{R_E (R_{B1} + R_{B2})}$$

$$I_C = \frac{\dfrac{V_{CC} R_{B2}}{R_{B1} + R_{B2}} - V_{BE}}{R_E + \dfrac{R_{B1} R_{B2}}{\beta (R_{B1} + R_{B2})}}$$

Collector Potential, $V_C = V_{CC} - I_C R_C$.

Darlington Pair

Current gain$= \beta_1 \beta_2 = \beta^2$ if each transistor has the same β.

$$\text{Input resistance} = \beta^2 \times \frac{R_E R_L}{R_E + R_L}$$

Operational Amplifiers

Inverting amplifier

$$\text{Gain, } A = -\frac{Z_f}{Z_i}$$

Noninverting amplifier

$$\text{Gain, } A = 1 + \frac{Z_f}{Z_1}$$

Summing amplifier

$$\text{Output, } V_o = -R_f \frac{V_{i1}}{R_{i1}} + \frac{V_{i2}}{R_{i2}} + \frac{V_{i3}}{R_{i3}}$$

Differential amplifier

$$\text{Output, } V_o = -\frac{R_f}{R_i} (V_{i1} - V_{i2})$$

RC Oscillators

Astable Multivibrator

$$\text{Frequency} = \frac{1}{0.7 (C_1 R_{B1} + C_2 R_{B2})} = \frac{1}{1.4 \, CR_B}$$

41

$$\text{if } C_1 = C_2 = C \text{ and } R_{B1} = R_{B2} = R_B$$

Phase Shift Oscillator

Three CR sections: $\text{Frequency} = \dfrac{1}{2\pi \sqrt{6}\, RC}$ Hz

Attenuation factor, $\beta = \dfrac{1}{29}$

Four CR sections: $\text{Frequency} = \dfrac{0.7}{2\pi\, CR}$ Hz

Attenuation Factor, $\beta = \dfrac{1}{18.4}$

Wien Bridge Oscillator

$$\text{Frequency} = \dfrac{1}{2\pi \sqrt{R1\,R2\,C1\,C2}} = \dfrac{1}{2\pi\, RC} \quad \text{Hz}$$

if R1 = R2 = R
and C1 = C2 = C

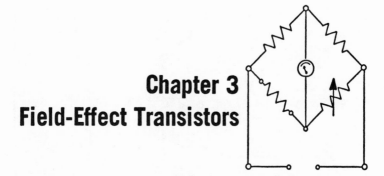

Chapter 3
Field-Effect Transistors

The action of the pnp or npn bipolar transistors in Chapter 2 involved two types of charge carrier—the electron and the hole. The *FET* is a unipolar transistor since its operation requires only one charge carrier which may be either the electron or the hole.

INTRODUCTION TO FIELD-EFFECT TRANSISTORS (FETS)

The two types of FET are the *Junction Field-Effect Transistor (JFET)* and the *Metal-Oxide Semiconductor Field-Effect Transistor (MOSFET)*; the latter is sometimes referred to as an *Insulated Gate Field-Effect Transistor (IGFET)*.

The JFET is essentially a doped silicon bar which is referred to as a channel and behaves as a resistor. The doping may either be p type or n type, thereby creating either a p channel or an n channel JFET. At the ends of the channel are two terminals which are referred to as the source and the drain. When a particular drain-source voltage (V_{DS}) is applied between the end terminals, the amount of current flow (I_D) between the source and the drain depends on the channel's resistance. The value of this resistance is controlled by a gate which may either consist of two n type regions diffused into a p type channel or two p type regions diffused into an n type channel. In either case the two regions are commonly joined to provide a single gate (two separate gates may be used in some mixer circuits). Cutaway views of both types with their schematic symbols are shown in Fig. 3-1. In the schematic symbols the

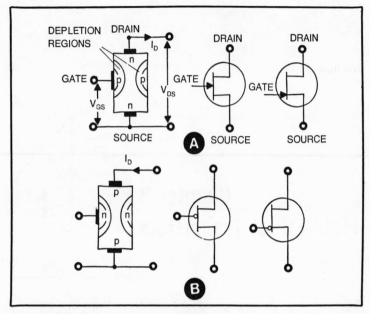

Fig. 3-1. N channel and P channel JFETs.

vertical line may be regarded as the channel; the arrow then points towards an n channel but away from a p channel. The gate line may either be symmetrically positioned with respect to the source and the drain, or may be drawn closer to the source.

If a reverse bias voltage is applied between the gate and the source of an n channel JFET, depletion layers will surround the two p regions which form the gate. If the reversed bias is increased the depletion layers will spread more deeply into the channel until they almost touch. The channel's resistance will then be extremely low so that the I_D is very small.

The *reverse* biasing of the gate/source junction may be compared with applying a negative voltage to a triode's grid relative to its cathode. Like the tube the FET is a voltage controlled device in the sense that only the input voltage to the gate controls the output drain current. This is in contrast with the bipolar transistor where the base/emitter junction is forward biased; the input voltage then controls the input current which in turn determines the output current.

With reverse biasing of the gate/source junction very little gate current flows. This means that the input impedance to a JFET is of the order of several megohms; this is a definite advantage of the FET over the bipolar transistor whose input impedance is relatively low. However when compared with the JFET the output current of a bipolar transistor is much more sensitive to changes in the input voltage; the result is a lower voltage gain available from the JFET.

JFET DRAIN AND TRANSCONDUCTANCE CURVES

In Fig. 3-2A the voltage (V_{DS}) between the source and the drain of the n channel JFET, is gradually increased from zero; at the same time the voltage between gate and source, $V_{GS} = 0$ V which is referred to as the shorted gate condition. Initially the available channel is broad so that the drain current, I_D, is directly proportional to V_{DS} and rises rapidly as V_{DS} is increased. However, the drain voltage creates a reverse bias on the junction between the channel and the gate. The increase in V_{DS} causes the two depletion regions to widen until finally they come into contact. This occurs when V_{DS} equals a value called the *pinch-off voltage*, V_p (Fig. 3-2B);

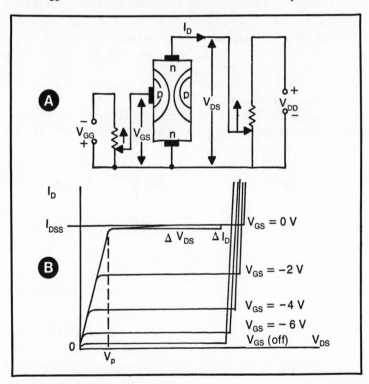

Fig. 3-2. JFET drain curves.

the available channel is then very narrow so that the drain current is limited (or pinched-off). Further raising of V_{DS} above the pinch-off point will only produce a small increase in the drain current. This situation continues until the drain voltage equals V_{DS} (max); at this point an avalanche effect takes place and the JFET breaks down. Over the operating range between V_p and V_{DS} (max) the approximately constant value of the drain current with the shorted gate is referred to as the I_{DSS} (drain to source current with shorted gate).

For each different negative value of V_{GS} a different drain current curve can be obtained. This family of curves is illustrated in Fig. 3-2B. Ultimately V_{GS} can be sufficiently negative so that the drain current is virtually cut off and equal to zero; this value of gate-source voltage is therefore referred to as V_{GS}(off).

At the cutoff condition the depletion layers nearly touch; this also occurred when V_{DS} was equal to V_p. Therefore V_{GS} has the same value as V_p although V_{GS} is a negative voltage while V_p is positive. The *transconductance curve* is the graph of drain current, I_D, plotted against the gate to source voltage, V_{GS}, while maintaining the drain to source voltage, V_{DS}, at a constant level. For example, in Fig. 3-3A, the drain voltage is set to 12 V while the gate is initially shorted to the source so that $V_{GS} = 0$. The recorded drain current would then equal the value of I_{DSS}. If the reverse gate voltage is now increased from zero; the drain current will fall until ultimately cut-off is reached when $V_{GS} = V_{GS}$ (off).

The shape of the transconductance curve is considered to be a parabola (Fig. 3-3B) so that there is a mathematical relationship between I_D and V_{GS}.

$$\text{Drain current, } I_D = I_{DDS}\left(1 - \frac{V_{GS}}{V_{GS}(\text{off})}\right)^{2} \qquad \textbf{Equation 3-1}$$

In this equation both V_{GS} and $V_{GS(\text{off})}$ are considered to be negative voltages.

In a FET amplifier the control which the gate voltage exercises over the drain current is measured by the transconductance, g_m. At a particular point on the curve the transconductance is defined by

$$g_m = \frac{\Delta I_D}{\Delta V_{GS}} \qquad \textbf{Equation 3-2}$$

and is normally measured in micromhos (microsiemens, μS). By differentiating the expression for I_D with respect to V_{GS},

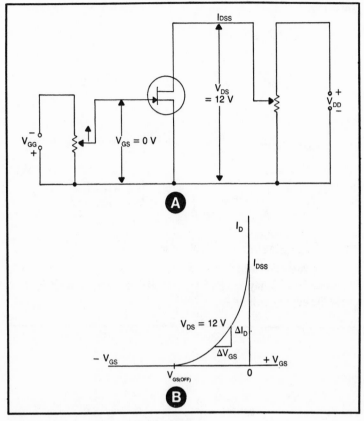

Fig. 3-3. JFET transconductance curve.

$$g_m = g_{mo}\left(1 - \frac{V_{GS}}{V_{GS(off)}}\right) \qquad \textbf{Equation 3-3}$$

where g_{mo} is the transconductance for the shorted gate condition.

The value of g_{mo} is $-\dfrac{2\,I_{DSS}}{V_{GSoff}}$; since $V_{GS(off)}$ is a negative voltage, g_{mo} is a positive quantity. The concept of transconductance also applies to the transfer characteristics of the triode and pentode tubes.

Example 3-1

A junction field-effect transistor has a pinch-off voltage equal to 4 V. If $I_{DSS} = 12$ mA, find the values of I_D and g_m when $V_{GS} = -2V$.

Solution

$$V_{GS(off)} = -V_p = -4 \text{ V}.$$

$$I_D = I_{DSS}\left(1 - \frac{V_{GS}}{V_{GS(off)}}\right)^2 = 12 \times \left(1 - \frac{(-2)}{(-4)}\right)^2$$
$$= 3 \text{ mA}.$$

$$g_{mo} = \frac{-2 \times 12}{-4} = 6 \text{ millimhos} = 6000 \text{ } \mu\text{mhos}.$$

$$g_m = g_{mo}\left(1 - \frac{V_{GS}}{V_{GS(off)}}\right) = 6000\left(1 - \frac{-2}{-4}\right)$$
$$= 3000 \text{ } \mu\text{siemens}.$$

METHODS OF BIASING THE JFET

The methods which follow are applied to n-channel FETS. P-channel FETS may be similarly biased by reversing the polarities of the dc supply voltages.

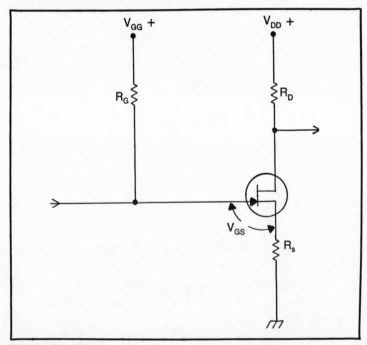

Fig. 3-4. Gate Bias.

48

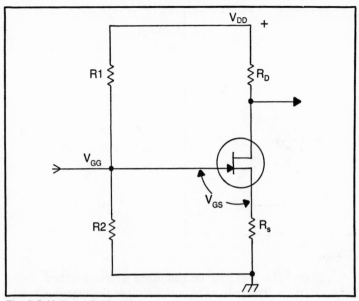

Fig. 3-5. Voltage divider bias.

Gate Bias

This method is similar to the base bias of the bipolar transistors. In Fig. 3-4, the drain current is given by

$$I_D = \frac{V_{GG} - V_{GS}}{R_s} \qquad \text{Equation 3-4}$$

$$\approx \frac{V_{GG}}{R_s} \text{ if } V_{GG} >> V_{GS} \qquad \text{Equation 3-5}$$

The equation $I_D \approx \dfrac{V_{GG}}{R_s}$ means that V_{GG} and R_s may be chosen to establish a value of I_D which is independent of the JFET characteristics. The requirement for a separate V_{GG} supply may be avoided by using voltage divider bias (Fig. 3-5). By comparing Figs. 3-4 and 3-5 and using Thévenin's Theorem,

$$V_{GG} = V_{DD} \times \frac{R2}{R1 + R2} \qquad \text{Equation 3-6}$$

$$R_G = \frac{R1R2}{R1 + R2} \qquad \text{Equation 3-7}$$

49

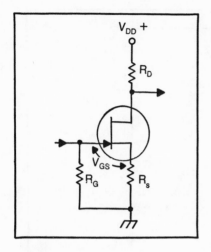

Fig. 3-6. Self Bias.

Self Bias

Self bias (Fig. 3-6) may be compared with the cathode bias used with tubes. The gate voltage is zero but the gate is biased negative with respect to the source by the amount of the voltage drop across R_s. Therefore

$$V_{GS} = -I_D R_s \qquad \text{Equation 3-8}$$

Self-bias, although a simple arrangement, does not swamp out V_{GS} and therefore the bias point depends on the characteristics of the JFET; this is its principal disadvantage.

Source Bias

Source bias (Fig. 3-7) is comparable with the emitter bias of a bipolar transistor. Once again the purpose is to swamp out the value of V_{GS} and achieve a drain current which is virtually independent of the JFET characteristics. Since the gate is at ground potential, the equation for the drain current is

$$I_D = \frac{V_{SS} - V_{GS}}{R_s} \qquad \text{Equation 3-9}$$

$$\approx \frac{V_{SS}}{I_S} \text{ if } V_{SS} >> V_{GS} \qquad \text{Equation 3-10}$$

It is easy to swamp out V_{GS} is a large negative voltage is available. The disadvantage of source bias is obvious in that it requires two separate supplies.

If a large negative voltage is not available, the problem may be solved by replacing R_s with a bipolar transistor in the current source bias circuit of Fig. 3-8. When the base/emitter junction is controlled by a forward bias action, the emitter junction is controlled by a forward bias action, the emitter current of the bipolar will equal the drain current of the FET so that:

$$I_D = I_E = \frac{V_{EE} - V_{BE}}{R_E} \qquad \text{Equation 3-11}$$

$$\approx \frac{V_{EE}}{R_E} \quad \text{if } V_{EE} >> V_{BE} \qquad \text{Equation 3-12}$$

Since $V_{BE} = 0.7$ V and only varies by 0.1 V from one transistor to another, a high drain current can be fixed by using a low voltage source for V_{EE}. If the low negative voltage is not available, the bipolar transistor may be forward biased by the voltage divider circuit of Fig. 3-9. Then by *Thévenin's Theorem,*

$$I_D = I_E = \frac{\dfrac{V_{DD} \times R2}{R1 + R2} - V_{BE}}{R_E} \qquad \text{Equation 3-13}$$

$$\approx \frac{V_{DD} \times R2}{(R1 + R2)R_E} \quad \text{provided } \frac{V_{DD} \times R2}{R_1 + R2} >> V_{BE}$$

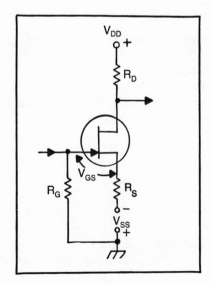

Fig. 3-7. Source bias.

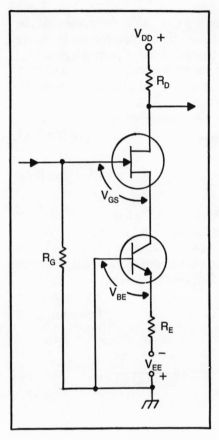

Fig. 3-8. Current source bias.

Current-source bias has the advantage of providing the best swamping action; its disadvantage is the requirement for the additional bipolar transistor.

Example 3-2

In Fig. 3-10 calculate the values of I_D and V_{DS} (ignore V_{GS}).

Solution

$$\text{Drain current, } I_D = \frac{12 \text{ V}}{5.6 \text{ k}\Omega} = 2.14 \text{ mA.}$$

Drain-source voltage, $V_{DS} = 35 \text{ V} - (6.8 \text{ k}\Omega + 5.6 \text{ k}\Omega) \times 2.14 \text{ mA}$

$$= 8.5 \text{ V, rounded off.}$$

Example 3-3

In Fig. 3-11 calculate the value of I_D if $V_{GS} = -2 \text{ V}$.

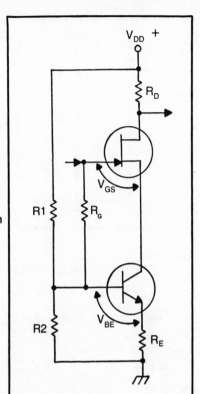

Fig. 3-9. Current source bias with a single supply.

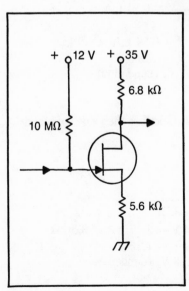

Fig. 3-10. Circuit for Example 3-2.

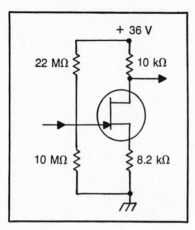

+ 36 V

22 MΩ   10 kΩ

10 MΩ   8.2 kΩ

Fig. 3-11. Circuit for Example 3-3.

Solution

Effective gate supply voltage is $\dfrac{10 \text{ M}\Omega \times 36 \text{ V}}{10 \text{ M}\Omega + 22 \text{ M}\Omega}$
= 11.25 V.

Then $I_D = \dfrac{11.25 \text{ V} + 2 \text{ V}}{8.2 \text{ k}\Omega} = 1.6$ mA, rounded off.

Example 3-4

In Fig. 3-12, $V_{GS} = -2$ V. Calculate the values of I_D and V_D.

Solution

Drain current, $I_D = \dfrac{2 \text{ V}}{2.2 \text{ k}\Omega} = 0.91$ mA.

Drain voltage, $V_D = +24$ V $- 0.91$ mA $\times 4.7$ kΩ.
= + 24 V − 4.277 V
= + 19.7 V, rounded off.

Example 3-5

In Fig. 3-13, $V_{GS} = -2$ V. Calculate the values of I_D and V_{DS}.

Solution

Drain current, $I_D = \dfrac{24 \text{ V} + 2 \text{ V}}{12 \text{ k}\Omega} = 2.17$ mA.

Drain voltage, $V_D = +24$ V $- 2.17$ mA $\times 3.3$ kΩ
= + 24 V − 7.16 V
= + 16.8 V, rounded off.

Source voltage, $V_S = +2$ V.

Drain-to-source voltage, $V_{DS} = +16.8 \text{ V} - (+2 \text{ V})$
$$= 14.8 \text{ V}.$$

Example 3-6

In Fig. 3-14, calculate the values of I_D and V_{DS} (assume $V_{GS} = -2$ V).

Solution

Assuming that the V_{BE} of the bipolar transistor is 0.7 V,

$$I_D = I_E = \frac{12 \text{ V} - 0.7 \text{ V}}{12 \text{ k}\Omega} = 0.94 \text{ mA}.$$

Then $V_E = -0.7$ V.
If $V_{GS} = -2$ V, $V_S = V_C = +2$ V and $V_{CE} = 2.7$ V.
Drain potential, $V_D = +36 \text{ V} - 0.94 \text{ mA} \times 12 \text{ k}\Omega$
$$= +24.7 \text{ V}.$$

Drain-to-source voltage, $V_{DS} = 24.7 - 2.0 = 22.7$ V.

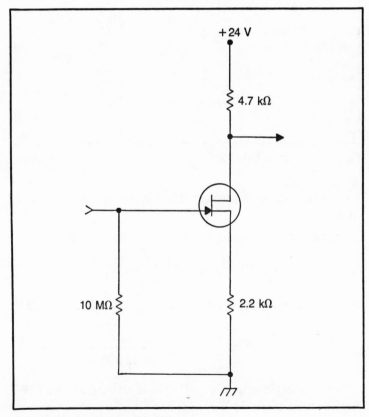

Fig. 3-12. Circuit for Example 3-4.

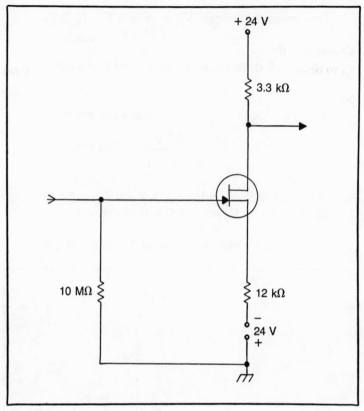

Fig. 3-13. Circuit for Example 3-5.

Example 3-7

In Fig. 3-15, calculate the value of V_{DS} (assume $V_{GS} = -2$ V).

Solution

Due to voltage divider action, the potential at point A is

$$+36 \text{ V} \times \frac{15 \text{ k}\Omega}{15 \text{ k}\Omega + 30 \text{ k}\Omega}$$

$= +12$ V which is equal to V_G. Since $V_{GS} = -2$ V, $V_S = +14$ V.

The emitter current, $I_E = I_D = \dfrac{12 \text{ V} - 0.7 \text{ V}}{12 \text{ k}\Omega} = 0.94$ mA.

The drain potential is $+36$ V $- 10$ k$\Omega \times 0.94$ mA $= +26.6$ V and $V_{DS} = 26.6$ V $- 14$ V $= 12.6$ V.

THE USE OF THE JFET AS A SIGNAL AMPLIFIER

The principle of the JFET amplifier is shown in Fig. 3-16A. (Lower case letters are used to indicate signal values.) The signal, v_g, to be amplified is applied between the gate and the source and produces variations, i_d, in the drain current. The resultant voltage variations across the drain load, r_d, produce voltage variations of opposite polarity between gate and ground. This output signal, v_d, is 180° out of phase with the input signal. This same phase inversion occurs with the common emitter arrangement of a bipolar transistor amplifier, and the grounded cathode tube amplifier.

Assuming that r_s is bypassed by a capacitor to avoid negative or degenerative feedback, the JFET behaves as a current source of

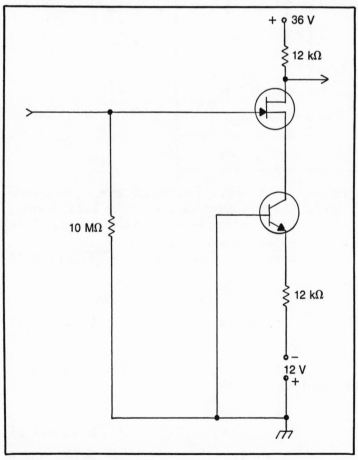

Fig. 3-14. Circuit for Example 3-6.

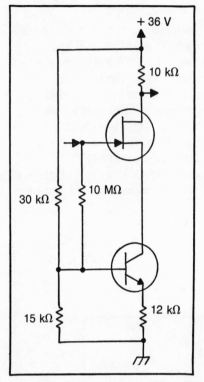

+ 36 V

10 kΩ

10 MΩ

30 kΩ

Fig. 3-15. Circuit for Example 3-7.

15 kΩ

12 kΩ

value $g_m v_g$ in parallel with a very high resistance, r_{ds}, which is the reciprocal of the drain characteristics slope (Fig. 3-16B). Normally r_{ds} exceeds 100 kΩ and may be neglected in the analysis. Then:

$$\text{Output signal, } v_d = g_m v_g \times r_d \qquad \textbf{Equation 3-14}$$

and,

$$\text{Voltage gain} = \frac{v_d}{v_g} = g_m r_d \qquad \textbf{Equation 3-15}$$

If the source resistance, r_s, is not bypassed, negative feedback is introduced into the circuit,

$$\text{Voltage gain} = \frac{r_d}{r_s + \dfrac{1}{g_m}} \qquad \textbf{Equation 3-16}$$

Provided $r_s \gg \dfrac{1}{g_m}$,

$$\text{Voltage gain} = \frac{r_d}{r_s} \qquad \textbf{Equation 3-17}$$

In the source follower circuit of Fig. 3-16C, $r_d = r_s$ and therefore:

$$\text{Voltage gain} = \frac{v_s}{v_g} = \frac{r_s}{r_s + \dfrac{1}{g_m}} \to 1 \text{ if } r_s \gg \frac{1}{g_m}$$

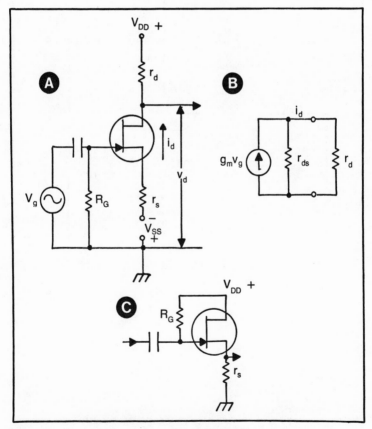

Fig. 3-16. The JFET as a small signal amplifier.

The low voltage gain is due to the negative feedback developed across r_s. However this also results in the source follower having an extremely high input impedance but a low output impedance. The same properties are possessed by the cathode follower and common collector circuits.

Example 3-8

In Fig. 3-17, the g_m of the JFET is 6000 μS. Calculate the voltage gain from gate to drain (neglect the value of r_{ds}). If the capacitor, C, is removed, what is the new value of the voltage gain?

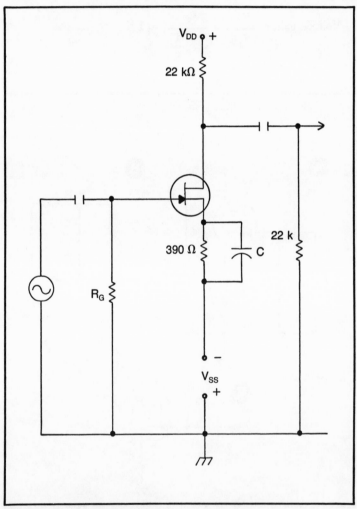

Fig. 3-17. Circuit for Example 3-8.

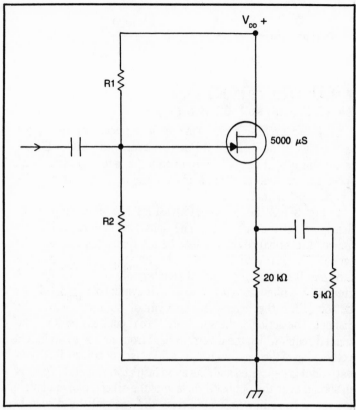

Fig. 3-18. Circuit for Example 3-9.

Solution

Total drain load, $r_d = 22\ k\Omega//22\ k\Omega = 11\ k\Omega$.

Voltage gain $= g_m r_d = 6000\ \mu S \times 11\ k\Omega$

$= 66$.

When C is removed,

New voltage gain $= \dfrac{r_d}{r_s + \dfrac{1}{g_m}} = \dfrac{11000}{390 + 167}$

$= 20$, rounded off.

Example 3-9

In Fig. 3-18, calculate the value of the voltage gain from gate to source.

Solution

Total source load, $r_s = 20\ k\Omega\ //5\ k\Omega = 4\ k\Omega$.

$$\text{Voltage gain} = \frac{r_s}{r_s + \dfrac{1}{g_m}} = \frac{4000}{4000 + 200} = 0.95.$$

THE METAL-OXIDE SEMICONDUCTOR
FIELD EFFECT TRANSISTOR (MOSFET)

To avoid excessive gate current it is necessary to apply a negative bias to the gate of a JFET. However with a MOSFET the gate current is still virtually zero even if the gate is positive with respect to the source. This is made possible by the MOSFET's different construction.

In Fig. 3-19A the n-channel MOSFET has only one p region which is called the substrate. The substrate may have its own terminal (4 terminal device) or may be internally connected to the source (3 terminal device); in this chapter it is assumed that the source and the substrate are either internally or externally connected. This is illustrated in the schematic symbol of Fig. 3-19B. As with the JFET the arrow in the symbol points towards the n-channel. The action of the substrate is to reduce the width of the channel through which the electrons pass from source to drain. On the other side of the narrow channel a thin layer of silicon dioxide (a metal oxide) is deposited and acts as an insulator. A metallic gate is then spread over the opposite surface of the silicon dioxide layer. Since the gate is now insulated from the channel the device is sometimes referred to as an *Insulated-Gate Fet* or *IGFET*.

In the operation of the n-channel MOSFET the drain supply voltage, V_{DD}, causes electrons to flow from source to drain through the channel while the gate voltage controls the channel's resis-

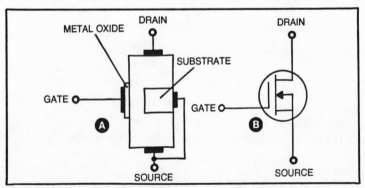

Fig. 3-19. The N channel DE MOSFET.

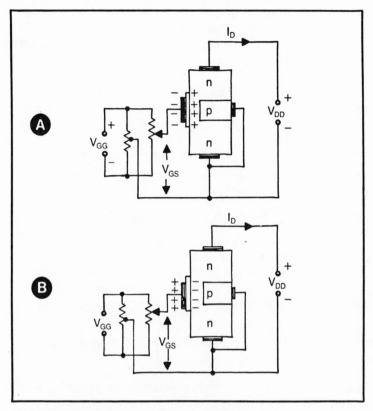

Fig. 3-20. Depletion and enhancement modes.

tance. If a negative voltage is applied to the gate with respect to the source (Fig. 3-20A), electrostatic induction will cause positive charges to appear in the channel. These charges will be in the form of positive ions which have been created by the repulsion of conduction-band electrons away from the gate; in other words, the number of conduction-band electrons existing in the n-channel has been reduced or depleted. If the gate is made increasingly negative, there will be fewer and fewer conduction-band electrons available until ultimately the MOSFET is cut off. This action is very similar to that of the JFET; since a negative gate causes a depletion of conduction electrons, this manner of operating a MOSFET is called the *depletion mode*.

Since the channel and the gate are insulated from each other, it is possible to apply a positive voltage to the MOSFET gate (Fig. 3-20B). The result will be to induce negative charges into the n-channel; these will be in the form of additional conduction-band electrons which are drawn into the channel by the action of the positive gate. The total number of conduction-band electrons has therefore been increased or enhanced; consequently this manner of operation for the MOSFET is called the *enhancement mode*.

Unlike the JFET the MOSFET may be operated with either a positive or a negative gate voltage; in either mode of operation the input resistance of a MOSFET is very high and is typically of the order of hundreds of G Ω.

Apart from the necessity of reversing the polarity of the drain and gate supply voltages, the operation of p-channel and n-channel MOSFETs are identical.

MOSFET Drain and Transconductance Curves

The appearances of the MOSFET curves are similar to those of the JFET and are illustrated in Figs. 3-21A and 3-21B. The only difference is the extension of the gate voltage into the positive region of the enhancement mode. The transconductance curve is still a parabola with its equation:

$$I_D = I_{DSS} \left(1 - \frac{V_{GS}}{V_{GS\,off}} \right)^2 \qquad \text{Equation 3-18}$$

In this equation $V_{GS(off)}$ is always a negative voltage but V_{GS} may either be positive or negative.

The type of MOSFET, which may either operate in the depletion or the enhancement mode, conducts when $V_{GS} = 0$ with a drain current value equal to I_{DSS}. For this reason the device is called a *normally on* or depletion-enhancement (DE) MOSFET. Such a MOSFET can be operated with zero bias since the dc operating point can be chosen at $V_{GS} = 0$, when the signal is applied to the gate, the operation of the MOSFET will swing back and forth between the depletion and the enhancement modes.

Biasing the DE MOSFET

The gate of the DE MOSFET may be biased either positively or negatively with respect to the source. Working in either the depletion mode or the enhancement mode can be provided by both voltage divider and source bias. However, self-bias and current-source bias can only be used to operate in the depletion mode. Zero bias of the DE MOSFET is achieved in the circuit of Fig. 3-22. Since $V_{GS} = 0$ and $I_D = I_{DSS}$, it follows that

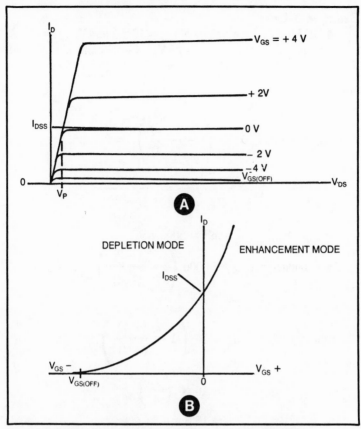

Fig. 3-21. Drain and transconductance curves of the MOSFET.

$$V_{DS} = V_{DD} - I_{DSS}R_D \qquad \text{Equation 3-19}$$

Provided $V_{DS} > V_p$, the DE MOSFET will automatically operate on the nearly flat section of the $V_{GS} = 0$ drain curve. The signal may also be directly coupled to the gate without the necessity for a coupling capacitor; this will allow a flat response for the amplifier at low frequencies.

The DE MOSFET as a Signal Amplifier

Like the JFET amplifier, the DE MOSFET behaves as a constant current source with a value of $g_m v_d$ in parallel with the very high value of r_{ds}. The equations for the signal output and the voltage gain are therefore the same for both the JFET and the DE MOSFET amplifiers.

Example 3-10

A DE MOSFET has values of $I_{DSS} = 10$ mA and $V_{GS(off)} = -4$ V. What are the values of I_D and g_m at (a) $V_{GS} = -2$ V, and (b) $V_{GS} = +1$ V?

Solution

(a) $V_{GS} = -2$ V.

Drain current, $I_D = 10 \left(1 - \dfrac{(-2)}{(-4)}\right)^2 = 2.5$ mA.

$$g_{mo} = \frac{-2 \, I_{DSS}}{V_{GS(off)}} = \frac{-2 \times 10}{-4}$$

$$= 5 \text{ mS} = 5000 \, \mu\text{S}.$$

Transconductance, $g_m = 5000 \left(1 - \dfrac{(-2)}{(-4)}\right) = 2500 \, \mu$S.

(b) $V_{GS} = +1$ V.

Drain current, $I_D = 10 \left(1 - \dfrac{(+1)}{(-4)}\right)^2$

$$= 10 \times \left(\frac{5}{4}\right)^2$$

$$= 15.6 \text{ mA}.$$

Transconductance, $g_m = 5000 \left(1 - \dfrac{(+1)}{(-4)}\right) = 6250 \, \mu$S.

Example 3-11

The DE MOSFET of example 3-10 is used in the circuit of Fig. 3-22. If $R_D = 1.5$ kΩ, calculate the values of V_{DS} and the amplifiers voltage gain (neglect the effect of r_{ds}).

Solution

The circuit is operating with zero bias and therefore $I_D = I_{DSS} = 10$ mA. Then, $V_{DS} = +24$ V $- 10$ mA $\times 1.5$ k$\Omega = 9$ V.

The value of V_{DS} exceeds the pinch-off voltage, $V_p = 4$ V and therefore the DE MOSFET will operate on the flat section of the drain curve for $V_{GS} = 0$ V. The voltage gain $= g_{mo} \times r_d = 5000$ μS $\times 1.5$ k$\Omega = 7.5$.

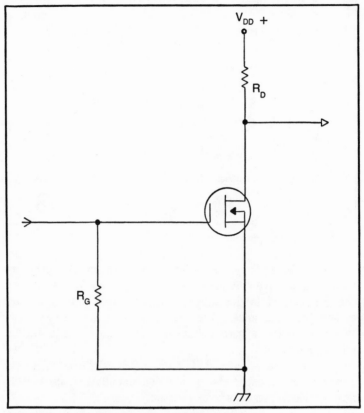

Fig. 3-22. The DE MOSFET with zero bias.

THE ENHANCEMENT-ONLY OR E MOSFET

In this type of MOSFET there is no longer a continuous n-channel between the drain and the source. The substrate stretches all the way across to the metal oxide layer (Fig. 3-23A) so that no current can flow if the MOSFET is in the depletion mode. When $V_{GS} = 0$ V, there will be a small number of conduction-band electrons created in the substrate by thermal energy but the current flow due to the drain supply is still extremely small. Consequently the E MOSFET is also referred to as a *normally-off* MOSFET. This normally-off condition is shown in the schematic symbol (Fig. 3-23B) by the broken line which represents the channel. Since Fig. 3-23A shows an n-channel E MOSFET, the arrow in the schematic symbol points towards the channel; with a p-type MOSFET the arrow would point away from the channel.

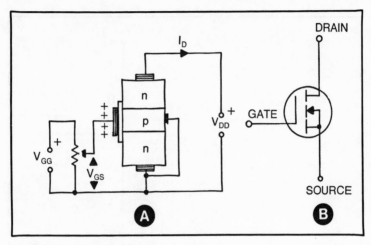

Fig. 3-23. The E MOSFET.

To produce an appreciable flow of drain current it is necessary to apply a positive voltage to the gate. If this voltage is low, the charges induced in the substrate are negative ions which are created by filling holes in the p-substrate with valence electrons. When the positive gate voltage is increased above a certain minimum threshold level, ($V_{GS} > V_{GS(th)}$), the additional induced charges are conduction band electrons which exist in a thin n-type inversion layer next to the metal oxide and allow an appreciable flow of electrons from source to drain.

Drain and Transconductance Curves of the E MOSFET

In Fig. 3-24A each drain curve represents a fixed positive value of V_{GS}. For the lowest curve $V_{GS} = + V_{GS(th)}$ and the E MOSFET is virtually cut off.

The transconductance curve is again parabolic in shape with its vertex at V_{GS} (Fig. 3-24B). The curve's equation is:

$$I_D = k(V_{GS} - V_{GS(th)})^2 \qquad \textbf{Equation 3-19}$$

where k is a constant value for a particular MOSFET.

The range of the threshold voltage is typically $+ 1\,V$ to $+ 5\,V$. To obtain the value of k, a point on the transconductance curve must be specified. For example if
$V_{GS(th)} = + 2\,V$ and $I_D = 12$ mA when $V_{GS} = \div 4\,V$, 12 mA $= k$ $(4\,V - 2\,V)^2$ $k = 0.003$.

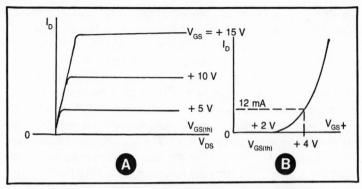

Fig. 3-24. Drain and transconductance curves of the E MOSFET.

The equation for the transconductance is:

$$g_m = 2 k (V_{GS} - V_{GS(th)}) \qquad \textbf{Equation 3-20}$$

Biasing the E MOSFET

E MOSFETs can use voltage divider and source bias but not self and current-source bias which can only provide operation in the depletion mode. However there is another circuit, drain feedback bias, which is only suitable for the enhancement mode (Fig. 3-25). A high value resistor of several MΩ is connected between the drain and the gate. Since the voltage drop across R_G due to the gate current is negligible, $V_{DS} = V_{GS} = V_{DD} - I_D R_D$. By arranging that the

Fig. 3-25. Drain feedback Bias.

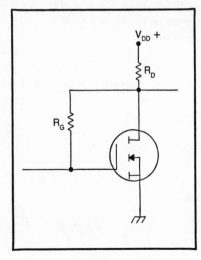

value of V_{DS} is well above the pinch-off voltage, the operation of the MOSFET will occur on the nearly flat section of the drain curve. Once I_D, V_{DD} and V_{GS} have been determined, the value of R_D may be chosen to provide the required operating conditions.

The action of drain feedback bias for the E MOSFET is similar to the bipolar's collector feedback or self-bias, which compensates for changes which occur in the FET's characteristics. For example if I_D is tending to decrease, both V_{DS} and V_{GS} will increase and this will level off the tendency for I_D to fall. The disadvantage of this type of bias is the degenerative feedback which occurs from the drain output to the gate input; this has the effect of reducing the amplifier's voltage gain.

Since the gate of an E MOSFET operates with a positive voltage on the gate, it is possible to use direct coupling between the amplifier stages (Fig. 3-26); not only is the circuitry simple, it has the advantage of an excellent flat response at low frequencies. The positive bias required by one stage is provided by the dc drain voltage of the previous stage.

The E MOSFET as a Small Signal Amplifier

The equations of the E MOSFET amplifier are the same as those for the JFET and DE MOSFET amplifiers previously discussed. For a common source stage the gain from gate to drain is $g_m r_d$.

Example 3-12

For an E MOSFET, $k = 0.001$ and $V_{GS(th)} = +2.5$ V. What are the values of I_D and g_m at the point on the transconductance curve for which $F_{GS} = +5.5$ V?

Solution

Drain current, $I_D = 0.001 (5.5 \text{ V} - 2.5 \text{ V})^2$ A
$$= 9 \text{ mA}.$$

Transconductance, $g_m = 2 \times 0.001 (5.5 \text{ V} - 2.5 \text{ V})$ S
$$= 6000 \ \mu\text{S}.$$

Example 3-13

It is required to bias the E MOSFET of example 3-12 at the point for which $V_{GS} = +5.5$ V. If the drain feedback circuit of Fig. 3-25 is used, calculate the value of R_D. What is the value of the voltage gain from gate to drain?

Solution

Drain load resistor, $R_D = \dfrac{24 \text{ V} - 5.5 \text{ V}}{9 \text{ mA}} = 2 \text{ k} \Omega$

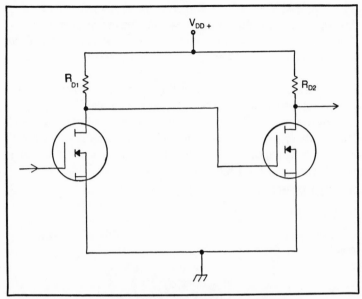

Fig. 3-26. Direct coupling between E MOSFET amplifiers.

Voltage gain from gate to drain $= g_m r_d$
$$= 6000 \ \mu S \times 2 \ k\Omega$$
$$= 12$$

COMPARISON BETWEEN BIPOLAR TRANSISTORS AND FETS

Compared with bipolar transistors FETS have the definite advantage of extremely high input resistances, so that they have practically no loading effect. The input resistance of JFETs can range up to 10 GΩ while for MOSFETs the values can extend to 10000 GΩ.

As discrete components FETs tend to be more expensive than bipolar transistors. However, in integrated circuits with a large number of active devices the MOSFET is easier to manufacture and it is possible to concentrate more MOSFETs than bipolars on a single chip; as a result a MOS IC tends to be cheaper than a comparable bipolar IC.

The transconductance curve of a FET is a parabola which is referred to as a square law characteristic. A small input signal will only operate over a limited section of the curve and therefore there will be an approximately linear relationship between the input and output signals. For larger signals the parabolic curves will intro-

71

duce appreciable waveform distortion into the amplifier's output; this degree of distortion may be unacceptable in some applications. However, a square law characteristic is ideal for a mixer circuit in which two signals of different frequencies are fed to a dual-gate FET.

For a bipolar transistor operating over the approximately flat sections of the collector curves, it is necessary that V_{CE} exceeds 1 volt. However, for a FET, V_{DS} must be greater than the pinch-off voltage which is much more than 1 volt. It follows that a FET will need higher voltage power supplies than a bipolar and this is clearly a disadvantage of the FET.

CHAPTER SUMMARY

Junction FET

Gate biased negatively with respect to the source (depletion mode only).

$$I_D = I_{DSS}\left(1 - \frac{V_{GS}}{V_{GS(off)}}\right)^2$$

$$g_{mo} = -\frac{2\,I_{DSS}}{V_{GSoff}}$$

$$g_m = g_{mo}\,1 - \left(\frac{V_{GS}}{V_{GS(off)}}\right)$$

Gate Bias

$$I_D = \frac{V_{GG} - V_{GS}}{R_S} \approx \frac{V_{GG}}{R_S} \quad \text{if } V_{GG} >> V_{GS}$$

Voltage Divider Bias

$$V_{GG} = \frac{V_{DD} \times R_2}{R_1 + R_2}$$

$$I_D = \frac{V_{GG} - V_{GS}}{R_S} \approx \frac{V_{GG}}{R_S} \quad \text{if } V_{GG} >> V_{GS}$$

Self Bias

$$V_{GS} = -I_D R_S$$

Source Bias

$$I_D = \frac{V_{SS} - V_{GS}}{R_S} \approx \frac{V_{SS}}{R_S} \quad \text{if } V_{SS} >> V_{GS}$$

Common Source Small-Signal Amplifier
180° phase change between the input and output signals.

$$v_d = i_d r_d$$

$$v_g = i_d (r_s + \frac{1}{g_m}), \text{ neglecting } r_{ds} = \frac{\Delta V_{DS}}{\Delta I_D}$$

$$\text{Voltage Gain} = \frac{v_d}{v_g} = \frac{r_d}{r_s + \frac{1}{g_m}}$$

If the source resistance is bypassed $r_s = 0$ and

$$\text{Voltage Gain} = g_m r_d$$

If $r_s >> \frac{1}{g_m}$, Voltage Gain $= \dfrac{r_d}{r_d}$

Source Follower
Zero phase change between the input and output signals.

$$\text{Voltage Gain} \approx \frac{r_s}{r_s + \frac{1}{g_m}} \rightarrow 1 \text{ if } r_s >> \frac{1}{g_m}$$

DE MOSFET
Gate biased either negatively or positively with respect to the source (depletion or enhancement mode). Equations are the same as those for the JFET except that self bias may only be used for the depletion mode.

E MOSFET
Gate biased positively with respect to the source (enhancement mode only). Voltage divider or source bias may be used.

$$I_D = k (V_{GS} - V_{GS(th)})^2$$
$$g_m = 2 k (V_{GS} - V_{GS(th)})$$

Drain Feedback Bias.

$$V_{DS} = V_{GS} = V_{DD} - I_D R_D.$$

The equations for the small signal amplifier are the same as those for the JFET and DE MOSFET.

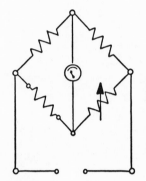

Chapter 4
Vacuum Tubes

Figure 4-1 shows a small area of a triode's static plate characteristics; the center of this area is the operating point Q. The word *static* means that the characteristic curves were obtained under controlled laboratory conditions, rather than under dynamic operation such as occurs in an amplifier circuit.

PARAMETERS OF THE TRIODE STATIC CHARACTERISTICS

If the grid voltage, E_c, is held constant, a small change in the plate voltage, Δe_b, will be accompanied by a small change in the plate current, Δi_b. The triode's ac plate resistance or plate impedance, r_p, is a measure of the control which the plate voltage has over the plate current, and is defined by:

$$\text{ac plate resistance, } r_p = \frac{\Delta e_b}{\Delta i_b} \qquad \textbf{Equation 4-1}$$

The value of r_p is typically of the order of kilohms, and may be derived from the reciprocal of the plate characteristic slope at the point Q. However, it is not a constant for a particular triode since its value depends on the actual operating point chosen.

The dc plate resistance,
$$R_P = \frac{E_b}{I_b} \; ,$$

the value of which also depends on the operating conditions as represented by the point Q.

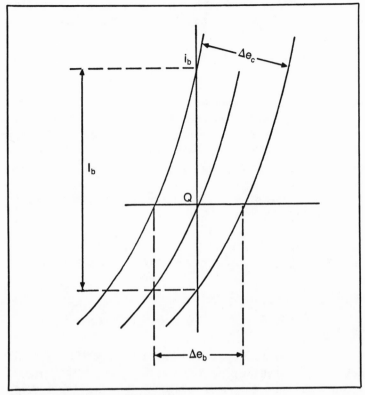

Fig. 4-1. Triode plate characteristics.

If the plate voltage, E_b is held constant, a small change in control grid voltage, Δe_c, will produce a corresponding small change in plate current, Δi_b. The triode's mutual (or transfer) conductance is a measure of the control which the grid voltage has over the plate current and is defined by:

Transconductance, $g_m = \dfrac{\Delta i_b}{\Delta e_c}$ **Equation 4-2**

The basic unit of conductance is the mho and the values of g_m are typically a few thousand micromhos. This value may be derived from the slope at the same point, Q, on the static transfer (mutual) characteristic. As with r_p, g_m is not a constant for a particular triode but depends on the choice of the operating point.

To hold the plate current, I_b, constant, a small change is in the plate voltage, Δe_b, may be compensated by an opposite small change in the control grid voltage, Δe_c. The triode amplification factor, μ, compares the controls which the plate voltage and the grid voltage exercise over the plate current, and is defined by:

$$\text{Amplification factor, } \mu = \frac{\Delta e_b}{\Delta e_c} \qquad \textbf{Equation 4-3}$$

The value of μ is primarily determined by the geometry of the triode and has no units. From the selection of triodes commercially produced, the values of the amplification factor range from 2 to 100, so that the tubes may be classified as low-μ (primarily for power amplification), medium-μ and high-μ triodes (used for voltage amplification).

If the parameters μ, r_p, g_m are all derived from the same operating point, Q, then:

$$\mu = \frac{\Delta e_b}{\Delta e_c} = \frac{\Delta e_b}{\Delta i_b} \times \frac{\Delta i_b}{\Delta e_c} = r_p \times g_m \quad \textbf{Equation 4-4}$$

For example, if $r_p = 10$ kΩ and $g_m = 2000$ micromhos, then $\mu = r_p g_m$ $= 10 \times 10^3 \times 2000 \times 10^{-6} = 20$ (a medium $-$ μ triode).

Example 4-1

A triode's operating point is defined by $E_b = +250$ V, $I_b = 10$ mA $E_c = 4$ V. When the plate voltage is changed from 240 V to 260 V, while maintaining the grid voltage at -4 V, the plate current varies between 9.4 mA and 10.6 mA. What are the triode's ac and dc plate resistance? If the plate voltage is kept constant at $+250$ V and the control grid voltage is shifted from -3.8 V to -4.2 V, the change of plate current is 0.8 mA. What is the triode's transconductance? If the operating point is kept constant, calculate the value of the amplification factor.

Solution

Change in plate voltage, $\Delta e_b = 260 - 240 = 20$ V. The corresponding change in the plate current, Δi_b, is $10.6 - 9.4 = 1.2$ mA. AC plate resistance,

$$r_p = \frac{\Delta e_b}{\Delta i_b} = \frac{20 \text{ V}}{1.2 \text{ mA}} = 16.7 \text{ k}\Omega.$$

DC plate resistance is given by:

$$R_p = \frac{E_b}{I_b} = \frac{250 \text{ V}}{10 \text{ mA}} = 25 \text{ k}\Omega$$

Change in grid voltage, $\Delta e_c = 4.2 - 3.8 = 0.4$ V.
The transconductance is,

$$g_m = \frac{i_b}{e_c} = \frac{0.8 \text{ mA}}{0.4 \text{ V}} = 2 \text{ millimhos} = 2000 \text{ micromhos}.$$

Amplification factor, $\mu = r_p g_m = 16.7 \times 10^3 \times 2000 \times 10^{-6}$
$= 33$, rounded off.

Example 4-2

In Example 4-1, the control grid voltage is changed from -4 V
to -3.6 V. To what value must the plate voltage be shifted in order
to restore the plate current to the 10 mA level?

Solution

Since the control grid voltage has been made less negative, the
plate current has increased and therefore the plate voltage must be
lowered in order to restore the plate current to its original value.
Required change in the plate voltage, $\Delta e_b = \mu \times \Delta e_c = 33.4 \times 0.4$
$= 13.4$ V, rounded off. New value of plate voltage $= 250 - 13.4 =$
236.6 V.

TRIODE AUDIO VOLTAGE AND POWER AMPLIFIERS

In this section, capital letters will be used to indicate no-signal
(quiescent or dc) values of plate voltage, plate current and grid
voltage, while lower case letters will represent their instantaneous
signal levels. For simplicity we shall consider that the audio signal
input is a single *sine wave* whose sound equivalent is a pure tone.

Audio Voltage Amplifier with Plate Load Resistor

In order to keep distortion to a minimum, a single-stage audio
frequency (af) amplifier must operate under *class A conditions* which
require that the plate current shall flow continuously and that the
control grid current shall not flow at all. This is somtimes expressed by saying that the angle of plate current flow is 360° (plate
current flows throughout the complete cycle of the audio input
signal) while the angle of control grid current flow is 0°.

Quiescent Conditions. Since no grid current is allowed to
flow, the current in the cathode circuit must equal the current in the
plate circuit, so that the currents through R_K and R_L are equal (Fig.
4-2A).

For class A operation, the triode is often biased to the center of
the approximately linear (straight) portion of the transfer charac-

teristic. This requires that the bias be positioned roughly half-way between zero and the cut-off point which represents the value of negative grid volts which is just sufficient to prevent the flow of plate current. The value of this cut-off bias is,

$$- \frac{E_{bb}}{\mu}$$

volts where E_{bb} is the plate supply voltage, and therefore the bias for class A operation is approximately,

$$- \frac{E_{bb}}{2\,\mu} \text{ volts.}$$

The bias points for other classes of operation are shown in Fig. 4-2B, and their related bias values are:

Class AB: $- \dfrac{0.75\,E_{bb}}{\mu}$ volts   **Equation 4-5**

Class B: $- \dfrac{E_{bb}}{\mu}$ volts (approximately)   **Equation 4-6**

Class C: Between $- \dfrac{2\,E_{bb}}{\mu}$ and $- \dfrac{4\,E_{bb}}{\mu}$ **Equation 4-7**

Cathode bias is often used to provide class A operation. The mean dc level of plate current passes through R_K and develops a voltage drop which is equal to the required value of bias.

Referring to Fig. 4-2A:

Cathode potential, $E_K = +\,I_b R_K$ **Equation 4-8**

Class A bias value $= -\,I_b R_K$ **Equation 4-9**

Voltage between plate and ground, $E_b = E_{bb} - I_b R_L$

Equation 4-10

Voltage between plate and cathode, $E_{PK} = E_b - I_b R_K$

$$= E_{bb} - I_b (R_L + R_K)$$

Equation 4-11

Plate power dissipation $= E_{PK} I_b = E_b I_b - I_b^2 R_K = E_{bb} I_b - I_2^2$

$$(R_L + R_K)$$ **Equation 4-12**

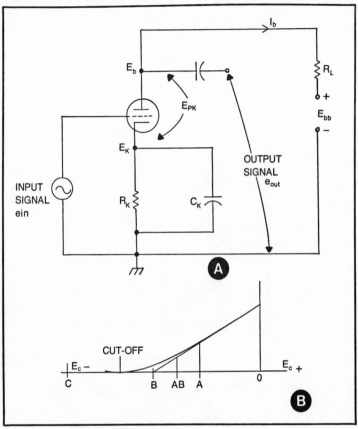

Fig. 4-2. Triode voltage amplifier.

DC plate input power (dc power from the B + supply) = $E_{bb}I_b$

Equation 4-13

Signal Conditions. Under signal conditions, the mean levels of the plate voltage, plate current and grid voltage are approximately the same as the values under quiescent conditions.

The audio sine wave voltage is applied in series with the bias between the control grid and cathode, creating a fluctuating dc plate current whose signal component is in phase with the signal voltage on the control grid. The plate voltage also has a fluctuating dc waveform with an ac component which represents the output audio signal; as shown in Fig. 4-3 this plate signal is 180° out of phase with the input grid signal. If cathode bias is used without the inclusion of C_K, the voltage on the cathode is in phase with the input signal on

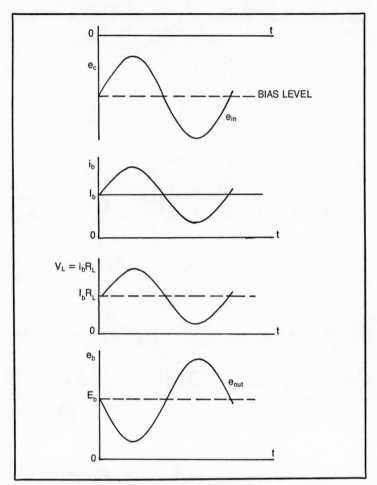

Fig. 4-3. Waveforms of triode voltage amplifier.

the control grid and the plate current, but is 180° out of phase with the signal voltage between plate and ground.

If the peak voltage of the audio signal input were to exceed the bias level, the grid would be driven positive with respect to the cathode during part of the grid voltage cycle. This would cause grid current to flow with the result that the output signal would be distorted. Therefore, under class A conditions, the highest rms value of the input signal is 0.707 × the bias value; this assumes that the bias point has been correctly chosen so that the signal does not take the grid voltage down to the cut-off region where further distortion would occur.

The voltage gain of the amplifier is:

$$A = \frac{\text{rms value of the audio signal output voltage } (e_{out})}{\text{rms value of the audio signal input voltage } (e_{in})}$$

$$= \frac{\text{rms (or peak-to-peak) value of } e_b}{\text{rms (or peak-to-peak) value of } e_c} = \frac{\mu R_L}{r_p = R_L}$$

Equation 4-14

This expression for the voltage gain is related to the equivalent circuit shown in Fig. 4-4. The negative sign for $-e_{in}$ indicates the 180° phase change which occurs between the input grid signal and the output plate signal. The ac plate resistance, r_p, may be regarded as the internal resistance of the equivalent generator. If the circuit of Fig. 4-2 and the next amplifier (Fig. 4-5) are rc coupled, the grid leak resistor, R_g, of the following stage is effectively in parallel with R_L and must be taken into account in the calculation of the voltage

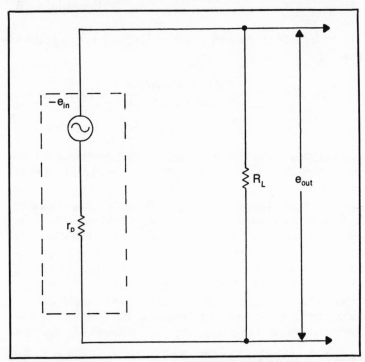

Fig. 4-4. Equivalent circuit of triode voltage amplifier under signal conditions.

gain. An alternative expression for the voltage gain is $g_m R$ (where R is the total equivalent resistance of r_p, R_L, and R_g in parallel). Notice that the value of the voltage gain cannot equal or exceed the amplification factor, μ, if a resistor is used as the plate load. The higher the value of R_L, the more nearly the voltage gain approaches the value of μ.

The signal power output will be determined by the amplifier components, the plate voltage, and the plate current.

Signal power output:

$$= \frac{\text{(peak-to-peak value of } e_b) \times \text{(peak-to-peak value of } i_b)}{8}$$

$$= \text{(RMS value of } i_b)^2 \times R_L$$

$$= \frac{\text{(RMS value of } e_b)^2}{R_L} \quad \text{watts}$$

Equation 4-15

The plate efficiency compares the signal output power with the dc plate input power, and is given by:

$$\text{Plate efficiency} = \frac{\text{signal power output}}{\text{dc plate input power}} \times 100\%$$

Equation 4-16

Cathode Capacitor, C_K. The cathode bias resistor is common to both the grid-cathode and plate-cathode circuits. Without the presence of C_K, the signal component of the plate current would develop a signal voltage across R_K. This signal voltage would be $180°$ out of phase with the audio input signal and would therefore represent negative or degenerative feedback. This would have the effect of reducing the amplifier voltage gain. To prevent degeneration C_K is a by-pass or decoupling capacitor which offers a low reactance (compared with the value of R_K) to the frequencies contained in the audio signal. Taking music as an example, the frequency range will extend from below 100 Hz to several kHz. A common criterion is to arrange that the reactance of C_K does not exceed $\frac{1}{10}$ th of the value of R_K at the lowest frequency to be by-passed. On this basis, the formula for C_K is:

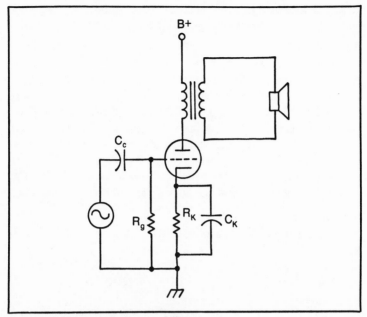

Fig. 4-5. Triode audio power amplifier.

$$C_K = \frac{1.50 \times 10^6}{f\, F_K} \text{ microfarads} \qquad \textbf{Equation 4-17}$$

where R_K is the value of the cathode resistor in ohms and f is the lowest frequency to be bypassed in Hz. For audio amplifiers, the values of C_K are normally several microfarads while for rf amplifiers, C_K is 0.01 μF or less. It should be pointed out that class A operation is also necessary in receiver stages such as the radio frequency and intermediate frequency voltage amplifiers; such stages commonly use cathode bias to provide the required quiescent conditions.

Triode Audio Power Amplifier

Figure 4-5 represents a triode audio power amplifier which is being used as the output stage of a receiver. The class A requirements are the same as for the voltage amplifier already described but the tube would probably possess a low μ, a low r_p and a high g_m since such a triode would have the ability to handle a large input signal voltage and also produce a high audio power output. Under optimum conditions of maximum audio power output, with minimum distortion, the required value for the plate load is $2\, r_p$. Since the primary winding of the matching transformer would possess a low resistance, the mean dc level of the plate-to-ground voltage would virtually be equal to the value of the B$^+$ supply.

Example 4-3

Under quiescent conditions in the circuit of Fig. 4-6 the plate current is 8 mA. What are the values of the plate-to-ground voltage, the cathode bias, the plate-to-cathode voltage, the plate dissipation and the dc input power? If the amplification factor of the tube is 18, what are the values of the cut-off and mid-point (class A) bias? Assuming that the transfer characteristic is linear from zero down to cut-off, what is the maximum possible value of the rms input signal which is assumed to be a single sine wave. Calculate the value of the voltage gain if the ac plate resistance is 10 kΩ.

Solution

Voltage drop across the plate load resistor $= I_b R_L = 8$ mA $\times$ 15 kΩ = 120 V.

Plate-to-ground voltage, $E_b = E_{bb} - I_b R_L = 250 - 120 = 130$ V

Value of the cathode bias $= I_b R_K = 8 \times 10^{-3} \times 680 = 5.4$ V, rounded off.

Plate-to-cathode voltage, $E_{PK} = E_b - I_b R_K = 130 - 5.4 = 124.6$ V.

Plate dissipation $= E_{PK} \times I_b = 124.6$ V $\times$ 8 mA $= 996.8$ mW $= 1.0$ W rounded off.

DC input power (plate input power) from the B$^+$ supply $= E_{bb} \times I_b = 250$ V $\times$ 8 mA $= 2000$ mW $= 2$ W.

$$\text{Value of the cut-off bias} = \frac{-E_{bb}}{\mu} = \frac{-250 \text{ V}}{18}$$

$$= -13.9 \text{ V rounded off.}$$

The value of the class A bias is -6.95 V, which is less than half the value of the -13.9 V cutoff bias. Therefore the highest allowable rms value for the input signal is $0.707 \times 6.95 = 4.91$ V, rounded off.

$$\text{Voltage gain} = \frac{\mu R_L}{r_p + R_L} = \frac{18 \times 15 \text{ k}\Omega}{10 \text{ k}\Omega + 15 \text{ k}\Omega}$$

$$= \frac{18 \times 15}{25} = 10.8$$

Example 4-4

In Example 4-3, the audio amplifier is now RC coupled to the next stage. If the following amplifier stage uses a 270 kΩ grid leak resistor, what is the new voltage gain of the first stage?

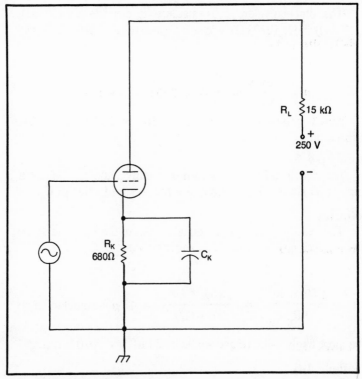

Fig. 4-6. Circuit for Example 4-3.

Solution

The effective plate load on the first stage consists of the 15 kΩ plate load resistor and the 270 kΩ grid leak resistor in parallel.

$$\text{Total plate load resistance} = \frac{15 \times 270}{15 + 270} = \frac{15 \times 270}{285}$$

$$= 14.2 \text{ k}\Omega \text{ rounded off.}$$

$$\text{New voltage gain} = \frac{18 \times 14.2}{10 + 14.2} = \frac{18 \times 14.2}{24.2}$$

$$= 10.6$$

$$\text{Alternatively,} \quad g_m = \frac{\mu}{r_p} = \frac{18}{10 \text{ k}\Omega}$$

$$= 1.8 \text{ millimhos} = 1800 \text{ micromhos.}$$

The total equivalent load resistance, R, consists of r_p (10 kΩ), R_L (15 kΩ) and R_g (270 kΩ) in parallel. Since the resistance of R_L and R_g in parallel is 14.2:

$$R = \frac{10 \times 14.2}{10 + 14.2} = 5.87 \text{ kΩ, rounded off.}$$

New voltage gain = $g_m R = 1.8 \times 10^{-3} \times 5.87 \times 10^3 = 10.6$, rounded off.

Example 4-5

The circuit in Fig. 4-6 is used to amplify audio signals in the range of 50 Hz to 15 kHz. Calculate the required value of C_K.

Solution

The reactance of C_K must equal 1/10th of the R_K value at the lowest frequency of 50 Hz. The required value of C_K is:

$$\frac{1.59 \times 10^6}{FR_K} = \frac{1.59 \times 10^6}{50 \times 680} = 47 \text{ μF, rounded off.}$$

The most likely value to use would be 50 μF with a 10 V rating.

Example 4-6

The audio signal input to the circuit of Fig. 4-6 is a sine wave of rms value 2.5 V. Assuming the values of μ and r_p in Example 4-3, what are the output peak-to-peak swings in the plate voltage and the plate current? Calculate the signal power output and the plate efficiency.

Solution

The voltage gain of the amplifier is 10.8 and therefore the rms value of the audio output signal is $2.5 \times 10.8 = 27$ V. The peak-to-peak voltage swing at the plate is $27 \times 2.828 = 76.4$ V, rounded off.

The peak-to-peak swing in the plate current is:

$$\frac{\text{Peak-to-peak swing in the plate voltage}}{R_L} = \frac{76.4 \text{ V}}{15 \text{ kΩ}} = 5.1 \text{ mA}$$

Signal power output =

$$\frac{(\text{peak-to-peak swing in } e_b) \times (\text{peak-to-peak swing in } i_b)}{8}$$

$$= 76.4 \text{ V} \times 5.1 \text{ mA} = 49 \text{ mW, rounded off.}$$

The signal power output may also be found from:

$$\frac{(\text{RMS value of } e_b)^2}{R_L} = \frac{(27 \text{ V})^2}{15 \text{ k}\Omega}$$

$$= 49 \text{ mW, rounded off.}$$

$$\text{Plate efficiency} = \frac{\text{signal power output}}{\text{dc plate input power}} \times 100\%$$

$$= \frac{49 \text{ mW}}{1.0 \text{ W}} \times 100 = 4.9\%, \text{ rounded off.}$$

Note that the plate efficiency of a class A voltage amplifier is always extremely low, since in this type of stage, the main requirement is a voltage gain with minimum distortion rather than a high signal power output.

Example 4-7

The audio power output stage of a receiver uses a triode whose ac plate resistance is 1.2 kΩ. If the loudspeaker impedance is 4 Ω, calculate the turns ratio of a matching transformer which provides optimum conditions.

Solution

For optimum conditions it is required to match the loudspeaker impedance of 4 Ω to a value of twice the r_p or 2.4 kΩ. The turns ratio is:

$$\frac{N_p}{N_s} = \sqrt{\frac{Z_p}{Z_s}} = \sqrt{\frac{2400}{4}}$$

$$= \sqrt{600} = 24:1, \text{ rounded off.}$$

NEGATIVE FEEDBACK IN AUDIO AMPLIFIERS

The introduction of negative feedback in an audio amplifier requires that a fraction, β, of the output signal is fed back in opposition to the input signal. In contrast with the disadvantage of reducing the amplifier gain, negative or degenerative feedback provides the following features:

☐ Stabilization of the amplifier voltage gain against changes in the parameters of the active device (tube or transistor).

☐ Reduction in the amplitude distortion caused by non-linearity in the tube or transistor characteristics.

□ Reduction in frequency and phase distortion produced by the interelectrode, junction, and stray capacitances.

□ Reduction in noise.

□ Changes in the stage input and output impedances.

Note that the second, third, and fourth advantages refer to the distortion and noise which are created within the stage itself. Negative feedback has no effect on the noise and distortion fed in from the previous stage.

Voltage Gain with Negative Feedback

In the block diagram of Fig. 4-7, the signal applied between grid and cathode is the sum of the input audio signal between grid and ground, V_i, and the negative feedback voltage, $-\beta V_o$. Therefore,

Signal between grid and cathode $= V_i - \beta V_o$

Equation 4-18

Output audio signal, $V_o = A \times$ (signal between G and K)

$$= A(V_i - \beta V_o) \qquad \text{Equation 4-19}$$

Amplifier gain with negative feedback,

$$A' = \frac{V_o}{V_i} = \frac{A}{1 + A\beta} \qquad \text{Equation 4-20}$$

If $A\beta$ is appreciably greater than 1, A' tends in value to,

$$\frac{A}{A\beta} = \frac{1}{\beta}$$

which is independent of A; consequently A' will be little affected by any changes in the tube or transistor parameters.

Since $A' = \dfrac{A}{1 + A\beta}$, $A = \dfrac{A'}{1 - A'\beta}$ and $\beta = \dfrac{1}{A'} - \dfrac{1}{A}$

$$= \frac{A - A'}{A A'} \qquad \text{Equation 4-21}$$

The feedback factor, β, may either be expressed as a fraction or as a percentage.

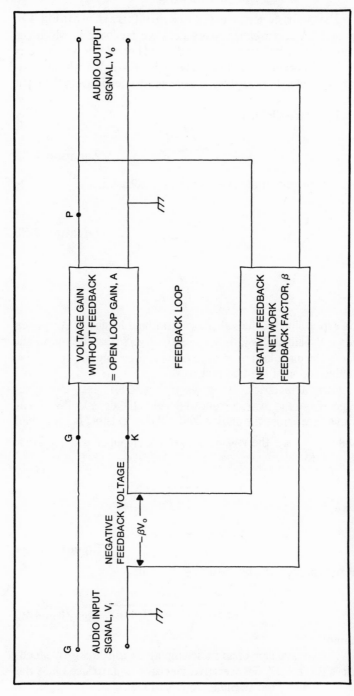

Fig. 4-7. Principles of negative feedback.

The two basic negative feedback circuits are shown in Fig. 4-8. Figure 4-8A represents voltage negative feedback in which the audio output signal voltage, V_o, is divided between R_1 and R_2 (C is only a dc blocking capacitor). The voltage $-\beta V_o$, which is developed across R_1, is applied as degenerative feedback to the input signal, V_i.

The feedback factor,

$$\beta = \frac{R_1}{R_1 + R_2} \qquad \textbf{Equation 4-22}$$

The voltage gain of the amplifier with feedback is:

$$A' = \frac{A}{1 - A\beta} \qquad \textbf{Equation 4-23}$$

where,

$$A = \frac{\mu R_L}{r_p - R_L}$$

This expression for the voltage gain without feedback, A, applies when the value of $R_1 + R_2$ is sufficiently large so that the equivalent value of the plate load resistance is not appreciably affected by the shunting action of the two resistors.

Current feedback, as shown in Fig. 4-8B, uses the signal component of the plate current to develop the degenerative feedback voltage across the unbypassed cathode resistor, R_K; β is then equal to $\dfrac{R_K}{R_L}$ and the voltage gain of the amplifier with feedback.

$$A' = \frac{A}{1 + A\beta}$$

where,

$$A = \frac{\mu R_L}{r_p + R_K + R_L} \qquad \textbf{Equation 4-24}$$

These equations can be used to show that:

$$A' = \frac{\mu R_L}{r_p + R_L + R_K (1 + \mu)} \qquad \textbf{Equation 4-25}$$

Example 4-7
The voltage gain of an audio amplifier without negative feedback is 35. If 20% degenerative feedback is introduced into the circuit, calculate the amplifier gain with feedback.

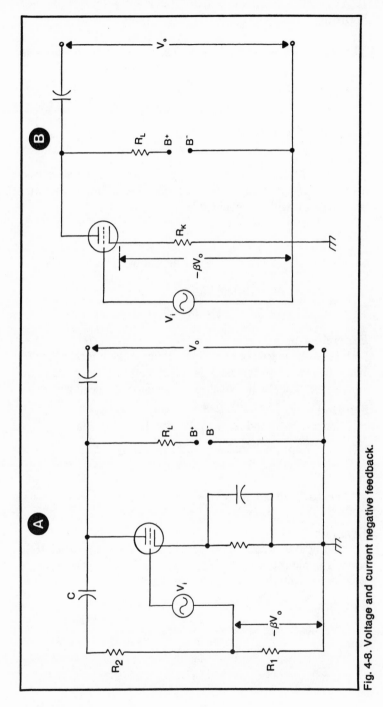

Fig. 4-8. Voltage and current negative feedback.

91

Solution

Since $A = 35$ and $\beta = \dfrac{20}{100} = 0.2$, the gain with feedback is:

$$A' = \frac{A}{1 + A\beta} = \frac{35}{1 + (35 \times 0.2)} = \frac{35}{1 + 7} = \frac{35}{8}$$

$= 4.4$ rounded off.

Example 4-8

The voltage gain of an audio amplifier with degenerative feedback is 8. If the negative feedback factor is 1/10, what is the amplifier gain without feedback?

Solution

Since $A' = 8$ and $\beta = \dfrac{1}{10}$, the gain without feedback is:

$$A = \frac{A'}{1 - A'\beta} = \frac{8}{1 - (8 \times 0.1)} = \frac{8}{0.2} = 40$$

Example 4-9

The voltage gain of an audio amplifier without feedback is 25. When degenerative feedback is introduced into the circuit, the voltage gain falls to 10. What is the feedback percentage?

Solution

Since $A = 25$ and $A' = 10$, the feedback factor is:

$$\beta = \frac{A - A'}{AA'} = \frac{25 - 10}{25 \times 10} = \frac{15}{250}$$

$$\text{Feedback percentage} = \frac{15 \times 100}{250} = 6\%$$

Example 4-10

In Fig. 4-9, what is the negative feedback percentage? If the triode's amplification factor is 24 and its ac plate resistance is 11 k, what is the voltage gain with feedback?

Solution

$$\text{Feedback factor,} = \frac{R_1}{R_1 + R_2} = \frac{33 \text{ k}\Omega}{470 \text{ k}\Omega + 33 \text{ k}\Omega}$$

$$= \frac{33}{503}$$

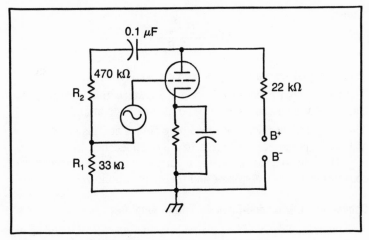

Fig. 4-9. Circuit for Example 4-10.

$$\text{Feedback Percentage} = \frac{33 \times 100}{503} = 6.6\%, \text{ rounded off.}$$

$$\text{Voltage gain without feedback, A} = \frac{\mu\, R_L}{r_p + R_L}$$

$$= \frac{24 \times 22}{11 + 22} = 16$$

$$\text{Voltage gain with feedback, A}' = \frac{16}{1 + (16 \times 0.066)}$$

$$= 7.9, \text{ rounded off.}$$

CATHODE FOLLOWER

The cathode follower circuit is shown in Fig. 4-10A and is an example of voltage negative feedback with a feedback factor, β, of unity. The circuit features are:

☐ No phase change between the cathode-ground output signal and the grid-ground input signal (the cathode output "follows" the grid input).

☐ A voltage gain of less than 1. The voltage is:

$$A' = \frac{A}{A + 1}$$

where,

$$A = \frac{\mu R_K}{r_p + R_K},$$

assuming that no lead is connected across R_K.

□ A higher input impedance and a lower output impedance as compared with a conventional grounded-cathode amplifier.

This circuit is an impedance matching device and may be used to match a high impedance source to a low impedance load.

The following compares the input and output impedance of the conventional triode amplifier and the cathode follower:

Conventional Grounded-Cathode Triode Amplifier

Input impedance: The parallel combination of R_g, C_{gk} and $(A + 1) C_{gp}$ (the result of Miller effect), where,

$$A = \frac{\mu R_L}{r_p + R_L}$$

and C_{gk} and C_{gp} are the grid-to-cathode and the grid-to-plate interelectrode capacitances.

Output impedance: The parallel combination of R_L, r_p, and C_{pk} (the plate-to-cathode interelectrode capacitance).

Triode Cathode Follower

Input impedance: $(A + 1) R_g$, $\frac{C_{gk}}{1 + A}$, and C_{gp} in parallel where,

$$A = \frac{R_K}{r_p + R_K}$$

Output impedance: R_K, $\frac{r_p}{\mu + 1}$, and C_{pk} in parallel.

Example 4-11

In Fig. 4-10A, $R_K = 10$ kΩ, $R_g = 1$ MΩ, $r_p = 8$ kΩ and $\mu = 20$. What is the voltage gain of the cathode follower? Calculate the input and output resistances of the stage.

Solution

Voltage gain =

$$\frac{A}{A + 1}$$

where,

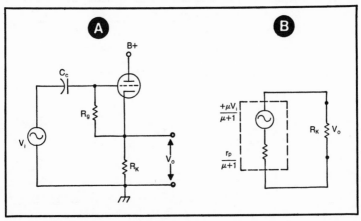

Fig. 4-10. The cathode follower circuit.

$$A = \frac{\mu R_K}{r_p + R_K} = \frac{20 \times 10}{8 + 10} = 11.1, \text{ rounded off.}$$

Voltage gain $= \frac{11.1}{12.1} = 0.92$, rounded off.

Input resistance $= (A + 1) R_g = 12.1 \, M\Omega$.

The output resistance consists of R_K (10 kΩ) in parallel with:

$$\frac{r_p}{\mu + 1} = \frac{8}{21} k\Omega = 381 \, \Omega, \text{ rounded off.}$$

Output resistance $= \frac{381 \times 10000}{10000 + 381} = 367 \, \Omega$, rounded off.

Note that the output resistance is approximately equal to:

$$\frac{1}{g_m} = \frac{r_p}{\mu} = \frac{8000}{20} = 400 \, \Omega.$$

PENTODE AUDIO VOLTAGE AND POWER AMPLIFIERS

Figure 4-11 illustrates a pentode af amplifier whose class A characteristics are similar to those of the triode amplifier previously discussed. However, since the cutoff bias depends on the screen grid voltage as well as the plate voltage, the previous expression for the cut-off bias $\frac{(- E_{bb})}{\mu}$ no longer applies. The cathode

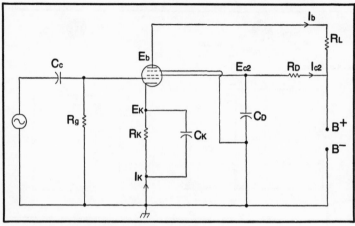

Fig. 4-11. Pentode audio voltage amplifier.

current, I_K, is the sum of the screen grid current (I_{c2}) and the plate current (I_b) so that $I_K = I_{c2} + I_b$. R_D is used as a voltage dropping resistor in order to apply the necessary positive potential to the screen grid and therefore the screen potential, E_{c2}, is E_{bb} minus the voltage drop across $R_D = E_{bb} - I_{c2} R_D$ C_D is the bypass capacitor for R_D so that the screen grid is virtually at ground potential as far as the signal is concerned. The value of C_D is typically chosen so that its reactance is equal to,

$$\frac{R_D}{10}$$

at the lowest frequency to be bypassed.   **Equation 4-26**

The value of the cathode bias is $I_K R_K = (I_{c2} + I_b) R_K$

and the plate potential, $E_b = E_{bb} - I_b R_L$.

Equation 4-27

Pentodes used for audio voltage amplification possess a high r_p of the order of 1 MΩ so that r_p may be ignored in the formula for voltage gain. The voltage gain is therefore $g_m R$ where R is the total equivalent resistance of the load resistor R_L, in parallel with the grid leak resistor, R_g, of the following stage (if present).

Pentode Audio Power Amplifier

The operation of the audio pentode power amplifier (Fig. 4-12) is similar to that of the triode power amplifier discussed earlier. Notice that it is common practice to connect the screen grid directly to B+. This allows the pentode to operate at its maximum g_m for a high power output. In addition, the power tube r_p will be appreciable lower than that of the voltage amplifier pentode.

Example 4-12

Under quiescent conditions in Fig. 4-11, $I_b = 3$ mA, $I_{c2} = 0.5$ mA. If $R_K = 680$ Ω, $R_L = 33$ kΩ, $R_D = 220$ kΩ and $E_{bb} = 250$ V. Calculate the values of the cathode bias and the plate and screen potentials. If the pentode's transconductance is 2200 micromhos, what is the amplifier's voltage gain? If the peak-to-peak sine wave voltage at the plate under signal conditions is 135 V, calculate the rms value of the input excitation on the control grid.

Solution

Cathode current, $I_K = I_b + I_{c2} = 3.0 + 0.5 = 2.4$ V rounded off.

Cathode bias $= I_K R_K = 3.5 = 10^{-3} \times 680 = 2.4$ V rounded off.

Plate potential, $E_b = + (E_{bb} - I_b R_L) = + (250 - 3\,\text{mA} \times 33\,\text{k}\Omega)$
$$= + (250 - 99) = + 151 \text{ V.}$$

Screen grid potential $= + (E_{bb} - I_{c2} R_D)$
$$= + (250 - 0.5\,\text{mA} \times 220\,\text{k}\Omega)$$
$$= + (250 - 110 \text{ V}) = + 140 \text{ V}$$

Voltage gain of the pentode $= g_m R_L = 2200 \times 10^{-6} \times 33 \times 10^3$
$$= 72.6$$
$$= 73, \text{ rounded off.}$$

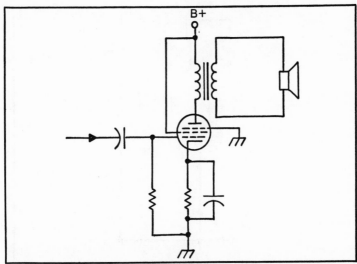

Fig. 4-12. Pentode audio power amplifier.

The peak-to-peak signal voltage input on the control grid is:

$$\frac{135}{72.6} = 1.86 \text{ V}$$

The rms value of the input signal is:

$$\frac{1.86}{2} \times 0.707 = 0.66 \text{ V rounded off.}$$

RF POWER AMPLIFIERS

Figure 4-13 shows an rf stage employing a beam power tube; note that a similar triode circuit would have to be neutralized in order to cancel the feedback through the plate/control grid interelectrode capacitance. The input signal is a sine wave and the plate load is a tank circuit which is commonly used in rf amplifiers. Since the resistance of L is very low, the mean dc level of the plate voltage is approximately equal to the plate supply voltage, E_{bb}. The screen potential is determined either by a single dropping resistor or by a voltage divider $R_1 R_2$ (Fig. 4-13).

Most rf power amplifiers are operated in class C to achieve a high plate efficiency. For these stages the bias is between two and

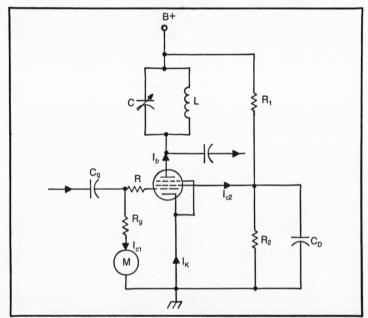

Fig. 4-13. Class C rf power amplifier stage.

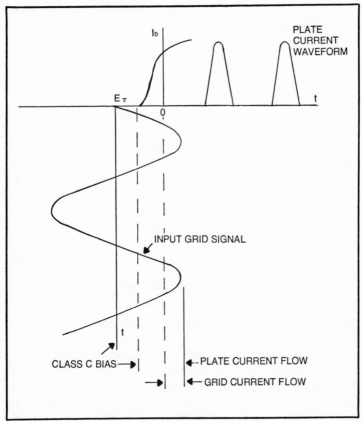

Fig. 4-14. Class C operation.

four times the cutoff value with an angle of plate current flow between 120° and 150° (Fig. 4-14). The plate current waveform is severely distorted but may be analyzed into a mean dc level together with a fundamental component (of the same frequency as that of the input signal) and all harmonics. However, since the plate load is a tank circuit, it may be tuned to the input frequency and its selectivity will then discriminate against the harmonics so that the voltage swing at the plate is virtually an undistorted sine wave.

$$\text{RF power output, } P_o = \frac{(\text{rms value of plate voltage swing})^2}{\text{dynamic resistance of the plate load}}$$

Equation 4-28

dc plate input power, $P_{in} = E_{bb} \times$ (mean dc level of plate current)   **Equation 4-29**

Plate dissipation, $P_D = P_{in} - P_o$ **Equation 4-30**

Plate efficiency as a percentage $= \dfrac{P_o}{P_{in}} \times 100\%$

Equation 4-31

If this type of stage is operated under class A conditions, the theoretical maximum plate efficiency is 50% with practical values up to 35%. For class B, the theoretical maximum is 78.5% and practical values extend to 60%. With class C, plate efficiencies range up to 85%. Class C stages require a high level of rf drive which produces a flow of control grid current. Referring to Fig. 4-13, the cathode current, I_K, is the sum of the plate current, I_b, the screen grid screen, I_{c2}, and the control grid current I_{c1}, so that

$$I_K = I_b + I_{c1} + I_{c2} \qquad \textbf{Equation 4-32}$$

The circuit normally employs grid leak bias (this is the same type of bias which oscillators commonly use) in which the control grid current charges C_g during a portion of one half-cycle of the input drive.

When the grid current ceases, C_g discharges slowly through R_g with a time constant of $C_g R_g$ which is high compared with the period of the input sine wave. As a result of this action, there is developed across R_g a dc bias level which is determined by the magnitude of the grid signal: consequently this type of bias is sometimes referred to as *signal bias*. If the drive fails, no signal bias will be generated so that some rf power amplifiers include a fixed safety bias or cathode bias in order to limit the plate current to a "safe" value.

The value of the signal bias is $-I_{c1} R_g$ where I_{c1} is the dc control grid current recorded by the meter, M. For a variety of purposes, a low value resistor R may be connected in series with the control grid. If such a resistor is present, its value must be added to that of R_g in calculating the magnitude of the signal bias.

Frequency Multipliers

For reasons of frequency stability, it is common practice to operate a transmitter rf oscillator stage at low frequency and low power, and then build up the frequency and power in the following stages. To increase the frequency, multiplier stages (sometimes called harmonic generators) are used; their circuitry is similar to that of Fig. 4-13, but their class C operation is achieved with a bias level which is several times the cutoff value. This reduces the angle of the plate current flow and the plate efficiency but increases the strength of the harmonic content, so that the tank circuit is then tuned to a particular harmonic contained in the plate current waveform. A first approximation of the output voltage of the multiplier stage will be an undistorted sine wave whose frequency is a whole number of times (twice for a doubler stage, three times for a tripler, etc.) the frequency of the input signal on the control grid. Since the output frequency from the plate circuit is different from the input frequency to the grid circuit, triode frequency multipliers stages are not required to be neutralized.

For a triode double stage, the angle of plate current flow is typically 90°, the bias level is approximately ten times the cutoff value and the plate efficiency is 50%. A triode tripler has about the same plate efficiency but the bias level is approximately 20 times the cutoff value and the angle of the plate current flow is reduced to 75°.

Example 4-13

In a class C rf power amplifier stage, E_{bb} is 600 V and the dc level of plate current is 1.5 A. If the plate efficiency is 80%, what are the values of the rf power output, and the plate dissipation?

Solution

DC plate input power = 600 × 1.5 A = 900 W.

RF power output = $900 \times \dfrac{80}{100} = \underline{720 \text{ W.}}$

Plate dissipation = 900 − 720 = $\underline{180 \text{ W.}}$

Example 4-14

In Fig. 4-13, R_g = 33 kΩ, R = 100 Ω and the reading of M is 2 mA. What is the bias on the control grid? If the dc levels of the cathode current and the screen grid current are respectively 225 mA and 35 mA, what is the mean dc level of plate current?

Solution

The total resistance associated with the control grid current of 2 mA is R_g + R = 33 kΩ + 100 Ω = 33.1 kΩ. The value of the grid leak bias is − (2 mA × 33.1 kΩ) = 66.2 V. Since $I_K = I_b + I_{c1} + I_{c2}$, $I_b = I_K − I_{c1} − I_{c2}$ = 225 − 2 − 35 = 188 mA.

Example 4-15

In a class C rf power amplifier stage, the power output is 1.5 kW, the plate efficiency is 80% and the dc level of the plate current is 1.2 A. Calculate the value of the plate supply voltage.

Solution

DC plate input power $= \dfrac{1500}{80} \times 100 = 1875$ W.

Plate supply voltage $= \dfrac{1875}{1.2} = 1560$ V, rounded off.

Note that in this problem, the plate dissipation is 1875 minus 1500 = 375 W.

Example 4-16

The frequency input to a tripler stage is 1 MHz. If the capacitance of the tank circuit is 225 pF, what is the required value for the associated inductance?

Solution

The tank circuit is tuned to the third harmonic of the frequency input and is therefore resonant at 3 MHz. The required value of the inductance is

$$L = \frac{0.0253}{f^2 C} = \frac{0.0253}{(3 \times 10^6) \times 225 \times 10^{-12}}$$

H = 12.5 μH, rounded off.

Example 4-17

The dc plate power input to a triode class C amplifier is 1375 W. If the plate dissipation is 225 W. What is the plate efficiency?

Solution

RF power output = 1375 − 225 = 1150 W.

Plate efficiency $= \dfrac{1375 - 225}{1375} \times 100\% = 84\%$, rounded off.

Example 4-18

In a class C rf amplifier employing a beam power tube, the dc levels of the cathode current, the plate current, and the screen grid current are respectively 325 mA, 280 mA, and 40 mA. If the stage employs signal bias with a 27 kΩ grid leak resistor, calculate the bias applied to the control grid.

Solution

Control grid current, $I_{c1} \times I_K - I_b - I_{c2} = 325 - 280 - 40 = 5$ mA.

Control grid bias $= I_{c1} R_g = -5$ mA $\times$ 27 k$\Omega = -135$ V.

Example 4-19

A transmitter uses a crystal-controlled oscillator which is followed by two doubler stages and a tripler stage. If the operating frequency is 22.02 MHz, what is the frequency provided by the crystal oscillator?

Solution

The total frequency multiplication factor provided by the two doubler stages and the tripler stage is $2 \times 2 \times 3 = 12$. The frequency of the crystal oscillator is $\dfrac{22.02}{12} = 1.835$ MHz.

Example 4-20

The master oscillator of a transmitter generates 865 kHz. The frequency multiplier stages consists of a doubler and two triplers. What is the transmitter operating frequency?

Solution

Total frequency multiplication factor = $2 \times 3 \times 3 = 18$

Transmitter operating frequency = $865 \times 18 = 15570$ kHz = 15.57 MHz

Example 4-21

The final stage of a 620 kHz AM transmitter is operated in class C and employs a single neutralized triode. On which one of the following frequencies is the transmitter most likely to cause interference in the AM broadcast band?

Solution

Since the final stage is operated in class C, it will generate harmonics which will be attenuated by such devices as a low pass filter and a Faraday screen. However, the radiation of the second harmonic on a frequency of $2 \times 620 = 1240$ kHz may produce interference in the AM broadcast band of 535 kHz to 1605 kHz. Note that the third harmonic whose frequency is $3 \times 620 = 1860$ kHz, lies outside this band.

Example 4-22

A transmitter has an operating frequency of 124.8 MHz and the master oscillator generates 5200 kHz. Which combination of harmonic generators will provide the correct frequency multiplication factor?

Solution

Total frequency multiplication factor = $\dfrac{124.8 \text{ MHz}}{5200 \text{ kHz}} = 24$.

This may either be achieved by three doublers and a tripler ($2 \times 2 \times 2 \times 3 = 24$) or by a doubler, a tripler and a quadrupler ($2 \times 3 \times 4 = 24$).

GROUNDED-GRID TRIODE CIRCUIT

This circuit (Fig. 4-15) is commonly used for rf voltage amplification in the vhf and uhf bands, as for example, in the first stage of a TV receiver. Its advantages are twofold:

☐ It contributes less noise than an amplifier using a conventional screen grid tube which suffers from partition noise due to the random effect in the division of the electron stream between the screen grid and plate circuits.

☐ The circuit does not require neutralization since the grounded grid provides an electrostatic screen between the output plate circuit and the input cathode circuit. This is particularly advantageous at high frequencies where the adjustment of the neutralizing circuit is more critical; in addition the elimination of the neutralizing capacitor reduces the input and output capacitance of the stage. Unlike the conventional grounded-cathode amplifier, there is no phase change between the input voltage signal on the plate. Both these signal voltages are 180° out of phase with the signal component of the plate current. From the equivalent circuit of Fig. 4-15B.

$$i_b = \frac{(\mu + 1) V_{in}}{r_p + Z_L} \qquad \text{Equation 4-33}$$

$$V_o = i_b Z_L = \frac{(\mu + 1) L_L}{r_p + Z_L} \times V_{in} \qquad \text{Equation 4-34}$$

$$\text{Voltage gain} = \frac{V_o}{V_{in}} = \frac{(\mu + 1) Z_L}{r_p + Z_L}$$

and the input impedance,

$$Z_{in} = \frac{V_{in}}{i_b} = \frac{R_p + Z_L}{\mu + 1} \qquad \text{Equation 4-35}$$

This value of input impedance is much lower than that of the conventional grounded-cathode amplifier discussed earlier. The low imput impedance is the main disadvantage of the grounded-grid circuit since it limits the amplification which can be obtained.

Example 4-23

The plate load of a grounded-grid triode amplifier is a tank circuit with a dynamic resistance of 20 kΩ. The tube has a μ of 15

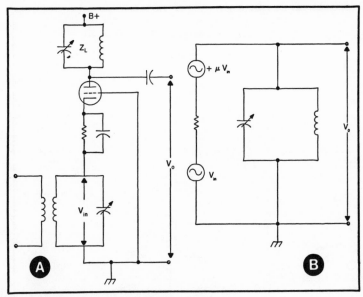

Fig. 4-15. The grounded-grid triode circuit.

and an r_p of 8 kΩ. Calculate the voltage gain of the stage and its input resistance.

Solution

$$\text{Voltage gain} = \frac{(\mu + 1)\,Z_L}{r_p + Z_L} = \frac{16 \times 20}{8 + 20} = \frac{320}{28}$$

$$= 11, \text{ rounded off.}$$

$$\text{Input resistance} = \frac{r_p + Z_L}{\mu + 1} = \frac{8 + 20}{16} = \frac{28}{16}$$

$$= 1.8 \text{ kΩ rounded off.}$$

TWO-TUBE CIRCUITS

Figure 4-16 shows the basic circuit of an audio frequency push-pull amplifier. The two control grid voltages are 180° out of phase so that the signal components of the plate currents are also 180° out of phase. However, the plate transformer is connected between the plates so that the audio signal output is proportional to the *difference* of the two plate currents; these currents will therefore combine in the primary winding to produce the magnetic flux which links with the secondary.

105

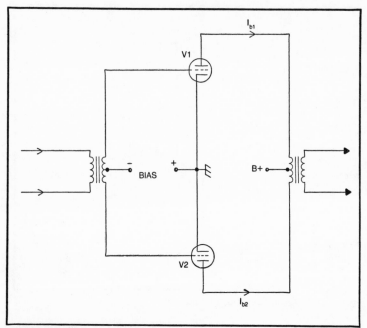

Fig. 4-16. Push-pull amplifier.

Push-Pull Amplifiers

The matched tubes may be biased to operate in class A, class AB_1, class AB_2 or class B (suffix 2 is used to denote the flow of control grid current while suffix 1 means that no grid current occurs). The main advantage of push-pull arrangement over a single tube amplifier is the elimination of second and other *even* harmonic distortion from the audio output signal (provided that the two tubes have matched characteristics).

Transmitters may also use the push-pull arrangement in the final class C rf power output stage. This will prevent second and even harmonic radiation and the strongest unwanted component will then be the third harmonic. Note that if triodes are used in such a circuit, they are normally required to be neutralized.

Push-Push Circuit

This arrangement (Fig. 4-17) only occurs in rf circuitry. The control grids are again fed 180° out of phase with the input sine wave signal but, in contrast with the push-pull circuit, the plates are joined together to one end of the tank circuit so that the output signal is proportional to the *sum* of the two plate currents. Consequently, all signal components which were eliminated from the output of the push-pull circuit, will appear in the output of the push-push circuit and vice-versa. As a result, the output of the push-push arrangement will contain only *even* harmonics, and therefore the circuit is mainly used as a doubler with the tank circuit tuned to the second harmonic of the input frequency.

Compared with the single tube doubler, the tuning of the tank circuit to the second harmonic will be more easily achieved in the push-push circuit, since the fundamental frequency and the third harmonic have already been eliminated from the output. Since the push-push stage is a harmonic generator, it will not require neutralization if triodes are used.

Tubes in Parallel

The parallel arrangement of tubes (Fig. 4-18) may be used in either af or rf circuits. The two control grids are fed in phase with the input signal and the plates are joined together to one end of the load so that the output signal is proportional to the sum of the two plate currents. With two tubes of the same type operated in parallel, the combination has twice the g_m, half the r_p and the same μ when compared with either one of the tubes. A high g_m and a low r_p are the main requirements of a power amplifier which may therefore consist of a number of commercially available tubes in parallel rather than a single non-standard tube.

Note that if triodes are parallel connected in an rf stage, they must be normally be neutralized.

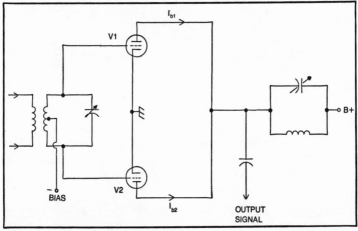

Fig. 4-17. The push-push stage.

Example 4-24

The input frequency to a class C push-pull power amplifier is 1.8 MHz. What is the frequency of the lowest harmonic appearing in the output of the amplifier?

Solution

Even harmonics are eliminated from the output of a push-pull stage so that the lowest harmonic will be the third which has a frequency of $3 \times 1.8 = 5.4$ MHz.

Example 4-25

The input frequency to a push-push circuit is 1200 kHz. The plate load is a tank circuit which is tuned to the lowest harmonic which is present in the output. If the inductance of the tank circuit is 45 μH, what is the required value of the associated capacitance?

Solution

The lowest harmonic which is present in the output, is the second whose frequency is 2×1200 kHz $= 2.4$ MHz. The required value of the capacitance is:

$$C = \frac{0.0253}{f^2L} = \frac{2.53 \times 10^{-2}}{(2.4 \times 10^6)^2 \times 45 \times 10^{-6}} F = 98 \text{ pF}$$

Example 4-26

Each of two triodes in parallel has an amplification factor of 8 and a transconductance of 9500 micromhos. Calculate the equivalent r_p and g_m of the parallel combination.

Solution

The r_p of each triode is:

$$\frac{\mu}{g_m} = \frac{8}{9500 \times 10^{-6}} = 842 \ \Omega$$

The equivalent r_p for the parallel combination is $\frac{842}{2} = 420$

Ω, rounded off.

Equivalent $g_m = 2 \times 9500 = 19000$ micromhos.

Example 4-27

A class C rf stage uses two neutralized triodes in parallel. If the dc plate input power to the stage is 1.2 kW and the plate efficiency is 70%, calculate the plate dissipation of each triode.

Solution

The total plate dissipation is $100 - 70 = 30\%$ of the plate input power. The plate dissipation of each triode is:

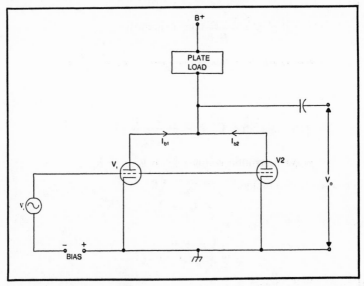

Fig. 4-18. Tubes in parallel.

$$\frac{30 \times 1.2}{100 \times 2} \text{ kW} = 180 \text{ W.}$$

CHAPTER SUMMARY

Triode Static Characteristics

$$\text{Plate resistance, } r_p = \frac{\Delta e_b}{\Delta i_b} \text{ (E_c constant)}$$

$$\text{Transconductance, } g_m = \frac{\Delta i_b}{\Delta e_c} \text{ (E_c constant)}$$

$$\text{Amplication Factor, } \mu = \frac{\Delta e_b}{\Delta e_c} \text{ (I_b constant)}$$

At the same operating point, $= r_p \times g_m$

Triode Audio Voltage Amplifier

Quiescent Conditions

$$\text{Cut-off bias} = \frac{-E_{bb}}{\mu}$$

$$\text{Class A bias} = \frac{-E_{bb}}{2\mu}, \text{ Class AB bias} = \frac{0.75 \, E_{bb}}{\mu}$$

$$\text{Class B bias} = \frac{-E_{bb}}{\mu} \text{ (approximately)}$$

$$\text{Class C bias} = \text{Between} \frac{-2 E_{bb}}{\mu} \text{ and } \frac{-4 E_{bb}}{\mu}$$

$$\text{Cathode bias} = -I_b R_k$$

$$\text{Cathode Capacitor, } C_K = \frac{1.59 \times 10^6}{f \times R_K} \mu F$$

$$\text{Plate-to-ground voltage, } E_b = E_{bb} - I_b R_L$$

$$\text{Plate-to-cathode voltage, } E_{pk} = E_b - I_b R_k$$
$$= E_{bb} - I_b (R_L + R_k)$$

$$\text{Plate power dissipated} = E_{pk} I_b$$
$$= E_b I_b - I_b^2 R_k$$
$$= E_{bb} I_b - I_b^2 (R_L + R_k)$$

$$\text{DC plate input power} = E_{bb} I_b$$

Signal Conditions

180° Phase change between input and output signals

$$\text{Voltage gain, } A = \frac{V_o}{V_i} = \frac{\mu R_L}{r_p + R_L}$$

$$= g_m R \text{ where } R = r_p \text{ // } R_L \text{ // } R_g$$

$$\text{Signal Power Output} = i_b \times e_b = i_b^2 RL = \frac{e_b^2}{R_L}$$

$$\text{Plate Efficiency} = \frac{\text{signal power output}}{\text{dc plate input power}} \times 100\%$$

$$\text{Input Impedance} = R_g \text{ // } C_{gk} \text{ // } (A + 1) C_{gp}$$

$$\text{Output Impedance} = R_L \text{ // } r_p \text{ // } C_{pk}$$

Triode Audio Power Amplifier

Optimum load = $2 \times r_p$

Negative Feedback in Audio Amplifiers

$$\text{Gain with feedback, } A' = \frac{A}{1 + A\beta} \longrightarrow \frac{1}{\beta} \text{ if } A\beta >> 1.$$

$$\text{Gain without feedback, } A = \frac{A'}{1 - A'\beta}$$

$$\text{Feedback Factor, } \beta = \frac{1}{A'} - \frac{1}{A} = \frac{A' - A'}{AA'}$$

Cathode Follower

Zero phase change between input and output signals

$$\text{Gain with feedback, } A' = \frac{A}{1 + A}$$

< 1. Feedback factor, $\beta = 1$.

$$\text{High input impedance, } Z_L = (A + 1)\, R_g\ //\ \frac{C_{gk}}{1 + A}\ \|\ C_{gp}$$

$$\text{Low output impedance, } Z_o = R_K\ //\ \frac{r_p}{\mu + 1}\ //\ C_{pk}$$

Pentode Audio Voltage Amplifier

Quiescent Conditions

Cathode current, $I_k = I_b + I_{c2}$

$$\text{Cathode bias} = -\, I_k R_k = -\, (I_b + I_{c2}) R_k$$

$$\text{Screen voltage, } E_{c2} = E_{bb} - I_{c2} R_D$$

Signal Conditions

$$\text{Voltage gain, } A = g_m R_L$$

RF Power Amplifiers

RF power output,

$$P_o = \frac{E_b{}^2}{\text{Dynamic Resistance of Plate Tank Circuit Load}}$$

dc Plate input power, $P_{in} = E_{bb} I_b$
Plate dissipation, $P_D = P_{in} - P_o$

$$\text{Plate efficiency as a percentage} = \frac{P_o}{P_{in}} \times 100\%$$

(class A < 35%, class B 50 to 60%, class C up to 80%)
Cathode current, $I_k = I_b + I_{c1} + I_{c2}$
Grid Leak bias $= -\, I_{c1} \times R_g$

Grounded-Grid Triode Amplifier

Zero phase change between input and output signals

$$\text{Voltage gain, } A = \frac{(\mu + 1) Z_L}{r_p + Z_L}$$

$$\text{Low input impedance} = \frac{r_p + Z_L}{\mu + 1}$$

Two-Tube Circuits

Push-Pull Amplifier

Grids are fed 180° out of phase; load is connected between the plates so that the output signal is dependent on the *difference* of the plate currents. With matched tubes even harmonic distortion is eliminated.

Push-Push Amplifier

Grids are fed 180° out of phase; plates are parallel-connected so that the output signal is dependent on the *sum* of the plate currents. The output contains even harmonics only and consequently the push-push circuit is mainly used as an rf doubler.

Parallel (Pull-Push) Amplifier

Corresponding electrodes of the two tubes are directly connected. With two tubes of the same type operated in parallel, the combination has twice the g_m, half the r_p and the same μ when compared with one of the tubes.

Chapter 5
Modulation

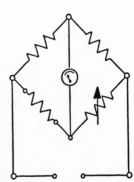

Modulation means controlling some feature of the rf carrier by the audio signal in such a way that the receiver is able to reproduce the information (speech, music, etc.). Since the carrier may be regarded as a high frequency sine wave, it only possesses three features which may be modulated—amplitude, frequency and phase (such quantities as period and wavelength are directly related to frequency). In amplitude modulation, the instantaneous amplitude (voltage) of the rf wave is linearly related to the instantaneous magnitude (voltage) of the af signal while the rate of amplitude variation is equal to the modulating frequency.

INTRODUCTION TO AMPLITUDE
MODULATION—PERCENTAGE OF MODULATION

In Fig. 5-1, the modulating signal is a single sine wave or test tone which is used to amplitude modulate an rf carrier. The extent of modulation is measured by the percentage modulation as defined by:

$$\text{Percentage modulation} = \frac{E_{max} - E_o}{E_o} \times 100\% \qquad \textbf{Equation 5-1}$$

Equation 5-1 is for positive peaks (upward modulation) where E_o is the amplitude of the unmodulated carrier. The percentage modulation on negative (downward modulation) peaks is

$$\frac{E_o - E_{min}}{E_o} \times 100\% \qquad \textbf{Equation 5-2}$$

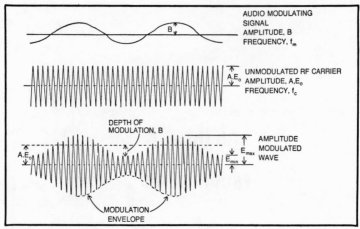

Fig. 5-1. The amplitude modulated wave.

Providing the modulation is symmetrical about the E_o level, the equation is:

$$E_o = \frac{E_{max} - E_{min}}{2} \qquad \textbf{Equation 5-3}$$

Which leads to the following expressions for percentage modulation:

$$\text{Percentage modulation} = \frac{E_{max} - \left(\dfrac{E_{max} + E_{min}}{2}\right)}{E_o} \times 100\%$$

$$\text{Percentage modulation} = \frac{\left(\dfrac{E_{max} + E_{min}}{2}\right) - E_{min}}{E_o} \times 100\%$$

Either form can be reduced to a more simple expression:

$$\text{Percentage modulation} = \frac{E_{max} - E_{min}}{2\,E_o} \times 100\% \qquad \textbf{Equation 5-4}$$

$$= \frac{E_{max} - E_{min}}{E_{max} + E_{min}} \times 100\% \qquad \textbf{Equation 5-5}$$

As an alternative to the modulation percentage, the degree of modulation is:

114

$$m = \frac{\text{percentage modulation}}{100} \qquad \textbf{Equation 5-6}$$

For a variety of reasons the modulation envelope for a symmetrical tone may contain unsymmeterical distortion which is referred to as carrier shift. In negative carrier shift the troughs of the modulation envelope are greater than the peaks and this will cause a decrease (compared with the unmodulated value) in the dc plate current reading of a plate modulated class C stage. Similarly, with positive carrier shift, the envelope's peaks exceed the troughs and the plate current will increase. Then:

Percentage carrier shift =

$$\frac{\text{dc level when modulated} - \text{dc level unmodulated}}{\text{dc level unmodulated}} \times 100\%$$

$$\textbf{Equation 5-7}$$

For a standard broadcast station, the carrier shift must not exceed 5%.

Increasing the amplitude of the test tone raises the modulation percentage, improves the signal-to-noise ratio at the receiver, and results in a higher audio power output. However, if the modulation percentage is increased to 100% and beyond (overmodulation), the modulation envelope is severely distorted and this distortion will ultimately appear in the output from the loudspeaker. Overmodulation also results in the generation of spurious sidebands which will cause interference to adjacent channels by heterodyning with the sidebands of those channels. Figure 5-2A shows the AM waveforms for various modulation percentages.

Other than measuring the percentage modulation from the AM waveform, it is common practice to use a trapezoidal display on an oscilloscope. This is achieved by feeding the AM signal for the vertical deflecting (Y) plates and the audio signal to the horizontal deflecting (X) plates. In addition to measuring percentage modulation, this method will clearly indicate whether there exists the required linear relationship between the instantaneous amplitude of the rf carrier and the instantaneous magnitude of the tone signal; non-linearity will appear either as a "barrel" or a "pincushion effect" on the trapezoidal display (Fig. 5-2B). The percentage of modulation is given by $\dfrac{P - Q}{P + Q} \times 100\%$ so that for 50% modulation, P = 3Q (*not* 2Q).   It should be emphasized that when AM is being used to transmit speech or music, the percentage of modulation varies from instant to instant. Permitted values may be quoted for:

☐ The minimum percentage modulation on average peaks of the audio modulation.

☐ The maximum modulation percentage on negative modulation peaks.

☐ The maximum modulation on positive modulation peaks.

☐ The maximum carrier shift.

Example 5-1

In Fig. 5-3, it is assumed that the modulation envelope is symmetrical about the E_0 level. If $E_{max} = 800$ V and $E_0 = 500$ V, what is the value of the percentage of modulation? Calculate the value of the instantaneous peak power if the AM signal is developed across an effective load of $100\ \Omega$.

Solution

$$\text{Percentage modulation} = \frac{E_{max} - E_o \times 100}{E_o}$$

$$= \frac{800 - 500 \times 100}{500}$$

$$= 60\%$$

The instantaneous peak voltage, E_{max} is 800 V and therefore the peak power is:
$$\frac{E_{max}^2}{R} = \frac{(800\ V)^2}{100\Omega} = 6400\ W$$

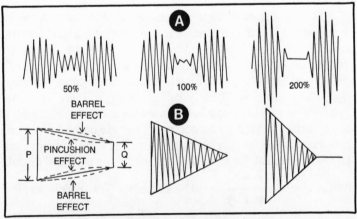

Fig. 5-2. Percentage of modulation and trapezoidal display.

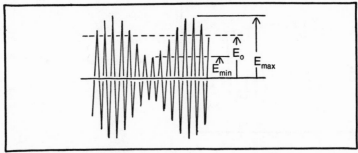

Fig. 5-3. Waveform for Example 5-1.

Note that the unmodulated carrier power is $\dfrac{(500V)^2}{100\Omega} = 2500$ W

and the instantaneous maximum power is $\dfrac{(200 \text{ V})^2}{100 \ \Omega} = 400$ W.

The next section will however show that the average power in this AM signal is 2950 W which is different from the arithmetic mean$\left(\dfrac{6400 + 400}{2} = 3400 \text{ W}\right)$ of the instantaneous peak and minimum power values. This difference is due to the fact that the instantaneous power curve is not symmetrical about the unmodulated carrier power level.

Example 5-2

A trapezoidal display (Fig. 5-4) is used to measure the percentage modulation of the AM signal in Example 5-1. If P = .3 cm, calculate the value of Q.

Solution

Since the percentage of modulation is 60%,

$$\frac{P - Q}{P + Q} = Q.6$$

Therefore:

$$\frac{3 - Q}{3 + Q} = Q.6$$

or,

$$Q = \frac{1.2}{1.6} = 0.75 \text{ cm}$$

Example 5-3

When unmodulated the plate current in the Final stage of an AM broadcast transmitter is 5.4 A. When modulated by a symmetrical audio tone, the plate current falls to 5.2 A. What is the percentage of negative carrier shift?

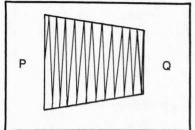

Fig. 5-4. Trapezoidal display for Example 5-2.

Solution

Percentage of negative carrier shift

$$= \frac{(5.4 - 5.2) \times 100\%}{5.4}$$

$$= 3.7\%$$

AM SIDEBANDS—BANDWIDTH OF AN AM SIGNAL

The act of modulation, whether amplitude, frequency or phase, creates additional rf frequencies which are known as sidebands. Each amplitude modulating frequency component creates a pair of sidebands, one upper and one lower, which are equally spaced in frequency on either side of the carrier. If a carrier of amplitude, A, and frequency f_c, is an amplitude B and frequency f_m, the resulting AM wave would have the appearance of Fig. 5-1, and would contain the following three rf components:

☐ An upper sideband of amplitude B/2 and frequency $f_c + f_m$.

☐ A carrier component of amplitude A and frequency f_c.

☐ A lower sideband of amplitude B/2 and frequency $f_c - f_m$.

The AM signal is therefore entirely rf in character and contains no audio components.

If the audio signal is speech or music which contains many instantaneous frequencies of varying amplitudes, each component will produce a pair of sidebands and the bandwidth occupied by the AM signal will be the frequency difference between the highest upper sideband and the lowest lower sideband transmitted. Therefore, the bandwidth is equal to twice the highest audio modulating frequency. For example, in the standard AM broadcast band of 535 to 1605 kHz, the channel width for each station is 10 kHz and therefore the highest audio modulating frequency is 5000 Hz. Since the sets of both upper and lower sidebands as well as the carrier are being transmitted, the emission is double-sideband AM telephony which is designated A3.

RF Power in the Sidebands

Each sideband component contains a certain rf power which is determined by the degree of modulation, m, and the unmodulated carrier power, P_c. In the simplest case of double-sideband amplitude modulation by a single audio tone, the total power contained in the pair of sidebands = $0.5\, m^2 P_c$; notice that the sideband power is proportional to m^2. Assuming that the audio tone produces 100% modulation, m = 1 and the total sideband power is 50% of the unmodulated carrier power. However, as far as the total power of both carrier and sidebands is concerned, the sideband power is only 33 1/3%.

As an example, a 1 MHz carrier whose unmodulated rf carrier power is 1 kW, is 100% modulated by a single 2 kHz tone. The resultant double-sideband AM wave contains a 250 W upper sideband of frequency 1002 kHz (1 MHz + 2 kHz), a 1 kW carrier component of frequency 1 MHz and a 250 W lower sideband of frequency 998 kHz (1 MHz − 2 kHz). The total sideband power = 2 × 250 = 500 W. The total power in the AM wave (carrier and sidebands) is 1 kW + 500 W = 1500 W. The bandwidth is 1002 − 998 = 4 kHz or twice the modulating frequency. The total sideband power (500 W) is therefore 50% of the carrier power (1 kW) but only 33 1/3% of the total power (1500 W).

Summarizing the equations:

For double-sideband amplitude modulation by a single tone;

Total sideband power = $0.5 \times m^2 P_c$ **Equation 5-8**

Power in each sideband = $0.25 \times m^2 P_c$ **Equation 5-9**

Total power in the AM wave is:

$$P_c + 0.5\, m^2\, P_c = P_c \left(1 + \frac{m^2}{2}\right)$$ **Equation 5-10**

Percentage of total sideband power as compared with the unmodulated carrier power is:

Equation 5-11

$$\frac{0.5\, m^2\, P_c}{P_c} \times 100 = 50\, m^2\% = 50\% \text{ (if m = 1)}.$$

Percentage of total sideband power as compared with the total power in the AM wave is:

Equation 5-12

$$\frac{0.5\, m^2\, P_c}{P_c\left(1 + \frac{m^2}{2}\right)} \times 100 = \frac{m^2}{2 + m^2} \times 100\% = 33\,1/3\% \text{ (if m = 1)}.$$

If the degree of modulation is increased from m_1 to m_2, the increase in total power $= 0.5\,m^2_2\,P_c - 0.5\,m^2_1\,P_c = 0.5\,P_c \times (m^2_2 - m^2_1)$. The percentage increase in total sideband power is given by:

$$\frac{0.5\,P_c \times (m^2_2 - m^2_1)}{0.5\,P_c \times m^2_1} \times 100 = \left[\frac{m^2_2 - m^2_1}{m^2_1}\right] \times 100$$

$$= \left[\left(\frac{M_2}{m_1}\right)^2\right] - 1 \times 100\% \qquad \textbf{Equation 5-13}$$

If the degree of modulation is decreased from m_2 to m_1, the percentage decrease in total sideband power is

$$\left[\frac{m^2_2 - m^2_1}{m^2_2}\right] \times 100 = \left[1 - \left(\frac{m^1}{m_2}\right)^2\right] \times 100\%$$

$$\textbf{Equation 5-14}$$

Types of AM Emission: Single Sideband System

The sidebands in an AM wave represent the audio information and in order to convey this information, it is not essential that the carrier and both sets of sidebands are transmitted. There are various types of AM emission and each type must be considered separately as regards the power content of the sidebands and the bandwidth. For example in the single-sideband suppressed carrier (SSSC) system, designated A3J, all the rf power is concentrated in one set of sidebands (either the upper or the lower). This improves the signal-to-noise ratio at the receiver as well as reducing the bandwidth required. However, compared with double-sideband operation, the SSSC system demands a higher degree of frequency stability for the carrier generated in the transmitter oscillator and also requires that a carrier component be reinserted at the receiver.

The advantage of power saving with the SSSC system is best illustrated by an example. Assume that the unmodulated carrier power is equal to 100 W and that the carrier is 100% double sideband modulated by a single audio tone. The total sideband power is $0.5\,m^2 P_c = 0.5 \times 1^2 \times 100 = 50$ W and the power in each sideband is 50 W/2 = 25 W. Since the total rf power is $100 + 50 = 150$ W, the percentage power saving in using the SSSC system is $\frac{150 - 25}{150} \times 100 = 83\,1/3\%$ (this result is independent of the value of carrier power closer). Alternatively, if the total rf power is kept constant at 150 W, the whole of this power can be concentrated in one sideband rather than being distributed over the carrier and two sidebands; the result is the improvement in the signal-to noise rates at the receiver.

Example 5-4

The unmodulated carrier power of a 1 MHz transmitter is 5 kW. The carrier is then 80% double sideband amplitude modulated by a 600 Hz tone. Calculate (a) the total sideband power (b) the power in each sideband and (c) the total rf power. What frequencies are contained in the AM signal and what is its bandwidth?

If the percentage of modulation is reduced from 80% to 50% what are the percentage decreases in total sideband power and total rf power?

Solution

(a) Total sideband power $= 1/2 \times m^2 \times P_c$

$$= \frac{1}{2} \times 0.8^2 \times 5000 \text{ W}$$

$$= 1600 \text{ W}$$

(b) Power in each sideband $= 1600$ W/2 $= 800$ W

(c) Total rf power $= 5$ kw $+ 1600$ W $= 6600$ W

The frequencies contained in the AM signal are 1MHz + 600 Hz = 1000.6 kHz (upper sideband), 1 MHz (carrier) and 1MHz − 600 Hz = 999.4 kHz (lower sideband). The bandwidth is the signal to twice the (highest) modulating frequency and is therefore 2 × 600 Hz = 1.2 kHz

Percentage decrease in total sideband power is:

$$\left[1 - \left(\frac{m_1}{m_2}\right)^2 \right] \times 100\% = 1 - \left[\left(\frac{0.5}{0.8}\right)^2 \right] \times 100\%$$

$$= 61\%, \text{ rounded off.}$$

Total rf power with 50% modulation is 5 kw $+ 1 \times 0.5^2 \times 5000$ W $= 5625$W

Percentage decrease in total rf power is:

$$\frac{(6600 - 5625)}{6600} \times 100 = \frac{975}{66} = 15\% \text{ rounded off.}$$

Example 5-5

When the carrier of Example 5-4 is 80% modulated, the emission is changed from double sideband, full carrier to single sideband, suppressed carrier. Calculate the percentage saving in total rf power assuming that the transmitter does not alter its received signal strength?

Solution

The total rf power output is changed from 6600 W to 800 W. The percentage saving in power is

$$\frac{(6600 - 800)}{6600} \times 100\%$$

$$= 88\%, \text{ rounded off}$$

CHANGE IN ANTENNA CURRENT DUE TO AMPLITUDE MODULATION

The act of amplitude modulation creates the additional sideband power and therefore the total rf power associated with the antenna is greater under modulated conditions. The antenna current is directly proportional to the square root of the rf power and will increase with the degree of modulation, m. If P_c is the rf carrier power associated with the antenna under unmodulated conditions and I_A is the corresponding antenna current, the additional sideband power with double-sideband amplitude modulation by a single tone is $0.5\ m^2\ P_c$ and the total power in the AM signal is:

$$P_c \times (1 + \frac{m^2}{2})$$

Therefore,

modulated antenna current, $I_{A'} = I \times \sqrt{\dfrac{P_c (1 + \frac{m^2}{2})}{P_c}}$

$$= I_A \times \sqrt{1 + \frac{m^2}{2}}$$

Equation 5-15

Increase in antenna current $= I_{A'} - I_A = I_A$

$$\left(\sqrt{1 + \frac{m^2}{2}} - 1 \right)$$

Percentage increase in antenna current $= \dfrac{(I_{A'} - I_A)}{I_A} \times 100$

$$= \left(\sqrt{\frac{m^2 + 1}{2}} - 1 \right) \times 100\%$$

Equation 5-16

For example, when comparing the unmodulated condition to the condition of 100% modulation by a single tone, the percentage increase in the antenna current is:

$$\left(\sqrt{1 + \frac{1^2}{2}} - 1 \right) \times 100 = (1.5 - 1) \times 100 = (1.225 - 1) \times 100$$

$$= 22.5\%$$

If the degree of modulation by a single tone is increased from m_1 to m_2, the increase in antenna current is:

$$I_A \left(\sqrt{1 + \frac{m_2^2}{2}} - \sqrt{1 + \frac{m_1^2}{2}} \right)$$

The percentage increase in antenna current is given by:

$$\frac{I_A \left(\sqrt{1 + \frac{m_2^2}{2}} - \sqrt{1 + \frac{m_1^2}{2}} \right) \times 100}{I_A \sqrt{1 + \frac{m_1^2}{2}}}$$

$$= \left(\sqrt{\frac{2 + m_2^2}{2 + m_1^2}} - 1 \right) \times 100\% \qquad \textbf{Equation 5-17}$$

Similarly, if the degree of modulation is decreased from m_2 to m_1, the percentage decrease in antenna current is given by:

$$\left(1 - \sqrt{\frac{2 + m_1^2}{2 + m_2^2}} \right) \times 100\% \qquad \textbf{Equation 5-18}$$

If you have difficulty in recalling these formulas, you can solve problems involving the percentage change in antenna current by assuming convenient values for the unmodulated carrier power, the antenna current and the effective antenna resistance. A suitable set of compatible values is:

unmodulated rf carrier power = 100 W
unmodulated antenna current = 1A
effective antenna resistance = 100 Ω

Example 5-6

An rf carrier is 70% amplitude modulated (double-sideband) by a single tone. What is the percentage increase in the antenna current as compared with its unmodulated value?

Solution

Let the unmodulated carrier power by 100 W which is associated with an antenna current of 1 A, and an effective antenna resistance, R, of 100Ω. The degree of modulation is $70/100 = 0.7$ and the total sideband power is $0.5\, m^2 P_c = 0.5 \times (0.7)^2 \times 100 = 24.5$ W. The total power in the AM signal, P, is $100 + 24.5 = 124.5$ W and the new antenna current is:

$$I_A = \sqrt{\frac{P}{R}} = \sqrt{\frac{124.5}{100.0}} = \sqrt{1.245} = 1.116A, \text{ rounded off.}$$

The percentage increase in antenna current is

$$\left(\frac{1.116 - 1}{1}\right) \times 100 = 11.6\%$$

Alternatively, the percentage increase in antenna current is:

$$\left(\sqrt{1 + \frac{m^2}{2}} - 1\right) \times 100 = \left(\sqrt{1 + \frac{(0.7)^2}{2}} - 1\right) \times 100$$
$$= 11.6\%$$

Example 5-7

An rf carrier is double sideband amplitude modulated by a single tone. If the degree of modulation is increased from 0.50 to 0.80, what is the percentage increase in the antenna current?
Solution

Assume that the unmodulated carrier power is 100 W, the unmodulated antenna current is 1 A and the effective antenna resistance is 100%

Degree of modulation, $m_1 = 0.50$

Total sideband power $= 0.5 \ m_1^2 \ P_c = 0.5 \times (0.5)^2 \times 100$
$$= 12.5 \ W$$

Total power in the AM signal $= 100 + 12.5 = 112.5W$

Antenna current $= \sqrt{\dfrac{112.5 \ W}{100 \ \Omega}} = 1.0607$ A, rounded off

Degree of modulation, $m_2 = 0.80$

Total sideband power $= 0.5 \ m_2^2 \ P_c$
$$= 0.5 \times (0.80)^2 \times 100 = 32W$$

Total power in the AM signal $= 100 + 32 = 132$ W

Antenna current $= \sqrt{\dfrac{132 \ W}{100 \ \Omega}} = 1.1489$ A, rounded off

The percentage increase in the antenna current is:

$$\left(\frac{1.1489 - 1.0607}{1.0607}\right) \times 100 = \left(\frac{1.1489}{1.0607} - 1\right) \times 100$$
$$= 8.3\% \text{ rounded off}$$

Alternatively, the percentage increase in antenna current is:

$$\left[\sqrt{\frac{2 + m_2^2}{2 + m_1^2}} - 1\right] \times 100$$
$$= \left(\sqrt{\frac{2.64}{2.25}} - 1\right) \times 100$$

$$= (1.1733 - 1) \times 100 - (1.0832 - 1) \times 100$$

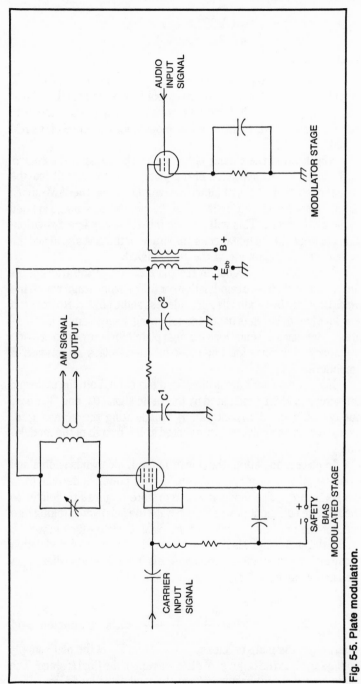

Fig. 5-5. Plate modulation.

$$= (\ 1.0832 - 1)\ \times 100$$
$$= 8.3\%, \text{ rounded off}$$

PLATE MODULATION

The plate modulated rf power amplifier (Fig. 5-5) is a class C amplifier in which the audio signal output is superimposed on the dc plate supply voltage, E_{bb}; the total voltage then applied to the plate circuit, corresponds to the required modulation envelope of the AM signal.

The level of the carrier signal input, the value of the control grid bias and the impedance of the plate load tank circuit may be adjusted so that the instantaneous amplitude of the AM signal output is approximately equal to the instantaneous voltage applied to the plate circuit. This will provide the necessary linear relationship between the instantaneous amplitude of the AM signal and the instantaneous magnitude of the audio signal.

Modulation may occur in the plate circuit of the transmitter final rf stage (high level modulation) or in an earlier stage where the modulator will be required to provide less audio power. However, if low level modulation is used, the following stages cannot be operated under class C conditions for high plate efficiency or to provide frequency multiplication but must be linear class A or class B amplifiers.

If a beam power tube is used for the rf state, both the plate and the screen grid are modulated by the audio signal (C_1 and C_2 are rf, but not af, bypass capacitors). By modulating the screen grid, excessive screen current is prevented at the trough of the modulation cycle.

In plate modulation, the power in the rf sidebands is obtained from the modulator stage while the carrier power is derived from the B+ supply. The modulator is therefore required to deliver to the rf stage sufficient power to generate the sidebands, taking into account the percentage value of the class C plate efficiency.

If the audio signal is a single tone and the degree of modulation required is m, the total sideband power is $0.5m^2\,P_c$ watts where P_c is the carrier power developed in the plate circuit.
Then,

$$P_c = \frac{E_{bb} \times I_b \times \eta_R}{100} \text{ watts} \quad \textbf{Equation 5-19}$$

where η_R is the plate efficiency percentage, E_{bb} is the plate supply voltage and I_b is the dc level of plate current in the final rf stage. The audio power output required from the modulator stage is:

$$\frac{0.5 \ m^2 \ P_c}{\eta_R} \times 100 = \frac{50 \ m^2 \ P_c}{\eta_R} \ watts.$$

Equation 5-20

As shown in Fig. 5-5, the modulator stage is a single tube audio power amplifier which will operate under class A conditions with relatively low plate efficiency.

The dc plate input power to the modulator stage is:

$$\frac{Audio \ power \ output}{\eta_m} \times 100 = \frac{50 \ m^2 \ P_c}{\eta_R \times \eta_M} \times 100 =$$

$$\frac{5000 \ m^2 \ P_c}{\eta_R \times \eta_M} = \frac{50 \ m^2 \times E_{bb} \times I_b}{\eta_M} \ watts$$

Equation 5-21

where η_M = plate efficiency percentage of the class A modulator stage. The plate dissipation of the modulator stage is equal to:

(dc plate input power to the modulator stage) $\times \ 1 - \left(\frac{\eta_M}{100}\right)$

$$= \left(\frac{100}{\eta_M} - 1\right) \frac{50 \ m^2 \ P_c}{\eta_R}$$

Equation 5-22

The effective load applied across the secondary of the output modulation transformer is $E_{bb} / I_b \ \Omega$. The turns ratio of the output transformer must be used to match this effective load to the optimum plate load required by the modulator tube (for example, if the modulator tube is a triode, the optimum plate load is $2r_p$ where r_p is the triode's ac plate resistance).

Example 5-8

The plate modulated final rf stage of an AM transmitter has a dc supply voltage of 800 V and a dc plate current level of 1.5 A. The stage is operated in class C with a plate efficiency of 75%, and is 80% modulated by a single tone. The modulator stage uses two triodes in parallel and has a plate efficiency of 30%. What are: (a) the total power in the sidebands, (b) the modulator output power, (c) the required audio power output to the modulator, (d) the required turns ratio for the modulator output transformer if each triode modulator tube has an ac plate resistance of 800 Ω, and (e) the plate dissipation in each of the triodes?

Solution

(a) DC plate input power = $E_{bb} \times I_b = 800 \times 1.5 = 1200$ W. The rf carrier power developed in the plate circuit of the final rf stage,

$$P_c = 1200 \times \frac{75}{100} = 900 \ W$$

Total sideband power, $P_s = 0.5\ m^2\ P_c = 0.5 \times (0.8)^2 \times 900$
$$= 288\ W$$

(b) The modulator output must provide the sideband power, taking into account the class C plate efficiency of the final rf stage.

Modulator output power $= \dfrac{P_s}{\eta_R} \times 100 = \dfrac{288}{75} \times 100 = 384\ W$

(c) The plate efficiency of the modulator stage is 30%. The dc plate power input to the modulator is:

$$\dfrac{\text{Modulator output power}}{\eta_M} \times 100 = \dfrac{384}{30} \times 100 = 1280\ W$$

Alternatively, the dc power plate input to the modulator is:

$$\dfrac{50\ m^2\ E_{bb}\ I_b}{\eta_M} = \dfrac{50 \times (0.8)^2 \times 800 \times 1.5}{30}$$
$$= 1280\ W$$

(d) The effective load on the transformer secondary is:

$$\dfrac{E_{bb}}{I_b} = \dfrac{800\ V}{1.5\ A} = 533\ \Omega$$

Effective r_p of the two triodes in parallel $= 800/2 = 400\ \Omega$. Optimum load required by the triodes $= 2 \times 400 = 800\ \Omega$. Required turns ratio for the modulator transformer $= \sqrt{800/533} = 1.23{:}1$

(e) The total plate dissipation of the modulator stage is
$$1.28 \times \dfrac{70}{100} = 0.896\ kW = 896\ W$$

The plate dissipation in each triode is $\dfrac{896}{2} = 450\ W$, rounded off.

Note that if the triodes had been connected in push-pull and not in parallel, the plate dissipation in each triode would still have been half of the total plate dissipation of the modulator stage.

FREQUENCY MODULATION

With frequency modulation, the instantaneous frequency of the rf wave is varied in accordance with the modulating signal while the amplitude of the rf wave is kept constant. The rf power output and the antenna current of the FM transmitter are therefore independent of the modulation. In the FM wave (Fig. 5-6), the instantaneous amount of the *frequency* shift away from its average unmodulated value is linearly related to the instantaneous *magnitude* (voltage) of the modulating signal while the rate at which the frequency shift occurs, is equal to the modulating frequency. Note carefully that the amount of the frequency shift in the rf wave is independent of the modulating frequency. Therefore, provided they are of the same amplitude, modulating tones of 200 Hz and 400 Hz will produce the same amount of frequency shift in the FM wave. However, it must be pointed out that in FM and TV broadcast transmitters, the higher audio frequencies above 800 Hz are progressively accentuated (pre-emphasized) in order to improve their signal-to-noise ratio at the receiver. The degree of pre-emphasis is measured by the time constant of a CR circuit whose audio output increases with frequency. This time constant is specified by the FCC as 75 microseconds. In order to restore the tonal balance, the receiver discriminator output is fed to an RC de-emphasis circuit with the same time constant.

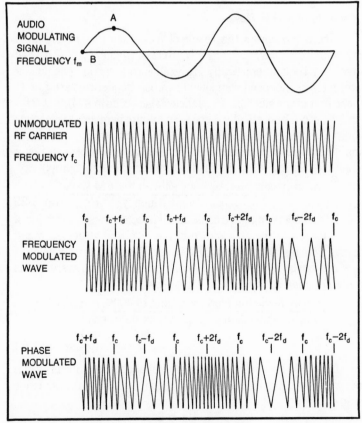

Fig. 5-6. Frequency and phase modulation waves.

129

When 100% modulation of an FM wave occurs, the amount of frequency shift reaches the maximum value allowed for the particular communications system. This maximum value is called the frequency deviation which, in the FM broadcast service (emission designation F3), is a shift of 75 kHz on either side of the unmodulated carrier frequency. The output frequency swing for 100% modulation is therefore ± 75 kHz. However, in the aural transmitter of a TV broadcast station, 100% modulation corresponds to a frequency deviation of 25 kHz while in the Public Safety Radio Services, the frequency deviation is only 5 kHz. The percentage modulation and the amount of frequency shift are directly proportional so that 40% modulation in the FM broadcast service would correspond to an output frequency swing of:

$$\pm \ \frac{40}{100} \times 75 = \pm 30 \text{ kHz}$$

Sidebands in an FM Wave

Figure 5-6 shows the result of frequency modulating an rf carrier of frequency, f_c, by a *single* tone of frequency f_m. The FM wave may be mathematically analyzed into a carrier component together with sideband components whose frequencies are $f_c \pm f_m$ (these first order sideband frequencies also occur in AM), $f_c \pm 2 f_m$, $f_c \pm 3 f_m$, etc. Theoretically there is an infinite number of sidebands whose frequency spacing is equal to f_m and whose individual amplitudes are determined by the modulation index, m_f. For a single modulating tone, the modulation index is defined by:

$$m_f = \frac{\text{maximum frequency shift in the FM wave}}{\text{modulating frequency}} \qquad \textbf{Equation 5-23}$$

If the modulating wave consists of speech of music, the value of m_f and therefore the appearance of the sideband structure would change from instant to instant. However, there is a certain value of m_f which can be quoted for a particular communication system; this is the *deviation ratio* which is defined as:

$$\frac{\text{frequency deviation (corresponding to 100\% modulation)}}{\text{highest modulating frequency to be transmitted}}$$

Equation 5-24

In the FM broadcast service, the frequency deviation is 75 kHz and with the highest audio frequency equal to 15 kHz, the deviation ratio is:

$$\frac{75 \text{ kHz}}{15 \text{ kHz}} = 5$$

In the TV broadcast aural transmitter, the highest audio frequency is again 15 kHz but with a frequency deviation of 25 kHz, the deviation ratio is:

$$\frac{25}{15} = 1.667$$

In the Public Safety Services, the maximum audio frequency is 3 kHz, the frequency deviation is 5 kHz and therefore the deviation ratio is:

$$\frac{5 \text{ kHz}}{3 \text{ kHz}} = 1.667$$

Most of the sidebands in an FM wave are low in amplitude and do not contribute significantly in reproducing the intelligence at the receiver. Provided that m_f is a whole number, the number of pairs of significant sidebands is $m_f + 1$ and therefore the bandwidth of the FM signal $= 2 (m_f + 1) f_m = 2 \times$ (the frequency shift in the FM wave) $+ 2f_m$. In the FM broadcast service, the particular combination of 100% modulation and the deviation ratio of 5, would produce a bandwidth of $2 \times 75 \text{ kHz} + 2 \times 15 \text{ kHz} = 180 \text{ kHz}$; the channel width allocated to such stations is 200 kHz.

Production of FM

The direct method of obtaining frequency modulation involves a varactor diode or a reactance tube, which is used with a variable frequency oscillator, such as a Hartley or a Colpitts. Since modulation is taking place at the master oscillator stage, the amount of audio power required is small. However, since the information is contained in frequency variations, the oscillator must possess a high degree of frequency stability; therefore an automatic frequency control (afc) circuit may be required to stabilize the generated frequency. Unlike an AM signal, the FM output from the oscillator may be followed by a number of class C frequency multiplier stages. The total multiplying factor will be applied not only to the carrier frequency but also to the instantaneous frequency swing created by the modulating signal. As a result, the frequency swing at the oscillator may be much smaller than the swing in the rf final stage; it is then easier to achieve the necessary linear relationship between the instantaneous frequency shift and the instantaneous voltage of the modulating signal.

Assuming that a single test tone produces a modulation percentage, m, in the FM broadcast service, the frequency swing in the rf final stage is

$$\pm \frac{m \times 75 \text{ kHz}}{100} \qquad \qquad \textbf{Equation 5-25}$$

If the total product factor provided by the frequency multiplier stages is M, the frequency swing at the oscillator stage is

$$\pm \frac{75m \text{ kHz}}{100M} \qquad \qquad \textbf{Equation 5-26}$$

It is interesting to note that when an rf wave is frequency modulated by more than one audio frequency, the principle of superposition, which applies to the sideband structure of an AM signal, does not similarly apply to FM; any form of single-sideband FM is therefore impossible. Moreover, if an FM receiver picks up two signals simultaneously on the same frequency, a "capture" effect takes place and only the stronger of the two signals is heard.

Example 5-9

For test purposes, a 10 kW FM broadcast transmitter is 80% modulated by a 2 kHz tone. Including the carrier and sidebands, what is the total power in the FM signal? Calculate the value of the output frequency swing.

Solution

Since the rf power in an FM signal is independent of the modulation, the total power remains at 10kW. In the FM broadcast service, 100% modulation corresponds to a frequency deviation of 75 kHz. The frequency swing for 80% modulation is:

$$\pm \frac{80}{100} \times 75 = \pm 60 \text{ kHz}$$

Example 5-10

The aural transmitter of a TV broadcast station is 60 modulated by a 500 Hz test tone. The amplitude and frequency of the tone are both halved. What is output frequency swing in the FM signal?

Solution

In the aural transmitter of a TV broadcast station, 100% modulation corresponds to a frequency deviation of 25 kHz. Since the percentage modulation is directly proportional to the tone amplitude (the effect of pre-emphasis may be neglected at 500 Hz and 250 Hz) but independent of its frequency, the new modulation percentage will be 30% which will correspond to an output frequency swing of

$$\pm \frac{30}{100} \times 25 = \pm 7.5 \text{ kHz}$$

Example 5-11

A 50 kW FM broadcast station is instantaneously 40% modulated by an audio frequency of 5 kHz. What is (a) The value of the modulation index and (b) the bandwidth of the FM signal?

Solution

(a) For an FM broadcast station, 40% modulation corresponds to a frequency shift of:

$$\frac{40}{100} \times 75 = 30 \text{ kHz}$$

The modulation index is:

$$\frac{30 \text{ kHz}}{5 \text{ kHz}} = 6$$

Since the modulation index is a whole number, the number of significant sidebands on either side of the carrier is $6 + 1 = 7$. Since adjacent sidebands are separated by the audio frequency of 5 kHz, the bandwidth is $2 \times 7 \times 5 = 70$ kHz.

Example 5-12

An FM transmitter is operating on 102 MHz and the oscillator stage is being directly modulated by a 3 kHz test tone so that its frequency swing is ± 2 kHz. The oscillator stage generates 4250 kHz when unmodulation is 75 kHz. What is the percentage modulation produced by the test tone?

Solution

The total product factor of the frequency multiplier stages is:

$$\frac{120 \text{ MHz}}{4250 \text{ kHz}} = 24$$

The output frequency swing $= \pm 2 \times 24 = \pm 48$ kHz.

Percentage modulation $= \dfrac{48}{75} \times 100 = 64\%$.

Example 5-13

When an FM broadcast transmitter is modulated by a 450 Hz tone, the output frequency swing is ± 30 kHz. If the tone frequency is lowered to 225 Hz but the amplitude is unchanged, what is the new percentage of modulation?

Solution

For tones of 450 Hz and 225 Hz the effect of the pre-emphasis may be neglected. Therefore the change in the tone frequency does not alter the modulation percentage which remains at:

$$\frac{30}{75} \times 100 = 40\%$$

Example 5-14

The aural transmitter of a TV broadcast station is 40% modulated by a 400 Hz test tone. The tone amplitude is doubled and the frequency is increased to 500 Hz. Neglecting any effect of pre-emphasis, what is (a) the new value of the modulation index and (b) the total number of significant sidebands?

Solution

When the tone amplitude is doubled, the new output frequency swing will be:

$$\pm\, 2 \times \frac{40}{100} \times 25 = \pm\, 20 \text{ kHz}$$

The new value of the modulation index will be:

$$\frac{20 \text{ kHz}}{500 \text{ Hz}} = 40$$

Since m_f is a whole number, the number of significant sidebands on either side of the carrier is $m_f + 1 = 40 + 1 = 41$. The total number of significant sidebands $= 2 \times 41 = 82$. Note that although there are a large number of significant sidebands, the separation between adjacent sidebands is only 500 Hz and therefore the required bandwidth is $82 \times 0.5 = 41$ kHz.

Example 5-15

An FM broadcast station is operating on 103.1 MHz. If its transmission is 60% modulated by a 3 kHz test tone, what is (a) the highest instantaneous frequency in the FM signal, and (b) the frequency of the highest significant upper sideband?

Solution

(a) For an FM broadcast station, 60% modulation corresponds to a frequency swing of:

$$\pm\, 75 \times \frac{60}{100} = \pm\, 45 \text{ kHz}$$

The highest instantaneous frequency is therefore:

$$103.1 \text{ MHz} + 45 \text{ kHz} = 103.145 \text{ MHz}.$$

(b) The modulation index, m_f is:

$$\frac{45 \text{ kHz}}{3 \text{ kHz}} = 15$$

Since m_f is a whole number, the number of significant sidebands on either side of the carrier is:

$$m_f + 1 = 16$$

The frequency of the highest upper significant sideband is 103.1 MHz + (3 × 16 kHz) = 103.148 MHz.

PHASE MODULATION

In phase modulation (Fig. 5-6) the instantaneous phase of the rf carrier wave is varied in accordance with the modulating signal while the amplitude of the rf wave is kept constant. The instantaneous amount of the phase shift away from its unmodulated value is linearly related to the instantaneous magnitude (voltage) of the modulating signal. Since a rate of change of phase is equivalent to a shift in frequency, the PM wave is similar in appearance to the FM wave and, in fact they cannot be distinguished except by reference to the modulating signal. The important differences are:

□ With PM, the output frequency swing is proportional to the product of the amplitude and the frequency of the modulating signal, while in FM, the swing is proportional to the amplitude alone. Therefore, if the carrier is being modulated by a single tone and the tone amplitude and frequency are both doubled, the output frequency swing in the FM signal would be quadrupled (neglecting any effect of pre-emphasis).

□ Relative to the cycle of the modulating signal, the instantaneous maximum (and/or minimum) frequency positions are 90° apart in the FM and PM waves. For example, in Fig. 5-6, point A in the modulating signal corresponds to the instantaneous maximum frequency in the FM wave; for the PM wave the maximum frequency occurs at point B which is one-fourth of a cycle or 90° from point A.

The main importance of PM is its use in the indirect method of creating FM. For reasons of frequency stability (and to avoid the requirement for an afc system) it is common practice in many FM transmitters to use a master crystal oscillator whose frequency is fixed and which therefore cannot be directly modulated. The modulated stage comes after the crystal oscillator and consists of a circuit which actually creates phase modulation. However, before reaching the modulated stage, the audio signal is passed through a correction network (not to be confused with the pre-emphasis circuit) whose voltage output is inversely proportional to frequency and which introduces an approximate 90° phase shift. Then as far as the undistorted audio signal input *to* the correction network is concerned, the output from the modulated stage is the required FM signal, but with regard to the output *from* the correction network, the modulated stage produces PM.

Example 5-16

When modulated by an audio tone of 250 Hz, a phase modulated stage produces and output frequency swing of ± kHz. The tone amplitude is doubled and its frequency is raised to 400 Hz. What is the new output frequency swing?

Solution

In a PM signal, the frequency swing is proportional to the product of the tone amplitude and the frequency. The new frequency swing is:

$$\pm\,5 \times 2 \times \frac{400}{250} = \pm\,16\ \text{kHz}$$

CALCULATION OF OPERATING POWER BY THE INDIRECT METHOD

The operating power of a transmitter is the actual rf power supplied to the antenna. It may either be calculated by the direct method (discussed in the next chapter) or by the indirect method which involves the plate input power to the final rf stage and an efficiency factor which is normally expressed as a decimal fraction but may be given as a percentage.

The operating power $= E_{bb} \times I_b \times F$ where E_{bb} is the dc plate supply voltage of the rf final stage I_b is the associated dc level of plate current and F is the efficiency factor.

For a standard AM broadcast station, the efficiency factor depends on the method of modulation (plate, grid or low level) and the maximum rated carrier output, but for FM and TV (aural) broadcast stations, the value of F is originally supplied by the manufacturer.

Example 5-17

The final rf stage of a standard broadcast station has a plate supply voltage of 2500 V and a dc level of plate current equal to 1.5 A. The stage uses plate modulation with an efficiency factor of 0.7. What is the operating power, as determined by the indirect method?

Solution

The operating power is $E_{bb} \times I_b \times F = 2500 \times 1.5 \times 0.7$
$$= 2625\ \text{W}.$$

Example 5-18

A transmitter uses an antenna with an effective resistance of 110 Ω and the antenna current is 4.5 A. The final rf stage has a plate supply voltage of 1500 V and a plate current of 1.9 A. What is the value of the efficiency factor F?

Solution

Operating power by direct method $= (4.5)^2 \times 100 = 2227.5\ \text{W}.$

Efficiency factor, $F = \dfrac{2227.5}{1500 \times 1.9} = 0.78$

CHAPTER SUMMARY

Amplitude Modulation

Positive peaks:

$$\text{Percentage modulation} = \frac{E_{max} - E_o}{E_o} \times 100\%$$

Negative peaks:

$$\text{Percentage modulation} = \frac{E_o - E_{min}}{E_o} \times 100\%$$

Symmetrical modulation:

$$\text{Percentage modulation} = \frac{E_{max} - E_{min}}{2\,E_o} \times 100\%$$

$$= \frac{E_{max} - E_{min}}{E_{max} + E_{min}} \times 100\%$$

Degree of modulation, $m = \dfrac{\text{percentage modulation}}{100}$

Percentage carrier shift =

$$\frac{\text{Modulated dc plate current} - \text{unmodulated dc plate current}}{\text{Unmodulated dc plate current}} \times 100\%$$

Trapezoidal Display.

$$\text{Percentage modulation} = \frac{P - Q}{P + Q} \times 100\%$$

Double sideband modulation:

$$\text{Total sideband power} = \frac{1}{2} \times m^2 \times P_c$$

Bandwidth = $2 \times$ highest modulating frequency.

Percentage increase in total sideband power $= \left[\left(\dfrac{m_2}{m_1} \right)^2 - 1 \right] \times$

100% if the degree of modulation is increased from m_1 to m_2.

Percentage decrease in total sideband power =

$\left[1 - \left(\dfrac{m_1}{m_2} \right)^2 \right] \times 100\%$, if the degree of modulation is

decreased from m_2 to m_1.

Single sideband modulation:
Bandwidth = highest modulating frequency.

Percentage power saving with single sideband =

$$\frac{\text{Total rf Power (double sideband)} - \text{Single sideband power}}{\text{Total rf power (double sideband)}} \times 100\%$$

Antenna Current (double sideband)

Percentage increase in antenna current =

$$\left(\sqrt{\frac{m^2}{2} + 1} - 1 \right) \times 100\%,$$

when the degree of modulation is increased from 0 to m. If the degree of modulation is increased from m_1 to m_2,

percentage increase in antenna current =

$$\sqrt{\frac{2 + m_2^2}{2 + m_1^2}} - 1 \times 100\%$$

If the degree of modulation is decreased from m_2 to m_1,

Percentage increase in antenna current =

$$\left(1 - \sqrt{\frac{2 + m_1^2}{2 + m_2^2}} \right) \times 100\%$$

Plate modulation:

$$\text{Carrier Power, } P_c = \frac{E_{bb} \times I_b \times \eta_R}{100} \text{ watts}$$

$$\text{Modulator Power output} = \frac{50 \, m^2 \, P_c}{\eta_R} \text{ watts}$$

DC input plate power to the modulator stage =

$$\frac{5000 \, m^2 \, P_c}{\eta_R \times \eta_M} = \frac{50 \, m^2 \, E_{bb} \, I_b}{\eta_M} \text{ watts.}$$

$$\text{Modulator plate dissipation} = \left(\frac{100}{\eta_M} - 1 \right) \frac{50 \, m^2 \, P_c}{\eta_R}$$

Frequency Modulation

$$\text{Modulation index, } m_f = \frac{\text{frequency shift in the FM wave}}{\text{modulating frequency}}$$

Deviation ratio =

$$\frac{\text{frequency deviations corresponding to 100\% modulation}}{\text{highest transmitted modulating frequency}}$$

Number of significant sidebands = 2 (m_f + 1)

Bandwidth = 2 (m_f + 1) f_m

Operating power by the indirect method = $E_p \times I_p \times F$ watts.

Chapter 6
Transmission
Lines and Antennas

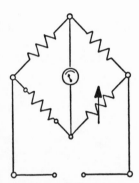

The purpose of a transmission line used at radio frequencies is to convey rf power from one position to another. Such a line is an example of distributed circuitry and possesses the following properties which are referred to as the primary constants:

- [ ] Resistance per unit length, R, (ohms per meter)
- [ ] Inductance per unit length, L, (henrys per meter)
- [ ] Capacitance per unit length, C, (farads per meter)
- [ ] Conductance per unit length, G, (siemens per meter)

(The above refers to the insulation between the conductors).

SURGE IMPEDANCE AND THE MATCHED LINE

The surge or characteristic impedance, Z_o, which is a secondary constant, is defined as the input impedance to an infinite length of the line and is measured in ohms. In terms of the primary constants,

$$Z_o = 4\sqrt{\frac{R^2 + \omega^2 L^2}{G^2 + \omega^2 C^2}} \ \Omega \qquad \textbf{Equation 6-1}$$

Where the angular velocity, $\omega = 1\,\pi\,f$ and f is the frequency of the generator which is feeding the line; at radio frequencies, this formula becomes,

$$Z_o = \sqrt{\frac{L}{C}} \ \Omega$$

which is a resistive quantity. The value of the surge impedance is determined by the physical construction of the line and the nature of the insulation between the conductors. For the two most common types of transmission line, the Z_o formulas are:

Parallel Conductor or Twin Lead

As an example, this is the type of line which is used to connect a TV receiver to its antenna (Fig. 6-1)

$$\text{Surge impedance, } Z_o = \frac{276}{\sqrt{\epsilon_r}} \log_{10}\left(\frac{s}{r}\right) \Omega$$

$$= \frac{276}{\sqrt{\epsilon_r}} \log_{10}\left(\frac{2s}{d}\right) \Omega$$

Equation 6-2

where,

   s = spacing between the centers of the conductor

   r = radius of each conductor

   d = diameter of each conductor

   ϵ_r = relative permittivity of the insulator between the con-
        ductors.

Note that s, r and d must be measured in the same units of length. For S1 units this would be the meter.

Coaxial Cable

$$\text{Surge impedance, } Z_o = \frac{138}{\sqrt{\epsilon_r}} \log_{10}\left(\frac{D}{d}\right) \Omega \quad \textbf{Equation 6-3}$$

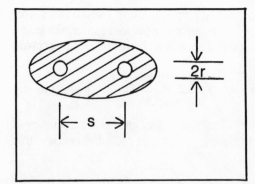

Fig. 6-1. The twin head transmission line.

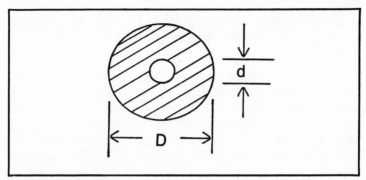

Fig. 6-2. The coaxial cable.

where,

  D= inner diameter of the outer conductor (Fig. 6-2)

  d = outer diameter of the inner conductor and

  ϵ_r = relative permittivity of the insulation between the conductors.

Again both D and d must be measured in the same units of length such as the meter.

Since at radio frequencies the phase angle associated with the surge impedance of the transmission line is virtually zero, the line may be terminated with a resistive load which is identical in value to Z_o; under these conditions the line is said to be matched. From the generator, traveling (progressive) waves of voltage and current move down the line in phase toward the end where their energy is completely delivered to the load. At any position on the line the ratio of the rms voltage, E, between the conductors to the rms current, I, flowing through the conductors, is equal to the surge impedance, Z_o; the power at the position,

$$P = \frac{E^2}{Z_o} = I^2 Z_o \text{ watts} \qquad \textbf{Equation 6-4}$$

Therefore, $E = \sqrt{PZ_o}$ volts and $I = \sqrt{\dfrac{P}{Z_o}}$ amperes (as in the Ohm's law formulas) **Equation 6-5**

The surge impedance is independent of the length of the line and consequently the input impedance at the generator must also be equal to Z_o.

Notice that the voltage and current waves travel down the line in step although their phases are continuously shifting with respect

141

to the voltage and current at the generator. This change is measured by the phase shift constant, β, which is equal to, $\dfrac{2\pi}{\lambda}$ radians per meter where λ is the wavelength existing on the line. Due to the presence of the primary constants R and G, there are losses associated with the line and therefore the voltage and current waves are attenuated as they travel from the generator towards the load. The degree of attenuation is measured by the attenuation constant, α, whose unit is the *neper per meter*. The secondary constants, α and β, are combined in the propagation constant, γ, where

$$\gamma = \alpha + j\beta \qquad \text{Equation 6-6}$$

As the waves move down the line, the alternating voltage and current are multiplied by the factor $\epsilon^{-\gamma x}$ where x is the distance in meters from the transmitter. It may be shown that:

$$\gamma = \sqrt{(R = j\omega L) \times (G + j\omega C)} \qquad \text{Equation 6-7}$$

This leads to:

$$\alpha = \frac{R}{2Z_0} + \frac{GZ_0}{2} \text{ nepers per meter} \qquad \text{Equation 6-8}$$

and, $\qquad \beta = \omega\sqrt{LC}$ radians per meter

Since 1 neper = 8.7 decibels, the attenuation may also be expressed in decibels per meter.

Adjacent points on the line which have identical phase conditions, are separated by a distance equal to the wavelength,

$$\lambda = \frac{V_\phi}{f}$$

, where V_ϕ is the phase velocity or the V_ϕ speed at which the voltage and current waves travel down the line. If an air dielectric is used, V_ϕ is approximately 3×10^8 meters per second (the velocity of light, c). If an insulator or dielectric other than air is used,

$$V_\phi = \frac{c}{\epsilon_r} = \frac{3 \times 10^8}{\epsilon_r} \text{ meters per second,}$$

Equation 6-10

where ϵ_r is the relative permittivity.

Since $\lambda = \dfrac{V_\phi}{f}$ $f = \dfrac{V_\phi}{\lambda}$ and $V_\phi = f \times \lambda$,

Equation 6-11

where f is expressed in hertz and λ in meters.

Since $V_\phi = f\lambda$ and $\beta = \dfrac{2\pi}{\lambda}$, $\lambda = \dfrac{2\pi}{\beta}$ meters

Equation 6-12

and, $\quad V_\phi = \dfrac{2\pi f}{\beta} = \dfrac{\omega}{\beta} = \dfrac{\omega}{\omega\sqrt{LC}} = \dfrac{1}{\sqrt{LC}}$

meters per second

Example 6-1

Each conductor of a parallel lead transmission line has a radius of 1.5 mm and the spacing between the centers of the conductors is 0.8 cm. If an air dielectric is used, what is the value of the line's surge impedance?

Solution

The line's surge impedance,

$$Z_o = \dfrac{276}{\sqrt{\epsilon_r}} \log_{10}\left(\dfrac{S}{r}\right) = \dfrac{276}{\sqrt{1}} \log_{10}\left(\dfrac{0.8}{0.15}\right)$$
$$= 276 \log_{10} 5.333 \approx 200 \ \Omega.$$

Example 6-2

The outer conductor of a coaxial cable has an inner diameter of 1.75 cm while the inner conductor has an outer diameter of 2.5 mm. Using Teflon® (dielectric constant = 2.1) as the insulator between the conductors, what is the value of the cable's surge impedance?

Solution

Cable's surge impedance, $Z_o = \dfrac{138}{\sqrt{\epsilon_r}} \log_{10}\left(\dfrac{D}{d}\right)$

where, d = 2.5 m = 0.25 cm. D = 1.75 cm

Therefore:

$$Z_o = \dfrac{138}{\sqrt{2.1}} \log_{10}\left(\dfrac{1.75}{0.25}\right) = \dfrac{138}{\sqrt{2.1}}$$

$\log_{10} 7 = 81 \ \Omega$, rounded off.

Example 6-3

The primary constants of an rf transmitter line are $R = 50$ mΩ per meter, $L = 1.6\,\mu$H per meter, $C = 7.5$ pF per meter and $G = 10$ nS per meter. If the frequency of the generator feeding the line is 300 MHz, calculate the line's (a) surge impedance (b) attenuation constant (c) phase shift constant (d) wavelength (e) phase velocity?

Solution

(a) Surge impedance, $Z_0 = \sqrt{\dfrac{L}{C}} = \sqrt{\dfrac{1.6 \times 10^{-6}}{7.5 \times 10^{-12}}}$

$$= 462\ \Omega$$

(b) Attenuation constant, $\alpha = \dfrac{R}{2Z_0} + \dfrac{GZ_0}{2}$

$$= \frac{50 \times 10^{-3}}{2 \times 462} + \frac{10 \times 10^{-9} \times 462}{2}$$

$$= 54 \times 10^{-6} + 2.3 \times 10^{-6}$$

$$= 56.3 \times 10^{-6}\ \text{nepers per meter}$$

$$= 490 \times 10^{-6}\ \text{decibels per meter.}$$

(c) Phase Shift constant, $\beta = \Omega\sqrt{LC}$

$$= 2 \times \pi \times 300 \times 10^6 \times$$

$$\sqrt{1.6 \times 10^{-6} \times 7.5 \times 10^{-12}}$$

$$= 6.53\ \text{radians per meter.}$$

(d) Line's wavelength, $\lambda = \dfrac{2\pi}{\beta}$

$$= 0.96\ \text{meter.}$$

(e) Phase velocity, $V_\phi = f \times \lambda$

$$= 300 \times 10^6 \times 0.96$$

$$= 288 \times 10^6\ \text{meters per second.}$$

UNMATCHED LINE

If an rf line is terminated by a resistive load not equal to the surge impedance, the generator will still send voltage and current waves down the line in phase but their energy will only be partially absorbed by the load. A certain fraction of the voltage and current waves which are incident at the load, will be reflected back towards the generator. In the two extreme cases of open-circuited and short-circuited lines, no energy can be absorbed by the load and total reflection will occur. At any position on the line the instantaneous voltage (or current) will be the resultant of the incident and reflected voltage (or current) waves. These combine to produce standing waves whose rms distributions on open-circuited and short-circuited lines are shown in Figs. 6-3A and B.

Considering the voltage standing wave distribution, there are certain stationary positions on the line at which minimum voltage occurs. These are known as voltage nodes or null points which are separated from each other by a distance equal to,

$$\frac{\lambda}{2}$$

where λ is the wavelength as it exists on the line. Half-way between the null points are the voltage antinodes or loops, which represent the maximum voltage variation. An antinode is therefore separated from an adjacent voltage node by,

$$\frac{\lambda}{4}.$$

Note that voltage antinodes coincide in their positions with current nodes and vice-versa.

If the line is terminated by neither an open circuit nor a short circuit but merely by a resistive load, R_L, which is either greater or less than the value of Z_o, the amount of reflection at the load will be decreased; the standing waves will therefore be reduced so that the nodes and antinodes will be less pronounced. Neglecting the losses on the line, the voltage and current distribution for the three cases of $R_L > Z_o$, $R_L = Z_o$ and $R_L < Z_o$ are shown in Fig. 6-4.

Reflection Coefficient

The fraction of the incident voltage and current which is reflected at the load is called the reflection coefficient ρ (rho). It may be shown that:

$$\rho = \frac{R_L - Z_o}{R_L + Z_o} \qquad \textbf{Equation 6-13}$$

A positive value of ρ indicates that the voltage wave is reflected with no phase change but the current wave will be reflected with a phase change of 180°. If ρ has a negative value, the voltage wave is reflected with a 180° phase reversal on reflection. These results are only true for loads which are purely resistive.

145

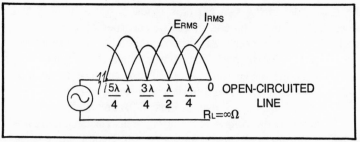

Fig. 6-3A. RMS voltage and current distribution on the open-circuited line.

If the load contains both resistance and reactance, ρ is a complex quantity having both a magnitude and a phase angle,

$$\rho = \frac{Z_L - Z_o}{Z_L + Z_o} = |P| \;\; \theta \qquad \text{Equation 6-14}$$

where $|P|$ (capital rho) is the magnitude of the reflection coefficient and θ is its phase angle. The magnitude of $|P|$ lies between zero (the perfectly matched line) and 1 (for open or short-circuited lines). The values of θ extend from $0°$ to $180°$.

Since the reflected voltage is $|P|$ times the incident voltage and the reflected current is $|P|$ times the incident current, it follows that the reflected power is $|P|^2$ times the incident power. Then the load power, ρ_L, is equal to the incident power minus the reflected power and is:

$$\rho_L = (1 - |P|^2) \times \text{incident power or } \frac{1 - |P|^2}{|P|} \times \text{reflected power}$$

Equation 6-15

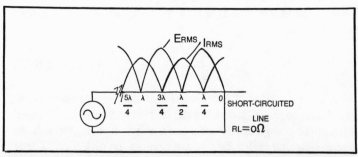

Fig. 6-3B. RMS voltage and current distribution on the short-circuited line.

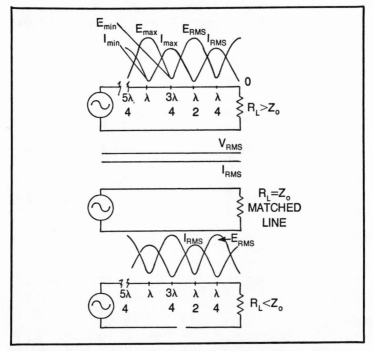

Fig. 6-4. Voltage and current distribution on a transmission line for various resistive terminations.

Voltage Standing Wave Ratio

Referring to Fig. 6-4, the rms value of the voltage antinode is E_{max} while the value of an adjacent node is E_{min}; the voltage standing wave ratio (vswr), s, is defined as, $\dfrac{E_{max}}{E_{min}}$

which is also equal in magnitude to, $\dfrac{I_{max}}{I_{min}}$.

For a perfectly matched line s $= 1$ while for the lossless line which is terminated by either an open or a short circuit, s is theoretically infinite. On a matched system, a value of s below 1.2 is normally regarded as adequate. Notice that s is not a complex quantity and possesses a magnitude only.

Since E_{max} is the result of an in-phase condition between the incident voltage and the reflected voltage, $E_{max} = E_i + E_r = E_i \times (1 + |P|)$ where the subscripts i and r represents *incident* and *reflected*. Similarly, E_{min} is the result of a 180° out of phase condition, and therefore $E_{min} = E_i \times (1 - |P|)$. The standing wave ratio is given by:

$$S = \frac{E_{max}}{E_{min}} = \frac{E_i\,(1 + |P|)}{E_i\,(1 - |P|)} = \frac{1 + |P|}{1 - |P|} \quad \text{Equation 6-16}$$

This leads to:

$$|P| = \frac{S - 1}{S + 1} \quad \text{Equation 6-17}$$

If R_L is greater than Z_0, the magnitude of ρ is given by:

$$|P| = \frac{R_L - Z_o}{R_L + Z_o} \quad \text{Equation 6-18}$$

and,

$$S = \frac{1 + |P|}{1 - |P|} = \frac{R_L}{Z_o} \quad \text{Equation 6-19}$$

If R_L is less than Z_o, the magnitude of ρ is

$$|P| = \frac{Z_o - R_L}{Z_o + R_L} \quad \text{Equation 6-20}$$

and,

$$S = \frac{Z_o}{R_L} \quad \text{Equation 6-21}$$

$$\text{Load power} = P_i \times (1 - |P|^2) = P_i \times \left(1 - \frac{S - 1}{S + 1}\right)^2$$
$$= \frac{4SP_i}{(S + 1)^2} \quad \text{Equation 6-22}$$

At the positions where the voltage antinodes and the current nodes coincide, the impedance of the line is a maximum and is resistive.

$$\text{Maximum impedance, } Z_{max} = \frac{E_{max}}{I_{min}} = \frac{E_i\,(1 + |P|)}{I_i\,(1 - |P|)}$$
$$= Z_o \times \frac{(1 + |P|)}{(1 - |P|)} = SZ_o$$

Equation 6-23

At the voltage node position, there is a minimum impedance which is given by:

$$Z_{min} = \frac{E_{min}}{I_{max}} = \frac{E_i\,(1 + |P|)}{I_i\,(1 + |P|)} = Z_o \times \frac{(1 - |P|)}{(1 + |P|)}$$

$$= \frac{Z_o}{s} \qquad \textbf{Equation 6-24}$$

Quarter-Wave Line

If a quarter-wave section of line whose surge impedance is Z_o, is terminated by a load Z_L (Fig. 6-5), the input impedance to the line is:

$$Z_{in} = \frac{Z_o^2}{Z_L} \qquad \textbf{Equation 6-25}$$

or,

$$Z_o = \sqrt{Z_{in} \times Z_L} \qquad \textbf{Equation 6-26}$$

The quarter-wave line used in this manner is sometimes called the,

$$\frac{\lambda}{4}$$

(impedance) transformer. The same impedance transformation can be achieved by using any odd multiple of,

$$\frac{\lambda}{4}$$

for the transformer length, but not by using an even multiple, since this would be equivalent to a multiple of,

$$\frac{\lambda}{2}$$

for which there is no impedance transformation.

Note that although the impedance matching transformer is electrically,

$$\frac{\lambda}{4}$$

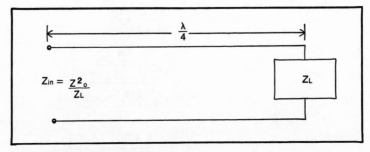

Fig. 6-5. The quarter wave line.

long, its physical length is shorter than,

$$\frac{\lambda}{4}$$

in free space and is given by:

$$\text{Length in feet} = \frac{246 \times \delta}{f} \qquad \textbf{Equation 6-27}$$

where δ is the velocity factor which is equal to the ratio of the phase velocity to the velocity of light, and f is the frequency in MHz. The value of δ varies from 0.66 for certain types of coaxial cable to 0.975 for an air-insulated parallel conductor line.

Example 6-4

A transmission line with an air dielectric and a surge impedance of $50\,\Omega$, is terminated by a load consisting of $40\,\Omega$ resistance in series with $65\ \Omega$ capacitive reactance. Calculate the reflection coefficient and the voltage standing ratio. What are the maximum and minimum values of impedance existing on the line?

If a 60 MHz rf generator delivers 80 watts to the line which is assumed to be lossless, what are the amounts of the reflected power and the power absorbed by the load. What is the distance between adjacent nulls on the line?

Solution

Load, $Z_L = 40 - j\,65\ \Omega$

Reflection coefficient, $\rho = \dfrac{Z_L - A_o}{Z_L + Z_o}$

$$= \frac{40 - j\,65 - 50}{50 + 40 - j\,65}$$

$$= \frac{-10 - j\,65}{90 - j\,65}$$

$$= \frac{65.76\ \underline{/-98.75°}}{111.01\ \underline{/-35.84°}}$$

$$= 0.6\ \underline{/-63°},\ \text{rounded off}$$

Therefore $|\rho| = 0.6$ and $\theta = -63°$

Voltage standing wave ratios, $S = \dfrac{1 + |\rho|}{1 - |\rho|} = \dfrac{1.6}{0.4} = 4.0$

Maximum impedance, $Z_{max} = SZ_o = 4.0 \times 50 = 200 \ \Omega$

Minimum impedance, $Z_{min} = \dfrac{Z_o}{S} = \dfrac{50}{4} = 12.5$

Reflected power $= (0.6)^2 \times 80 = 29$ watts, rounded off

Power absorbed by the load $= 50 - 29 = 21$ watts

Since the transmission line uses an air dielectric,

Wavelength, $\lambda = \dfrac{300 \times 10^6}{60 \times 10^6} = 5$ meters.

Distance between adjacent rules $= \dfrac{\lambda}{2} = 2.5$ meters

THE SMITH CHART

The Smith Chart used to solve transmission line problems by graphical means rather than by mathematical equations. While separate Smith Charts may be constructed for each value of surge impedance, it is more common to use a universal chart (Fig. 6-6) where all impedances (or admittance are normalized as a result of dividing their phasors by the surge impedance, Z_o (or the surge admittance, γ_o). This means that the universal chart is automatically referred to a transmission line with a surge impedance of 1 ohm or a surge admittance of 1 siemens.

In the central portion of the chart the circular coordinates represent the normalized values of the components of impedance of admittance along a mismatched transmission line. The complete circles are the coordinates of resistance or conductance while the two sets of partial circles represent those of reactance or susceptance. A voltage standing wave ratio (vswr) circle whose center is the center of the chart and which passes through a particular impedance or admittance automatically contains all the other values which exist on the lossless transmission line. The length of the circle's radius is a measure of the line's voltage standing wave ratio. Which is one of the following eight radially scaled parameters located at the side of the universal chart. These are

A. Voltage standing wave ratio, $S = \dfrac{E_{max}}{E_{min}} = \dfrac{1 + |\rho|}{1 - |\rho|}$

B. Voltage standing wave ratio in dB $= 20 \log_{10} S$.

C. Transmission loss scale in dB $= 10 \log |\rho|$.

D. Loss Coefficient (or an unmatched line as compared with the same line when matched) $= \dfrac{1 + S^2}{2S}$

E. Reflection loss in dB $= -10 \log (1 - |\rho|^2)$

F. Return loss in dB $= 20 \log |\rho|$

G. Power Reflection Coefficient $= \dfrac{\text{Reflected Power}}{\text{Incident Power}} = |\rho|^2$

H. Voltage Reflection Coefficient $= \dfrac{\text{Reflected Voltage}}{\text{Incident Voltage}}$

$$= \dfrac{S - 1}{S + 1}$$

All these parameters apply equally well to either an impedance or an admittance method of analysis. Corresponding impedance and admittance values lie at diametrically opposite ends of all circles whose centers are the center of the chart. The first peripheral scale surrounding the central portion measures the phase angle, $\theta°$, of the voltage reflection coefficient, ρ, in degrees. The two outermost peripheral scales show the distances in wavelength is either direction (towards the generator or towards the load) as measured from the null positions on the line. The three peripheral scales apply to all the impedance or admittance values which lie on a radial line through the center of the chart.

The use of the universal Smith Chart is illustrated by the following examples:

Example 6-5

Solve example 2-4 with the use of the Smith Chart.

Solution

   Step 1: Normalize the value of the load. Normalized load,

$$Z_{LN} = \quad Z_L/Z_o = \frac{40 - j65}{50} = 0.8 - j\,1.3$$

   Step 2: Plot Z_{LN} on the Smith Chart as point X(Fig. 6-7). Draw a line from the chart's center, passing through X, and extend the line to the peripheral scales. As read on the innermost scale, the angle of the reflection coefficient is $\underline{/-63°}$.

   Step 3: On the radial scale "G", mark off a length equal to the distance from the center of the chart to the point X. The magnitude of the reflection coefficient $|\rho|$ is shown to be 0.6.

   Step 4: On scale G read off the corresponding value of the power reflection coefficient. This value of $|\rho|^2$ is 0.36 which can then be used to obtain the other results required by example 6-4.

Example 6-6

A 100 Ω transmission line with an air dielectric is terminated by a load of 50 $-$ j80 Ω. Determine the values of swr, reflection

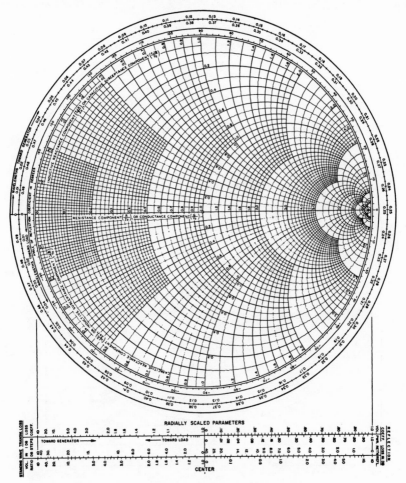

RADIALLY SCALED PARAMETERS

Fig. 6-6. Universal Smith chart with lettered radial scales.

coefficient and the percentage of reflected power. If the power incident at the load is 100 mW, calculate the power in the load. If the generator frequency is 3 GHz, and the line is 73 cm long, find the input impedance at the generator. See Fig. 6-8.

Solution

Step 1. Normalize the load so that $Z_{LN} = \dfrac{50 - j80}{100}$

$$= 0.5 - j0.8$$

Step 2. Plot Z_{LN} or the Smith Chart and draw the vswr circle through Z_{LN} (Fig. 6-8).

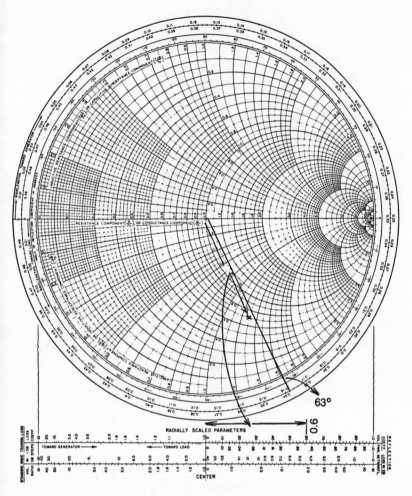

Fig. 6-7. Smith chart analysis for Example 6-5.

Step 3. Mark off a length equal to the circle's radius on the reflection coefficient $|\rho| = 0.56$, percentage of reflected power = scales A, G, H. The values read off are: vswrs = 3.5, voltage $|\rho|^2 \times 100 = 32\%$. Then the reflected power is $\dfrac{32}{100} \times 100 =$

32 mW and the power is the load is $100 - 32 = 68$mW.

Step 4. From the center of the chart draw a line through Z_{LN} and extend the line to the peripheral scales. Since all distances on the chart are measured in terms of wavelength, it is necessary to determine the line's λ which is equal to:

$$\frac{c}{f} = \frac{3 \times 10^{10}}{3 \times 10^{9}} \text{ cm} = 10 \text{ cm};$$

therefore 73 cm is equivalent to 7.3 λ.

Identical impedance values on a mismatched line repeat every half wavelength which will be the distance covered by one complete revolution on the Smith Chart. A distance of 7.3λ will require 4 complete revolutions (7.0λ) and an additional rotation of 0.3λ in the clockwise direction towards the generator.

On the inner peripheral wavelength scale, the distance from the Z_{LN} position to the null position, N, is 0.118λ. We must then travel towards the generator a further (0.3 − 0.118λ = 0.182λ on the outermost peripheral scale and arrive at point G).

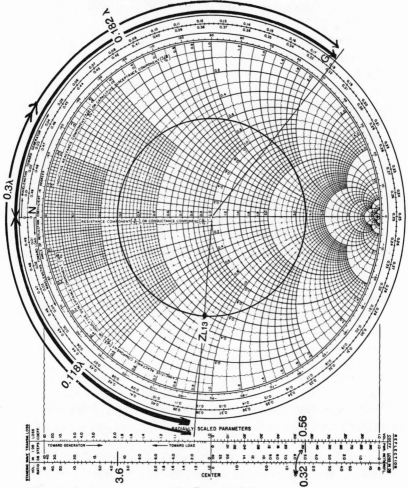

Fig. 6-8. Smith chart analysis for Example 6-6.

Step 5. Draw a line from G to the center of the chart. The point Z_{GN} of intersection between this line and the vswr circle represents the normalized input impedance at the generator; therefore $Z_{GN} = 1.18 + j1.43$ and the "denormalized" value of the input impedance at the generator is $(1.18 + j1.43) \times 100 = 118 + j143\,\Omega$.

Example 2-7

The vswr on a 200 Ω transmission line is 2.5. If a null point is located at a position 3.38λ from the load, find Z_L, Z_{max}, Z_{min} and give the value of the swr in dB.

Solution

Step 1. On the A scale determine the length corresponding to a vswr of 2.5 and then draw the vswr circle with this length as its radius (Fig. 6-9); using the B scale, the vswr is read off as 8 db.

Step 2. The point N represents the normalized value of the null impedance, Z_{min}; therefore $Z_{min} = 0.4 \times 200 = 80\Omega$. Similarly the maximum impedance occurs at point A so that $Z_{max} = 2.5 \times 200 = 500\,\Omega$.

Step 3. Z_{LN} is found by moving a distance of 3.38λ from the null position in the counterclockwise direction towards the load. The first three wavelengths are equivalent to six complete revolutions on the chart; the additional 0.38λ on the inner wavelength scale then brings as to the point Z_{LN} on the vswr circle. The "denormalized" load impedance is $(0.65 + j0.7) \times 200 = 130 + j140\,\Omega$.

Example 6-8

The vswr on a 50Ω line is 1.8 and the position of a null point is located on a slotted line. When the load is replaced by a short circuit, the position of the null point shifts a distance of 0.15λ towards the load. Find Z_{LN} as well as the magnitude and phase angle of the reflection coefficient. How far from the load is the first voltage maximum (give the answer as a fraction of the wavelength)?

Solution

This example illustrates a common method of determining the value of an unknown load impedance. A slotted line is used to locate the position of a voltage null with the line terminated by the load. The load is then removed and replaced by a short circuit. The result is a shift in the position of the null on the slotted line. According to the nature of the load (inductive or capacitive), the direction of the shift may be either towards the generator or the load and the amount of the shift must be 0.25λ or less. If the shift is either zero or exactly 0.25λ, the load is a resistance whose value is respectively less or greater than zero. Knowing the amount and the direction of the null shift, Z_{LN} may be determined by carrying out the following steps:

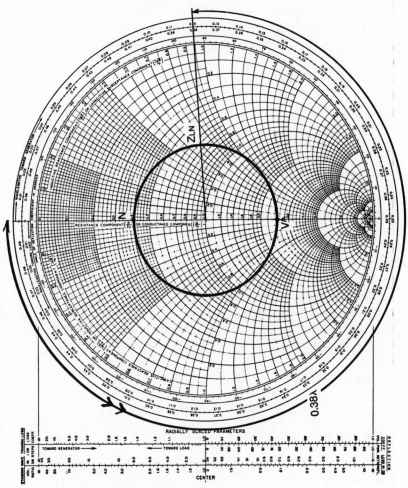

Fig. 6-9. Smith chart analysis for Example 6-7.

Step 1. From the null position (point N) travel a distance of 0.15λ on the inner wavelength scale in the counterclockwise direction towards the load (Fig. 6-10). Arriving at point L draw a line from L to the center of the chart. The point of intersection between the line and the vswr = 1.8 circle, is the normalized value of the load impedance, $Z_{LN} = 1 - j0.6$.

Step 2. The "denormalized" load impedance is $Z_L = Z_{LN} \times Z_o = (1 - j0.6) \times 50 = 50 - j30\ \Omega$.

Step 3. The line passing through L intersects the angle, $\theta°$, of the reflection coefficient scale at $-72°$. Marking off the radius of the vswr circle on the radial scale G shows that $|\rho| = 0.28$.

Step 4. The voltage maximum nearest to the load exists at the point M. The required distance is found by moving from L to M on the wavelength scales in the clockwise direction towards the generator. This distance is equal to LN (inner scale) + NM (outer scale) = $0.15\lambda + 0.25\lambda = 0.4\lambda$.

Example 6-9

A 200 Ω line with an air dielectric is terminated by a load impedance of $150 + j80\Omega$ and is excited by a 1 GHz generator. Find the position on the line of a single matching stub, and determine the length of the stub.

Solution

One use of a stub is to match a general load impedance to the surge impedance of the cable which feeds the load. The stub itself may be regarded as a section of transmission line which is terminated by a movable short (Fig. 6-11A). The single movable stub is placed across (in parallel with) the twin line feeder and by sliding the stub along the line, a position is found so that the combination of the stub and the load represents an entirely resistive impedance whose value is equal to the feeder's Z_0. The purpose of the Smith Chart analysis (Fig. 6-11B) is therefore to determine the length L_1 and L_2.

Step 1. The normalized load impedance Z_{LN}, is

$$\frac{150 + j80}{200} = 0.75 + j0.4$$

and the wavelength is $\dfrac{C}{f} = \dfrac{3 \times 10^{10}}{1 \times 10^9}$ cm = 30 cm.

Step 2. Plot Z_{LN} on the Smith Chart and draw the vswr circle. Since the stub is across the line an admittance analysis must be used. Y_{LN} is therefore found at the opposite end of the diameter passing through Z_{LN}.

Step 3. From Y_{LN}, move round the vswr circle in the clockwise direction towards the generator until you reach the point of intersection, P, between the vswr circle and the circle for which the conductance, G = 1. The distance covered in the move is equivalent to the distance $L_1 = 0.15\lambda + 0.145\lambda = 0.295\lambda = 8.85$ cm. At the position P, the normalized admittance due to the load is $Y_{PN} = 1 + j0.54$ S which represents conductance in parallel with capacitive susceptance.

Step 4. To achieve a match with the line's surge impedance, the stub must eliminate the capacitive susceptance by contributing an equal amount of inductive susceptance, $- j0.54$. This value is

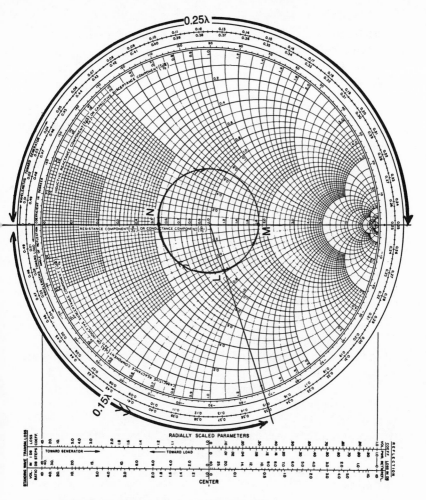

Fig. 6-10. Smith chart analysis for Example 6-8.

therefore entered at point S, on the chart. The short at the end of the stub has infinite conductance and is represented by the point G. Since this short is the stub's load termination, we must travel from S to G on the inner wavelength scale in a counter clockwise direction towards the load. The length of the stub, L_2, is therefore $0.25\lambda - 0.08\lambda = 0.17\lambda = 0.17 \times 30$ cm $= 5.1$ cm.

Another solution to the problem is represented by the point Q. However, the distance L_1 would then be very short (although any multiple of,

$$\frac{\lambda}{2}$$

could be added to L_1) and the distance L_2 would be much longer.

Example 6-10

In Example 6-9, the line is to be matched to the load by means of a,

$$\frac{\lambda}{4}$$

transformer. Find the two possible positions for locating the transformer and calculate the Z_0 of the transformer in each case.

Solution

The $\lambda/4$ transformer must be inserted at either of the positions M, N where the line impedance is resistive; only then can the line impedance be matched to the resistive value of Z_0. On the outer wavelength scale in Fig. 6-11B, position M is at a distance of $0.25\lambda - 0.099\lambda = 0.151\lambda = 0.151 \times 30$ cm $= 4.52$ cm from the load, while position N is a further quarter wavelength back along the line for a total distance of,

$$\frac{30}{4} + 4.52 = 12.02 \text{ cm.}$$

The line impedance at M is $Z_{max} = 1.68 \times 200 = 336 \, \Omega$, so that the required surge impedance for the $\lambda/4$ transformer is $\sqrt{336 \times 200} = 260 \, \Omega$, rounded off (Equation 6-26). At N, $Z_{min} = 0.58 \times 200 = 116 \, \Omega$ and the necessary transformer surge impedance $= \sqrt{116 \times 200} = 150 \, \Omega$, rounded off.

Example 6-11

A load is to be matched to a 100 Ω line by means of two fixed stubs which are $3\lambda/8$ apart. At the reference plane corresponding the position of the first stub, the admittance is 0.016-j0.008 S.

Solution

This problem is solved by means of the following steps:

Step 1. The surge admittance of the line is $1/100 = 0.01$S. Therefore the normalized admittance, Y_{N1}, at the reference plane of the first stub $(0.016 - j0.008)/0.01 = 1.6 - j0.8$.

Step 2. Enter Y_{N1} on the Smith Chart (Fig. 6-12) and observe that it lies on the 1.6 conductance circle. Rotate this circle through three quarters of a revolution in the clockwise direction; this rotation will correspond to the $3\lambda/8$ spacing between the stubs. The center of the circle after rotation will lie on the line passing through $+ j1.0$ and $- j1.0$.

Step 3. Determine the point P_2 of intersection between the newly constructed circle and the circle for which $G = 1$. Draw the vswr circle through P_1; then P_1 and P_2 are $3\lambda/8$ apart.

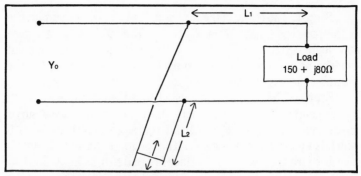

Fig. 6-11A. The single matching stub.

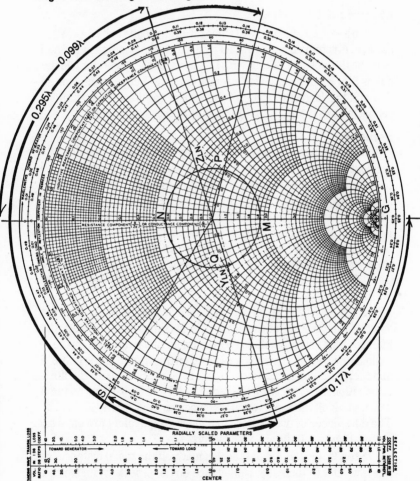

Fig. 6-11B. Smith chart analysis for Example 6-9.

Step 4. The effect of the first stub is to change the admittance at the reference plane from Y_{n1} to P_1. This stub must therefore contribute $- j1.78 - (-j0.8) = -j0.92$, which corresponds to point C_1. The short circuit which terminates the stub is point S. The length of the stub is therefore $0.25 \lambda - 0.118\lambda = 0.132 \lambda$

Step 5. The second stub must change the admittance from P_2 to the center of the chart, where the match to the line's surge impedance occurs. This stub must therefore contribute $- j1.5$ which is entered at the point C_2. The length of the second stub is measured from C_2 to S; this distance is equal to $0.25 \lambda - 0.156 \lambda = 0.094\lambda$.

Example 6-12

On a slotted line the swr is measured and found to be 3.6. When the load is removed and replaced by a short, the position of the null point on the slotted line moves 0.11λ towards the generator and the swr is 8.5. Find the one way attenuation in dB between the slotted line and the load, the value of the swr at the load (with the load connected), and the normalized value of the load.

Solution

When there are appreciable losses associated with the line, the incident voltage and current waves are attenuated as they travel from the generator towards the load. Assuming that the load is mismatched to the line, the reflected voltage and current waves will be further attenuated as they move back from the load towards the generator. Consequently the vswr value will be highest at the load position and will gradually decrease in the direction of the generator. On the Smith Chart the change in the value of the vswr (scale A) may be used to determine the line's "one-way" attenuation in dB (scale C − attenuation in 1 dB steps).

Step 1. When the "short" is placed at the end of the line, the vswr at the position of the "short" is maximum and theoretically infinite—this corresponds to the maximum radial distance on the A scale. However, the vswr as measured on the slotted line is only 8.5 and therefore the change from $S = \infty$ to $S = 8.5$ is due to the line's attenuation. After locating the $S = \infty$ and $S = 8.5$ positions on the A scale, mark off the same radial distances on the C scale (Fig. 6-13). The differences between these distances is equivalent to a one-way attenuation of 1.0 dB approximately.

Step 2. On the A and C scales mark off the radial distance for the vswr of 3.0. Increase the distance on the C scale by an amount corresponding to the one-way attenuation of 1.0 dB and then apply

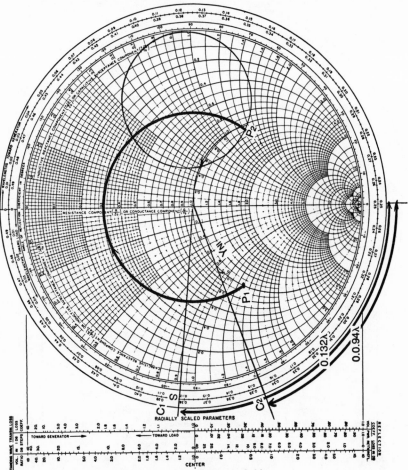

Fig. 6-12. Smith chart analysis for Example 6-11.

the same increase in distance to the A scale. The result is an swr of approximately 4.5 at the load.

Step 3. Draw the vswr circle for S=4.5. On the outer wavelength scale move clockwise through a distance of 0.11λ from the null position, N, towards the generator. When the point P is reached draw a straight line from P to the center of the chart. The intersection between this line and the vswr circle reveals the normalized load impedance, Z_{LN}, as $0.37 + j0.77$.

Example 2-13

It is desired to achieve a vswr of 2.5 on an unmatched line by the introduction of attenuation. If the swr at the load is 5.4, find the required one-way attenuation in dB. Determine the loss coefficient for the swr of 5.4.

163

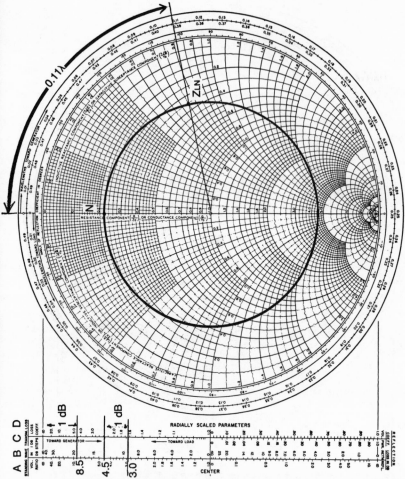

Fig. 6-13. Smith chart analysis for example 6-12.

Solution

This problem may be solved by using the radial scales only.

Step 1. Locate the $S = 2.5$ and $S = 5.4$ positions on the A scale and mark off the same radial distances on the C scale. The difference between these distances is equivalent to a one-way attenuation of 2.0 dB approximately.

Step 2. A more accurate estimate of the attenuation may be obtained by using scale F (return loss in dB) which represents the two-way loss. On this scale $S = 2.5$ and $S = 5.4$ correspond respectively to losses of 7.4 dB and 3.4 dB. The one-way attenuation is therefore $7.4 - 3.4 = 2$ dB.

Step 3. On scale D mark off the radial distance for S = 5.4. The corresponding loss coefficient is approximately 2.8.

HERTZ AND MARCONI ANTENNAS

A radio wave in free space consists of electric and magnetic fields which are at right angles to each other and to the direction of propagation; such an arrangement is known as a transverse electric magnetic (TEM) wave. The two fields are in time phase and the wave as a whole moves the velocity of light which in air is approximately 186,000 miles per second or 3×10^8 meters per second. The wave's plane of polarization is defined by the direction of the electric field and the direction of propagation so that a vertically polarized wave consists of a vertical electric field and a horizontal magnetic field; such a wave will be radiated by (or received by) a vertical antenna. The two basic types of antenna used for transmission and reception are the Hertz dipole and the Marconi unipole.

The Hertz dipole is essentially a thin rod which is electrically one half-wavelength,

$$\frac{(\lambda)}{2}$$

long and is commonly fed at its center. This antenna carries standing waves and Fig. 6-14 shows the relevant rms voltage and current distribution. When the dipole is electrically,

$$\frac{\lambda}{2}$$

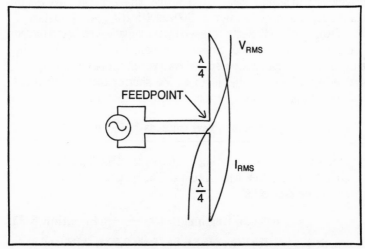

Fig. 6-14. Voltage and current distribution on the Hertz antenna.

long at the operating frequency, it is resonant and presents a load of approximately 70 Ω resistance to the center feedpoint. This value of 70 Ω is, therefore, the effective or radiation resistance of the antenna under resonant operating conditions.

The electrical half-wavelength, or,

$$\frac{\lambda}{2}$$

in free-space, is equal to:

$$\frac{1}{2} \times \frac{300}{f} = \frac{150}{f} \text{ meters} \qquad \textbf{Equation 6-28}$$

where f is the frequency in MHz at which the dipole is being operated. However, antenna lengths are generally measured in feet and then the formula is:

Electrical wavelength or the wavelength is free space,

$$\lambda_o = \frac{984}{f} \text{ feet and therefore,}$$

$$\text{Electrical half-wavelength} = \frac{1}{2} \times \frac{984}{f} = \frac{492}{f} \text{ feet}$$

$$\textbf{Equation 6-29}$$

where f is the frequency in MHz.

Since a radio wave is propagated through a distance of one wavelength in a time equal to the period, an electrical wavelength may be regarded as equivalent to 360 electrical degrees in distance.

Owing to "end effects" caused by the capacitance between the ends of the antenna and ground, the velocity of a wave on the antenna is less than in free-space. As a result the *physical* length of the resonant Hertz dipole is about 5% shorter than the *electrical* half-wavelength and may be found from the formula:

$$\text{physical length of a half-wave antenna} = \frac{468}{f} \textbf{Equation 6-30}$$

feet where f is the operating frequency in MHz. This formula strictly applies to a wire antenna. The general formula for a half-wave dipole is:

$$\text{physical length in feet} = \frac{492 \, \delta}{f}, \quad \textbf{Equation 6-31}$$

where δ is a factor whose value lies from 0.90 to 0.98, and is determined by the antenna's construction.

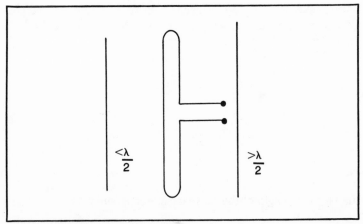

Fig. 6-15. Parasitic antenna elements.

Note that the Hertz dipole which may be mounted either horizontally or vertically, is an electrically balanced antenna which is operated remote from ground. At the feedpoint, the load of the dipole is usually matched to the surge impedance of the transmission line in order to reduce to a minimum the standing waves and the losses on the line.

It is common practice to place a reflecting rod (parasitic element) at the back of the dipole (Fig. 6-15) in order to increase the radiation in a particular direction or to increase the signal received from that direction. This is one way in which the gain of the antenna can be increased and is discussed later in this chapter. The physical length of the reflector is greater than that of the dipole and may be calculated from the expression,

$$\frac{492}{f}$$

feet, where f is the dipole's resonant frequency in MHz. The parasitic reflector is mostly used with a folded dipole (Fig. 6-15) which, at resonance, represents a load of approximately 300 Ω as opposed to 70 Ω for a thin dipole. Another parasitic element is the director which is shorter than the dipole and is placed in front of the antenna: it also serves to increase the antenna gain.

Low frequencies correspond to long wavelengths and therefore the size of the dipole becomes impractical for frequencies below a few MHz. In these bands, use is made of the quarter-wave unipole or Marconi antenna which is mounted vertically with its lower end close to the ground. Figure 2-16 shows the rms voltage and current standing wave distribution on the Marconi antenna which, at its resonant operating frequency, presents a load of approximately 35 Ω resistance to the feedpoint.

The electrical quarter-wavelength is:

$$\frac{75}{f} \text{ meters}$$

or,   **Equation 6-32**

$$\frac{246}{f} \text{ feet}$$

and,

the physical length of the resonant Marconi antenna $= \dfrac{234}{f}$ feet

Equation 6-33

where f is the frequency in MHz.

Example 6-14

A resonant Hertz antenna is operated at a frequency of 48 MHz. What is (a) its electrical length and (b) its physical length? A reflector rod is placed behind the Hertz dipole in order to increase the antenna gain. What should be the length of the reflector rod?

Solution

(a) Electrical half-wavelength of the Hertz antenna

$$= \frac{492}{f \text{ (MHz)}} = \frac{492}{48} = 10.25 \text{ ft.}$$

(b) Physical length of the Hertz antenna

$$= \frac{468}{f \text{ (MHz)}} = \frac{469}{48} = 9.75 \text{ ft.}$$

The length of the reflector rod is equal to the electrical half-wavelength of 10.25 ft.

Example 6-15

An antenna tower is 175 ft high and is operated at a frequency of 358 kHz. What percentage of the electrical wavelength is the height of the tower?

Solution

$$\text{Electrical wavelength in feet} = \frac{984}{f \text{ (MHz)}} = \frac{984}{0.835}$$

The percentage of the electrical wavelength represented by the height of the tower is:

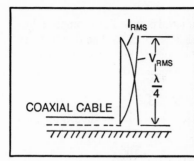

Fig. 6-16. Voltage and current distribution on the Marconi antenna.

$$\frac{175}{984/0.835} \times 100 = \frac{175 \times 0.835}{984} \times 100$$

$$= 14.9\%, \text{ rounded off.}$$

Example 6-16

Two Marconi antennas which are operated at 950 kHz, are separated by 150 electrical degrees. What is the physical length of each antenna and what is their distance apart in feet?

Solution

Physical length of each antenna $= \dfrac{234}{0.95} = 246$ ft.

Electrical wavelength $= \dfrac{984}{f\ (\text{MHz})} = \dfrac{984}{0.95} = 1036$ ft.

The distance between the antennas is $1036 \times \dfrac{150}{360}$

$$= 432 \text{ ft, rounded off.}$$

FACTORS AFFECTING THE FIELD STRENGTH

The electric field strength (or field intensity), ϵ, at a certain position from a transmitting antenna is measured in volts (or millivolts or microvolts) per meter and determines the signal voltage induced in a receiving antenna. The value of ϵ for a dipole is given by

$$\epsilon = \frac{60 \times I}{d} \text{ volts per meter} \qquad \textbf{Equation 6-34}$$

where, I = antenna current in amperes at the feedpoint

d = distance in meters from the transmitter antenna.

The field strength is therefore directly proportional to the antenna current and inversely proportional to the distance from the transmitting antenna. Since the transmitter radiated power is proportional to the square root of the radiated power. For example a thin center-fed dipole has a radiation resistance of 73.2 so that if the rf power delivered to the antenna is 1 kilowatt, the antenna current is:

$$I = \sqrt{\frac{P}{R}} = \sqrt{\frac{1000}{73.2}} \ A$$

The field strength at a position one mile (= 1609.3 meters) from the antenna, is:

$$= \frac{60 \times I}{d} = \frac{60 \times \sqrt{\frac{1000}{73.2}}}{1609.3}$$

$$= 0.1378 \text{ volts per meter}$$
$$= 137.8 \text{ millivolts per meter}$$

This value is used as the FCC standard to determine the gain of more sophisticated antennas.

In displaying the radiation pattern of a transmitting antenna, the positions where the value of the field strength is the same, may be joined to form a particular field strength contour.

Example 6-17

At a position 3 miles from a transmitting antenna, the field strength is 650 μV per meter. If the antenna current is doubled, what is the new field strength (a) at the same position and (b) at a position 5 miles from the transmitting antenna?

Solution

(a) The field strength is directly proportional to the antenna current. The new field strength is therefore $2 \times 650 = 1300 \ \mu$V per meter = 1.3 mV per meter.

(b) The field strength is inversely proportional to the distance from the transmitter antenna. Therefore the new field strength at a position 5 miles from the transmitting antenna is $1300 \times \frac{3}{5} = 780 \ \mu$V per meter.

Example 6-18

At a position 5 miles from the antenna of a 5 kW transmitter, the field strength is 400 μV per meter. If the power is now reduced to 3.5 kW, what is the new distance of the 600 μV per meter contour from the antenna?

Solution

Since the field strength is directly proportional to the square root of the radiated power, the new field strength at the 5 mile position is $400 \times \sqrt{\frac{3.5}{5.0}} \ \mu$ V per meter. With the field strength inversely proportional to the distance from the antenna, the new distance to the 600 μ V per meter contour is,

$$\frac{5 \times 600}{400 \times \sqrt{\frac{3.5}{5.0}}} = \frac{5 \times 600}{400} \times \sqrt{\frac{5.0}{3.5}}$$

$$= \frac{5 \times 600}{400} \times 1.428$$

$$= 9.0 \text{ miles, rounded off.}$$

Example 6-19

At a position 3 miles from a transmitter antenna, the field intensity is 15 mV per meter. The antenna current is now increased to 25 A and the new field intensity at the same position is 20 mV per meter.

Solution

The field intensity is directly proportional to the antenna current. Therefore:

$$\frac{\text{Original antenna current}}{\text{New antenna current}} = \frac{\text{Original field strength}}{\text{New field strength}}$$

or,

$$\text{Original antenna current} = 25 \times \frac{15}{20} = 18.75 \text{ A}$$

Example 6-20

A 25 kW transmitter produces a field strength of 25 mV per meter at a position which is 5 miles from the antenna. When the transmitter power output is increased, the new field strength at the same position is 35 mV per meter. What is the percentage increase in the transmitter power?

Solution

The square of the field strength is directly proportional to the transmitter power. Therefore:

$$\frac{\text{New transmitter power}}{\text{Old transmitter power}} = \left(\frac{\text{New field strength}}{\text{Old field strength}}\right)^2$$

or,

$$\text{new transmitter power} = 25 \times \left(\frac{35}{25}\right)^2 = 49 \text{ kW}$$

Percentage increase in transmitter power

$$= \frac{49 - 25}{25} \times 100 = \left(\frac{49}{25} - 1\right) \times 100 = 96\%$$

OPERATING POWER

Using the direct method, a transmitter operating power is determined from the rf current delivered by the transmitter to the antenna and the antenna's effective resistance.

The operating power, $P = I_A^2 R_A$ watts

I_A = antenna current in amperes

R_A = effective antenna resistance in ohms

Equation 6-35

Then,

$$I_A = \sqrt{\frac{P}{R_A}}$$ **Equation 6-36**

and,

$$R_A = \frac{P}{I_A^2}$$ **Equation 6-37**

The indirect method of calculating the operating power was described earlier in this book.

Antenna Gain

If more parasitic elements such as reflectors and directors are attached to a simple dipole (or more antennas are added to produce an array), the radiated RF carrier power is concentrated in particular directions and the antenna gain is increased. This gain may either be considered in terms of field strength or power.

From measurements taken at a particular position, the field gain is the ratio of the field strength produced by the complex antenna system to the field strength created by a simple ideal dipole (assuming that this dipole would be capable of directly replacing the complex antenna). Since the square of the field intensity is directly proportional to the radiated power, the power gain of the antenna is equal to (field gain)^2 and is either expressed as a ratio or in dB. However, it should be noted that the term "antenna system power gain" is sometimes used and this generally takes into account the transmission line loss.

Effective Radiated Power

The Effective Radiated Power (ERP) in a particular direction is given by:

ERP = (RF carrier power input to the transmission line) ×
(antenna system power gain ratio)

Equation 6-38

172

= (RF carrier power delivered to the antenna) × (antenna power gain ratio)   **Equation 6-39**

= (RF carrier power delivered to the antenna) × (antenna field gain ratio)^2 **Equation 6-40**

In addition,
Antenna power gain is dB
= 10 $\log_{10}$ (antenna power gain ratio)   **Equation 6-41**
= 20 $\log_{10}$ (antenna field gain ratio)   **Equation 6-42**
= power gain of antenna system in dB + transmission
line loss in dB.   **Equation 6-43**

Antenna Base Current Ratio

Non-directional AM stations use a single antenna tower and transmit the radio signal with equal strength in all directions from the station. Directional AM stations utilize more than one antenna tower. By establishing the position of each tower, the power radiated by each tower, and the phase of the signal in each tower, different signal strengths can be radiated in various directions. Directional antenna systems are used to improve the signal over desired areas and to reduce the signal in the direction of other stations to prevent interference.

To determine if a directional antenna system in radiating the signal according to a specified radiation pattern, an instrument called an antenna monitor is installed at the station. The antenna monitor enables the operator to determine if the radio frequency current in each tower is of the correct value and if the phase of the signal radiated by each tower is also correct. Some antenna monitors indicate the ratio of current in each tower to the current in one tower called the reference tower.

If the signal arrives at each tower at the same time, the current in each tower is said to be "in phase." In most directional antenna systems, the time the radio frequency signal reaches each tower from the transmitter is not the same. The time difference or phase is measured in degrees. For each directional antenna tower, the station license contains a list of the required signal phases and antenna base current ratios. The antenna base current ratio for a tower is calculated by dividing the current meter reading for that tower by the current meter reading of the designated reference tower.

As an example,

Antenna base current ratio for tower 2

$$= \frac{\text{Antenna current meter reading of tower 2}}{\text{Antenna current meter reading of the reference tower}}$$

Equation 6-44

This ratio, either calculated or read on the antenna monitor, must not deviate normally by more than 5 percent from the value on the station license. Since directional AM broadcast stations employ multiple radiating elements, the operating power of these stations, as determined by the direct method, is equal to the product of the resistance common to all the antenna towers (common point resistance, R_c) and the square of the current common to all the antenna towers (common point current, I_c).

Operating power of a directional AM station

$$= I_c^2 \, R_c \text{ watts} \qquad \textbf{Equation 6-45}$$

Example 6-21

The RF current delivered to an antenna is 8 A and the antenna effective resistance is 125 Ω. What is the operating power as calculated by the direct method?

Solution

Operating power $= I_A^2 \, R_A = (8 \text{ A})^2 \times 125 \, \Omega = 8000$ W.

Example 6-22

10 kW of RF carrier power is delivered by a transmitter to the input of a coaxial cable. If the antenna system power gain and the antenna power gain are respectively 8 dB and 8.3 dB, what is (a) the effective radiated power and (b) the transmission line loss?

Solution

(a) Effective radiated power = (rf power input to the transmission line) × (antenna system power gain ratio). Corresponding to 8 dB, the power gain ratio is Antilog$\left(\dfrac{8}{10}\right)$ = 6.309. To complete the solution, multiply the power gain ratio by the transmitter power of 10 kW. Then the effective radiated power is $6.309 \times 10 = 63$ kW, rounded off.

(b) Transmission line loss in dB = 8.3 − 8.0 = 0.3 dB Power delivered to the antenna = 10 antilog $\dfrac{-0.3}{10}$ kW

$$= 9330 \text{ W}$$

The power loss in the line is 10000 − 9330 W = 670 W,

Example 6-23

25 kW of rf carrier power is delivered by a transmitter to the input of a coaxial cable. If the transmission line loss is 0.35 dB and

the antenna field gain is 2.5, what is the effective radiated power?
Solution

Power gain of the antenna $= 20 \log_{10}$ (Antenna field gain) $= \log_{10} 2.5 = 7.965$ dB. Antenna system power gain $= 7.965 - 0.35 = 7.615$ dB. The corresponding power ratio is Antilog

$$\frac{7.615}{10} = 5.77$$

Therefore the effective radiated power is $5.77 \times 25 = 144$ kW, rounded off.

Example 6-24

A matched coaxial cable delivers 9.25 kW of rf carrier power to the antenna. At the antenna, the transmission line current is 11.2 A while at the transmitter end of the line, the current is 11.9 A. What is the transmission line loss in dB? If the antenna system power gain is 7.5, calculate the effective radiated power?
Solution

$$\text{Transmission line gain in dB} = 20 \log_{10} \frac{I_{out}}{I_{in}}$$

$$= 20 \log_{10}\left(\frac{11.2}{11.9}\right)$$

$$= -0.53 \text{ dB, rounded off}$$

Therefore, the transmission line loss $= +0.53$ dB. As an alternative to using the transmission line loss in dB, we may calculate the power at the transmitter end of the cable by considering that the power on a matched line at any position is $I^2 Z_o$. Therefore

$$\frac{\text{Power at the transmitter end of the cable}}{\text{power delivered to the antenna}} = \left(\frac{11.9}{11.2}\right)^2$$

The power at the transmitter end of the cable is:

$$9.2 \times \left(\frac{11.9}{11.2}\right)^2 = 10.4 \text{ kW, rounded off.}$$

The effective radiated power is $10.4 \times 7.5 = 78$ kW, rounded off. Note that the antenna system power gain was given as a ratio and not in dB.

Example 6-25

The RF power input to a coaxial cable is 5 kW. If the matched transmission line is 90% efficient and the antenna field gain is 2.7, calculate the effective radiated power.

Solution

$$\text{RF power input to the antenna} = 5 \times \frac{90}{100} = 4.5 \text{ kW}$$

Effective radiated power $= 4.5 \times (2.7)^2 = 32.8$ kW, rounded off.

Example 6-26

A transmitter RF carrier power output to the transmission line is 10 kW. The transmission line loss is 0.4 dB and the effective radiated power is 50 kW. What is (a) the antenna field gain and (b) the antenna system power gain?

Solution

(a) The RF carrier power input to the antenna is $10 \times \text{antilog}_{10}$

$-\left(\frac{0.4}{10}\right) = 9.12$ kW, rounded off. The antenna field gain is $\sqrt{\dfrac{50}{9.12}}$

$= 2.3$, rounded off.

(b) Antenna system power gain ratio $= \dfrac{50 \text{ kW}}{10 \text{ kW}} = 5$. The

antenna system power gain in dB is $10 \ \log_{10} 5 = 7$ dB, rounded off.

Example 6-27

The daytime antenna current is 7.5 amperes when the rf power delivered to an antenna is 10 kilowatts. If the nighttime power is reduced to 6 kilowatts, what is the value of the antenna current at night?

Solution

The antenna current is directly proportional to the square root of the power delivered to the antenna.
Therefore,

$$\frac{\text{Antenna current at night}}{\text{Antenna current during the day}} = \sqrt{\frac{\text{Nighttime antenna power}}{\text{Daytime antenna power}}}$$

$$\frac{\text{Antenna current at night}}{7.5} = \sqrt{\frac{6}{10}}$$

The antenna current at night is 5.8 A, rounded off. Note that the antenna resistance is either

$$\frac{P}{I_A^2} = \frac{10000}{7.5^2} = 178 \ \Omega$$

using the "day" figures, or

$$\frac{60000}{5.8^2} = 178 \ \Omega$$

from the "night" figures. The values of the antenna resistance during the day and at night are, of course, the same.

Example 6-28

The rf power delivered to an antenna at night is 5 kilowatts and the corresponding antenna current is 6 amperes. If the daytime current is increased to 10 amperes, calculate the power delivered to the antenna during the day?

Solution

The power, P_A, delivered to the antenna is directly proportional to the square of the antenna current, I_A.
Therefore,

$$\frac{P_A \ (\text{day})}{P_A \ (\text{night})} = \left(\frac{I_A \ (\text{day})}{I_A \ (\text{night})}\right)^2$$

$$P_A \ (\text{day}) = \left(\frac{10}{6}\right)^2$$

The power delivered to the antenna during the day is:

$$5 \times \left(\frac{10}{6}\right)^2 = \frac{500}{36} = 14 \ \text{kW} \ , \text{ rounded off.}$$

Example 6-29

The directional antenna system of a standard broadcast station consists of five towers whose common point resistance is 85 Ω. If the associated common point current is 12.5 A, calculate the operating power for the broadcast station.

Solution

Operating power = $I_c^2 \ R_c = (12.5A)^2 \times 85 \ \Omega$
$$= 13281.25 \ \text{W} = 13.5 \ \text{kW, rounded off.}$$

Example 6-30

A standard broadcast station has a directional antenna system which consists of five towers. Tower one is the reference tower and its antenna current is the correct specified value of 2.5 A. The antenna currents of Towers two, three and four are respectively 3.5 A, 4.0 A and 2.1 A. What is the antenna base current ratio for Tower three?

Solution

The antenna base current ratio for Tower three is

$$\frac{4.0}{2.5} = 1.6$$

Example 2-31

A standard broadcast station uses a directional antenna array which consists of five towers. Tower one is the reference tower and carries a current, as specified, of 3.5 amperes. Towers two, three, four and five carry currents of 4.5 amperes, 2.8 amperes, 5.2 amperes and 4.2 amperes while their base current ratios on the station license are respectively 1.3, 0.8, 1.6 and 1.2. Which tower current is incorrect?

Solution

From the measured values, the antenna base current ratios are:

$$\text{Tower two, } \frac{4.5}{3.5} = 1.2857$$

$$\text{Tower three, } \frac{2.8}{3.5} = 0.8$$

$$\text{Tower four, } \frac{5.2}{3.5} = 1.4857$$

$$\text{Tower five, } \frac{4.2}{3.5} = 1.2$$

The currents for Towers three and five are exactly correct and the antenna current base ratio for Tower two deviates by less than 5% from the specified value. However, the antenna base current ratio for Tower four must lie between

$$(\frac{5}{100} \times 1.6) + 1.6 = 1.68 \text{ and } 1.6 - 0.08 = 1.52,$$

and therefore this tower current is incorrect.

Example 6-32

A standard broadcast station has a directional antenna system consisting of five towers. As measured, the antenna currents for Towers one, two, three, four and five are respectively 3.8 A, 2.8 A, 1.7 A, 4.2 A and 5.3 A. It is specified that the tower currents must be in the proportion of 1.36 : 1.00 : 0.61 : 1.50 : 1.79. Which tower current is furthest away from its correct value?

Solution

Since the proportion value of Tower two is 1.00, it is easiest to calculate the current ratios with respect to this particular tower current.

Then,

$$\frac{\text{Tower one current}}{\text{Tower two current}} = \frac{3.8}{2.8} = 1.357$$

$$\frac{\text{Tower three current}}{\text{Tower two current}} = \frac{1.7}{2.8} = 0.607$$

$$\frac{\text{Tower four current}}{\text{Tower two current}} = \frac{4.2}{2.8} = 1.5$$

$$\frac{\text{Tower five current}}{\text{Tower two current}} = \frac{5.3}{2.8} = 1.8928$$

Tower five current is furthest away from its correct value.

VHF/UHF DIRECTIONAL ANTENNA ARRAYS

Apart from adding parasitic elements, directional antenna arrays may be formed by using more than one dipole. For example a horizontal dipole by itself would radiate equally well in all directions contained in the vertical plane. However, if two horizontal dipoles are spaced λ/2 apart vertically and these are then fed in phase, maximum radiation will occur in the two horizontal directions where the distances to the centers of the dipoles are equal. By contrast there will ideally be no resultant radiation in the vertical directions since the two distances would differ by λ/2 ; this would introduce a 180° phase difference between the two dipole fields at any position along the vertical directions so that the fields would tend to cancel.

Further directivity can be introduced by mounting two horizontal dipoles side by side, feeding them in phase but separating their centers by about a wavelength. Along certain directions in the horizontal plane the distances to the centers of the dipoles will differ by λ/2 and cancellation will occur.

The combination of vertical and horizontal spacing is shown in Fig. 6-17. The horizontal array consists of four dipoles which are shunt fed in phase. The dipoles have a vertical spacing of half a wavelength and are mounted about a wavelength apart horizontally. Parasitic reflectors reduce back radiation so that the final beam is concentrated along the direction X.

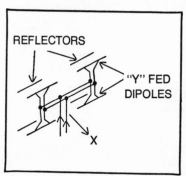

Fig. 6-17. Horizontal antenna array.

CHAPTER SUMMARY

Transmission lines

Surge impedance, $Z_o = 4\sqrt{\dfrac{R^2 + \omega^2 L^2}{G^2 + \omega^2 C^2}}$ Ω

$$\approx \sqrt{\dfrac{L}{C}} \ \Omega$$

Twin lead line,

$$Z_o = \dfrac{276}{\sqrt{\epsilon_r}} \ \log_{10}\left(\dfrac{S}{r}\right) \Omega$$

$$= \dfrac{276}{\sqrt{\epsilon_r}} \ \log_{10}\left(\dfrac{2s}{d}\right) \Omega$$

Coaxial cable,

$$Z_o = \dfrac{138}{\sqrt{\epsilon_r}} \ \log_{10} \dfrac{D}{d} \ \Omega$$

Propagation constant, $Y = \alpha + j\beta$

Attenuation constant, $\alpha \ \dfrac{R}{2Z_o} + \dfrac{GZ_o}{2}$ nepers per meter

Phase shift constant, $\beta = \omega\sqrt{LC} = \dfrac{2\pi}{\lambda \text{Line}}$ radians per meter

Phase velocity, $V_\phi = \dfrac{\omega}{\beta} = \dfrac{1}{\sqrt{LC}}$ meters per second.

Unmatched line

Reflection coefficient, $\rho = \dfrac{Z_L - Z_o}{Z_L + Z_o} = |\rho| \ |\theta$

Reflected power $= |\rho|^2 \times$ incident power

Load Power $= (1 - |\rho|^2) \times$ incident power $= \dfrac{1 - |\rho|^2}{|\rho|^2}$ $\times$ reflected power

Voltage standing wave ratio, $S = \dfrac{E_{max}}{E_{min}} = \dfrac{1 + |\rho|}{1 - |\rho|}$

Voltage standing wave ratio in dB $= 20 \log_{10} S$

Maximum impedance, $Z_{max} = SZ_o$

Minimum impedance, $Z_{min} = \dfrac{Z_o}{S}$

Load Power $= \dfrac{4S}{(S + 1)^2} \times$ incident power

Quarter-wave line

Input impedance, $Z_{in} = \dfrac{Z_o{}^2}{Z_L}$

Surge impedance of $\dfrac{\lambda}{4}$ transformer, $Z_o = \sqrt{Z_{in} \times Z_L}$

Smith Chart

Normalized impedance, $Z_N = \dfrac{Z}{Z_o}$

Transmission loss in dB $= -10 \log_{10} |\rho|$

Loss coefficient $= \dfrac{1 + S^2}{2S}$

Reflection loss in dB $= -10 \log_{10} (1 - |\rho|^2)$

Return loss in dB $= 20 \log_{10} |\rho|$.

Antennas

Electrical wavelength, $\lambda = \dfrac{300}{f(MHz)}$ meter

$\qquad\qquad\qquad\quad = \dfrac{984}{f(MHz)}$ feet

Physical length of half-wave (Hertz) antenna $= \dfrac{468}{f(MHz)}$ feet

Physical length of quarter wavelength (Marconi) antenna

$\qquad\qquad = \dfrac{234}{f(MHz)}$ feet

Electric Field intensity, $\epsilon = \dfrac{60\ I}{d}$ volts per meter

The field intensity is proportional to the square root of the transmitted power

Effective radiated power

$\qquad$ = (RF carrier power input to the transmission line) × (antenna system power gain ratio).

$\qquad$ = (RF carrier power delivered to the antenna) × (antenna power gain ratio)

$\qquad$ = (RF carrier power delivered to the antenna) × (antenna field gain ratio)^2

Antenna power gain in dB

$\qquad$ = 10 $\log_{10}$ (antenna power gain ratio)

181

= 20 $\log_{10}$ (antenna field gain ratio)

= power gain of the antenna system in dB + transmission line loss in dB

Antenna Base current ratio

$$= \frac{\text{Antenna tower current}}{\text{Antenna current in designated reference tower}}$$

Direct Method: operating power (single antenna) = $I_A^2 \times R_A$ watts

operating power (directional antenna) = $I_c^2 \times R_c$ watts

Chapter 7
Introduction
to Waveguides

At microwave frequencies the losses in coaxial cables, especially the dielectric loss, are very serious; and hollow conductors or waveguides prove far more efficient. At 3 GHz the loss in coaxial cables is about 0.6 dB/meter while in waveguides it is about 0.02 dB/meter. Waveguides are hollow tubes which are usually rectangular in cross section, but for special purposes they may be circular.

In normal feeders the transmission of energy as waves of voltage and current is a convenient approach, but in waveguides it is usual to consider a movement of electromagnetic waves. This electromagnetic energy progresses along the guide by a series of reflections from its sides as in Fig. 7-1 and, provided that the inner surface of the guide is a good conductor such as copper or copper alloy, very little attenuation occurs.

In normal radiated or TEM waves, the electric field, E and the magnetic field, H, are mutually at right angles to the direction of propagation. In waveguides the combination of incidents and reflected waves gives rise to a component of the E or the H field in the direction of the guide. Varied field patterns or modes may result in the guide, but these fall into two main groups:

☐ TE waves in which the E field is transverse only, while the H field has a component along the guide.

☐ TM waves in which the H field is transverse only, while the E field has a component along the guide.

The distance along the guide occupied by one complete field pattern is called the guide wavelength, λg.

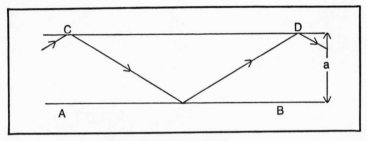

Fig. 7-1. Path of an EM wave in a waveguide.

In most cases, rectangular waveguides with a TE_{10} mode as in Fig. 7-2 are employed. Occasional use is made of a circular waveguide with an TM mode as in Fig. 7-3. In the TE_{10} mode the two figures in the suffix indicate the number of halfwave patterns of the E field along the narrow and wide sides of the guide respectively. For the TM_{01} mode these figures show the number of half-wave patterns of the H field along the circumference and the diameter respectively.

The nature of the voltage and current in the waveguide may be derived by considering

☐ That a voltage exists between opposite ends of the E lines.

☐ That currents in the walls of the waveguide flow at right angles to the H lines.

DEVELOPMENT OF THE TE_{10} WAVE

When the incident TEM wave strikes the conducting surface AB (Fig. 7-4A) the reflection takes place in accordance with the following conditions:

☐ The resultant E field obtained by combining the incident and reflected waves must be perpendicular to the surface, since there can be no component along the surface if it is a perfect conductor.

☐ The resultant H field obtained by combining the two waves must lie along the surface.

☐ The E and H fields are mutually at right angles to each other and to the direction of the motion of the wave.

In normal practice b is made roughly 0.7 to 0.8λ; For example when λ is 10 cm, b is about 3 inches or 7 cm, but when λ is 3 cm, b is about 1 inch or 2.4 cm.

The narrower dimension 'a' of the rectangular guide is not so critical except for higher transmitter power operation in which the spacing should be sufficient to prevent voltage flashover. Typically 'a' is 1 inch for 10 cm guides and ½ inch for 3 cm guides. It is important that 'a' should be less than $\frac{\lambda}{2}$, otherwise the direction of the E field and consequent polarization of the wave would be uncertain.

If the guide is filled with a dielectric the velocity of the wave and the dimensions of the above patterns are reduced by a factor $_r$ where $_r$ is the dielectric constant. Because of the increased losses, dielectric filling has only limited use.

WAVEGUIDE ATTENUATORS

If λ is greater than 2b or the cut-off wavelength, an evanescent mode is produced in which the E and H fields suffer rapid exponential attenuation along the guide; such narrow guides may be used to provide loose coupling.

Reflection losses increase with the resistance of the inner surface of the walls of the guide. For this reason the interior of the

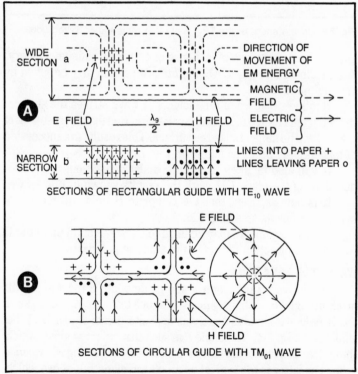

Fig. 7-2. Field patterns in rectangular and circular waveguides.

185

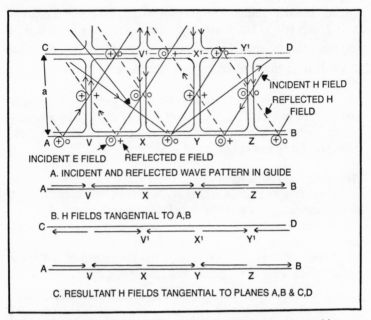

Fig. 7-3. Development of the TE$_{10}$ wave in a rectangular waveguide.

guide must be kept free of moisture or corrosion and, if necessary, dry air blown through it. Deliberate attenuation may be given by coating the narrow.

It follows that when the incident H wave strikes the surface, the reflected H wave must be in such a direction that the resultant of the two will be tangential to the surface. This results in a succession of tangential H fields as shown in Fig. 7-3B.

It will also be seen that the boundary conditions are reproduced along the plane CD, with the results shown in Fig. 7-3C.

It is now apparent that the complete H field will form as a series of loops as shown in Fig. 7-3A.

Similar arguments may be used to show the build-up of the E field whose direction indicates the plane of polarization.

WAVEGUIDE EQUATIONS

For a given wavelength λ and guide width b the waves will make an angle, θ, with the guide walls such that successive peaks of the H field are simultaneously at opposite points A and B of the guide as in Fig. 7-4. The angle θ is such that $\dfrac{\lambda}{2b} = \sin \theta$, which shows that as λ is increased, θ also increases, becoming 90° when λ = 2b. The latter is the critical or cut off wavelength λ_c above which the energy will not progress along the guide.

Wavelength in Guide, λ_g

Figure 7-4 shows that $\dfrac{\lambda}{\lambda_g} = \cos\theta$ and $\dfrac{\lambda}{2a} = \sin\theta$

Equation 7-1

It follows that as θ increases, the length of the field pattern, λ_g, also increases.

Since $\cos^2\theta + \sin^2\theta = 1$, $\left(\dfrac{\lambda}{\lambda_g}\right)^2 + \left(\dfrac{\lambda}{2a}\right)^2 = 1$

or $\dfrac{1}{\lambda_g{}^2} + \dfrac{1}{(2a)^2} = \dfrac{1}{\lambda^2}$

Equation 7-2

Therefore,
$$\lambda = \frac{\lambda_g}{\sqrt{1 + \left(\dfrac{\lambda_g}{2a}\right)^2}}$$

Equation 7-3

and $\lambda_g = \dfrac{\lambda}{\sqrt{1 - \left(\dfrac{\lambda}{2a}\right)^2}} = \dfrac{\lambda}{\sqrt{1 - \left(\dfrac{f_c}{f}\right)^2}}$

where f_c is the cut-off frequency whose corresponding wavelength is 2a.

The phase shift constant, $\beta = \dfrac{2\pi}{\lambda_g}$ radians per meter

Equation 7-4

Group Velocity, V_g

This is the velocity at which the wave energy progresses along the guide; it is less than the free-space velocity, c, of the wave and is given by:

$$V_g = c \times \cos\theta = c \times \frac{\lambda}{\lambda_g}$$

Equation 7-5

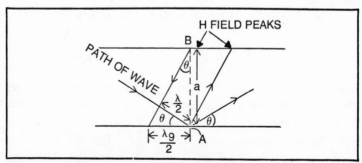

Fig. 7-4. Wavelength inside a rectangular waveguide.

187

Phase Velocity, V_p

This is the velocity of the field patterns; it is greater than c and is given by

$$V_p = \frac{c}{\cos\theta} = c \times \frac{\lambda_g}{\lambda} \qquad \text{Equation 7-6}$$

It follows that

$$V_p \times V_g = c^2 \qquad \text{Equation 7-7}$$

Wave Impedance in the Guide

This varies with the mode and the frequency and is given by:

$$\text{Wave Impedance, } Z_w = \frac{\text{transverse E field intensity}}{\text{transverse H field intensity}}$$

$$\text{Equation 7-8}$$

It may be proved that:

$$Z_w = 120\pi \frac{\lambda g}{\lambda} \text{ ohms for TE modes}$$

$$\text{Equation 7-9}$$

This is somewhat larger than the impedance of a wave in free space, which is 120π ohms or 377 ohms approximately. Hence some form of matching to free space is essential since an open-ended waveguide must result in a certain degree of mismatch.

Example 3-1

An X-band (8.2 - 12.4 GHz) waveguide has a wide dimension of 2.85 cm and a narrow dimension of 1.26 cm. What is the cut off wavelength for the TE_{10} dominant mode? If the transmitted frequency is 10 GHz, calculate the values of the free space wavelength, the angle of incidence θ, the guide wavelength, the phase velocity, the group velocity, the phase shift constant and the waveguide impedance.

Solution

$$\text{Cut-off wavelength for the wide dimension} = 2 \times 2.85$$
$$= 5.7 \text{ cm.}$$

$$\text{Free-space wavelength} = \frac{3 \times 10^8 \text{ m/s}}{10 \times 10^9 \text{ Hz}} = 0.03 \text{ m} = 3 \text{ cm}$$

Since the cut-off wavelength is greater than the free-space wavelength, the wave will propagate down the guide in the dominant TE_{10} mode.

$$\text{Angle of incidence, } \theta = \text{Inv. Sin} \frac{\lambda}{2a} = \text{Inv. Sin} \frac{3}{5.7}$$
$$= 31.76°.$$

Guide wavelength, $\lambda g = \dfrac{\lambda}{\text{Cos } \theta} = \dfrac{3}{\text{Cos } 31.76°} = 3.53$ cm.

Phase velocity, $v_\phi = \dfrac{c}{\text{Cos } \theta} = \dfrac{3}{\text{Cos } 31.76°}$

$= 3.53$ megameters per second.

Group velocity, $vg = c \text{ Cos } \theta = 300 \times \text{Cos } 31.76°$

$= 255$ magameters per second.

Phase shift constant, $\beta = \dfrac{2\pi}{\lambda g} = 178$ radians per meter.

Waveguide impedance, $Zw = 377 \times \dfrac{\lambda g}{\lambda} = \dfrac{377 \times 3.53}{3}$

$= 444 \ \Omega$

STANDING WAVES IN A WAVEGUIDE

When a rectangular waveguide is terminated by a transverse plate, which behaves as a short-circuit, the waves are reflected, giving rise to standing waves or patterns of the E and H fields as in Fig. 7-5. The maximum values of these E and H waves, like those of the corresponding waves of the voltage and current in Fig. 7-5 B are $90°$ or $\dfrac{\lambda g}{4}$ apart. The resulting impedance distribution along the guide, shown in Fig. 7-5C, is similar to that caused by standing waves in transmission lines.

As with other feeders, a mismatch causes reflection with consequent standing waves of voltage and current, which create standing patterns of E and H fields. Again the Standing Wave Ratio is a measure of the degree of mismatch or reflection and is given by:

$$\text{SWR,S} = \frac{\text{Max E field strength}}{\text{Min E field strength}}$$

$$\text{or SWR,S} = \frac{\text{Min H field strength}}{\text{Max H field strength}}$$

Summary of the Effects of Standing Waves

☐ Only a fraction of the incident power is absorbed by the load.

$$\frac{\text{Load Power}}{\text{Incident Power}} = \frac{4S}{(1 + S)^2}$$

If $S = 1.67$ power to the load is 94% of the incident power

☐ The voltages at the tinodes increase as S increases; this could given rise to arcing.

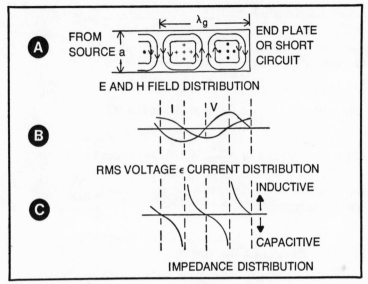

Fig. 7-5. Standing waves in a rectangular waveguide.

☐ Waveguide losses are increased.

☐ Impedance at the feed point is dependent on the electrical length of the guide run; this may cause frequency instability.

COUPLING TO AND FROM WAVEGUIDES

Various methods of coupling to or from waveguides may be used. Examples are:

☐ Probes usually employed with magnetrons, klystrons and test equipment.

☐ Slot coupling which is favored in duplexers. They are normally mutual coupling devices.

The simple E probe of Fig. 7-6A is an extension of the inner conductor of a coaxial cable protruding into the guide parallel to the E field. The coupling increases with the degree of insertion of the probe. By virtue of its length the probe may tend to resonate to some wavelength and, if this is undesirable, the tuning may be "flattened" by increasing the probe capacitance in the form of a door-knob or cross-bar as shown.

When launching an TE_{10} wave from a magnetron or klystron, the E probe is placed approximately $\frac{\lambda_g}{4}$ (or an odd multiple of) from the short-circuited end of the guide as in Fig. 7-6C. Such a probe behaves like a unipole from which energy is radiated along the

190

guide. Energy passing toward the short circuit is reflected with phase inversion so that it returns in phase with the forward moving waves. In some cases the short circuit end plate is in the form of a moveable piston which is adjusted for optimum output.

The H probe, which is less used, takes the form of a loop between the coaxial inner and outer conductors. It is inserted in the guide as in Fig. 7-6B so that the loop is at right angles to the H field.

Slots or holes cut in the walls of a guide may provide coupling to or from it. Such radiating or coupling slots are at right angles to the wall currents (parallel to the H lines) which are therefore interrupted. Some examples of radiating slots are shown in Fig. 7-7A. Such slots may be used to couple the waveguide to duplexers and directional couplers.

The degree of coupling increases with the size of the slot, especially its width. For loose coupling small circular slots may be used as in directional couplers.

Slots parallel to the direction of the wall currents are partically non-radiating. Such slots are useful for the insertion of movable probes as when measuring the standing wave ratio (Fig. 7-7B).

An open-ended guide as in Fig. 7-7C is also a radiating slot which presents some degree of mismatch to free-space since the wave impedance of the guide is somewhat greater than that of free-space. To improve this match for use in antenna coupling, the

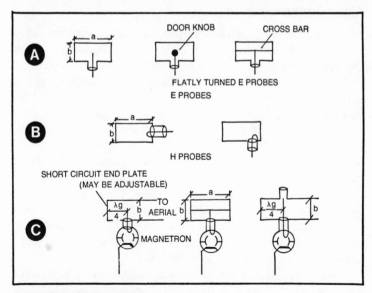

Fig. 7-6. Waveguide probes.

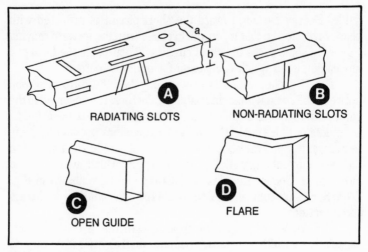

Fig. 7-7. Waveguide slots and flares.

dimension of the guide may be increased in the form of a flare or horn as in Fig. 7-7D; this serves to reduce the wave impedance of the guide.

An alternative way of improving the match is the use of a baffle in the form of a suitable thickness of dielectric placed across the end of the guide.

JOINTS, BENDS AND IRISES

Joints. Sections of 3 GHz waveguides may be joined by bolted flanges as in Fig. 7-8A; a copper gasket is inserted to ensure good contact at the inner surface of the guide and to exclude moisture.

When mechanical or electrical insulation is required between sections, a quarter-wave flange with a small air gap as in Fig. 7-8B may be used. Standing waves within the flange give rise to a short-circuit action at the inner surface of the guide, which therefore behaves as a continuous conductor. Mechanical insulation is usually provided by a section of flexible guide made of rubber with a metallic inner surface.

In the smaller 10 GHz guides a choke joint as shown in Fig. 7-8C may be used. Again standing waves within the joint give rise to a short-circuit action at the surface of the guide; this occurs at the center of the wide side of the guide where wall currents are large, namely where good contact is essential.

Rotating Joint. Rotating joints in waveguides are required to allow antenna rotation or elevation or beam-switching. They may take the form of a portion of circular waveguide inserted in the normal run of a rectangular guide. A typical example is shown in Fig. 7-9A, in which irises have been added to ensure that TE_{10} waves enter and leave the joint. A simple account of the purpose of each iris is indicated in Fig. 7-9A, while Fig. 7-9B shows the E field pattern only.

Bends. Rectangular guides may be bent in the plane of the narrow or wide sides in two ways which are commonly used:

☐ Gradual bends with a radius of curvature greater than λ_g as in Fig. 7-10A.

☐ Right-angle bends as in Fig. 7-10B with an inclined surface at the corner to ensure continuity of the fields around the bends. Here the distance "c" approaches the guide dimensions "a" or "b".

Twists. A gradual twist in a rectangular guide may be used to change the plane of polarization of the E field as in Fig. 7-11.

T Junctions. These are simple waveguide junctions which may take either of the forms shown in Fig. 7-12. Energy fed into any one of the guides will pass equally to the other two. The out-going E fields may be seen to be 180° out of phase in the E type junction, but in phase in the H type.

Irises (Diaphragms). These are transverse metal strips inserted in the guide and presenting reactive effects similar to stubs. Some common examples are given in Fig. 7-13. Inductive irises tend to concentrate the H field in the guide, while capacitive irises have the same effect on the E field. Suitable combinations of both can be used to give a parallel resonant action as in Fig. 7-13C. The band pass action of Fig. 7-13C may be improved by making the iris in the form of a rhumbation section.

Where adjustable reactance for matching purposes is required the insertion of an iris into the guide may be varied. Any loss-free obstruction in a guide will act as an iris, namely as a reactance.

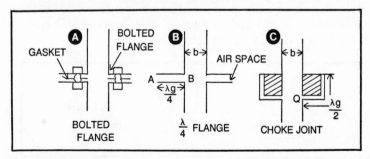

Fig. 7-8. Wave joints.

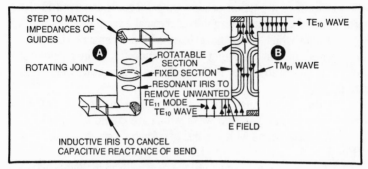

Fig. 7-9. Rotating waveguide joint.

WAVEGUIDE TERMINATIONS

Matched Terminations. Occasionally it is desirable to absorb unwanted energy at a waveguide termination so as to reduce reflection and standing waves. This can be done very effectively by means of a tapered portion of resistive material inserted in the guide. In some cases this takes the form of iron dust in s resin bond shaped as a wedge or tetrahedron as in Fig. 7-14A. A simple match may take the form of a resistive probe as in Fig. 7-14B by making the resistance of the probe equal to the impedance of the waveguide. A short circuit termination may be produced by a transverse plate blocking the guide or even by a transverse metal strip.

DIRECTIONAL WAVEGUIDE COUPLERS AND HYBRID COUPLERS

A number of waveguide devices having directional properties are employed in some microwave mixers. These include:

Directional Slot Couplers. In the device of Fig. 7-15A a small part of the energy passing along the lower waveguide from A to B is coupled to the upper guide through the two small slots as shown. By virtue of the path lengths such energy will add in the direction of C but will tend to cancel out in the direction of D; hence A is loosely coupled to C but not to D.

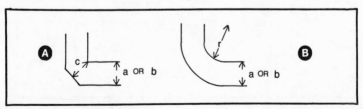

Fig. 7-10. Waveguide bends.

194

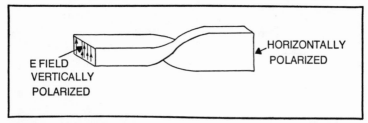

Fig. 7-11. Waveguide twist.

In the alternative device of Figs. 7-15B and 7-15C, energy passing through the small circular slots is 180° out of phase by virtue of the fact that they are set on either side of the center line of the guide. Allowing also for the differences of the path lengths, it may be seen that some of the energy entering at A may pass to C but not to D.

Hybrid or Magic T Coupler. This hybrid is a combination of E and H type T junctions as shown in Fig. 7-16A in which energy passes freely between all guides except A and C; this action is seen in the section of Fig. 7-16B in which the narrow section of guide A acts as an attenuator to a TE_{10} mode from guide C.

The directional properties may be summed up as follows.

Input	Output
A	Outputs at B and D in phase; no output at C.
C	Ouputs at B and D 180° out of phase; no output at A.

Hybrid Ring or Ratrace Coupler. This device is a combination of four E or H type T junctions as shown in Fig. 7-17. Consideration of path lengths and phase differences show the same directional properties as those listed for the magic T, but unlike the latter this device is sensitive to a change in wavelength.

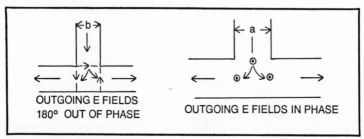

Fig. 7-12. T junctions.

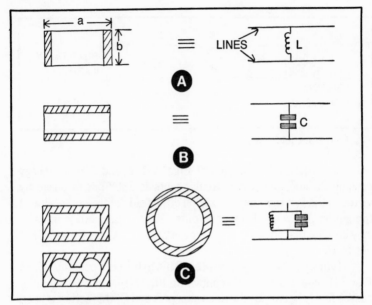

Fig. 7-13. Waveguide irises.

Coaxial Hybrid Ring. This is a simple coaxial equivalent of the ratrace used in some balanced mixers (Fig. 3-18A). In Fig. 3-18B a phase inversion is introduced by inductive coupling which

effective path length of $\frac{3\lambda}{4}$ between C and D.

Consideration of the path lengths shows the same directional properties as those listed for the magic T.

WAVEGUIDE MEASUREMENTS

A number of devices are used to measure the E or H field strength in a waveguide with a view to obtaining the values of standing wave ratio and/or power. The commoner devices include:

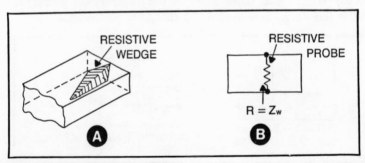

Fig. 7-14. Waveguide terminations.

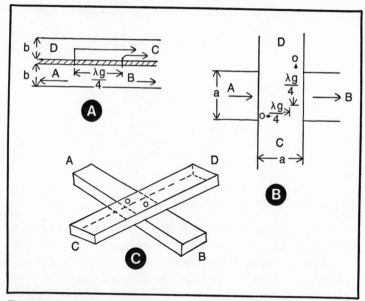

Fig. 7-15. Directional slot couplers.

Crystal Detector. The detected current (Fig. 7-19) is proportional to the RF voltage induced in the E (or H) probe which is proportional to the strength of the E (or H) field at that point in the waveguide.

Neon Indicator. The Neon Indicator of Fig. 7-20A takes the form of a pencil-type neon inserted through a non-radiating slot into the E field of the guide. The height to which ionisation extends is proportional to the strength of the E field at that point. By moving the neon along the slot it is possible to obtain the value of the swr.

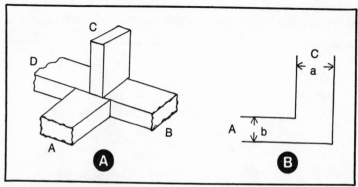

Fig. 7-16. Magic T coupler.

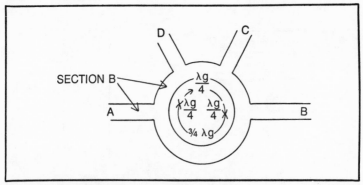

Fig. 7-17. Ratrace coupler.

The multi-neon indicator of Fig. 7-20B uses several such neons so that the SWR is readily measured without requiring any movement.

Thermocouple Power Meter. The dc output of the thermocouple is proportional to the temperature of the heater wire and therefore to the square of the current induced in the H probe of the waveguide in Fig. 7-21A. The output is therefore proportional to the RF power associated with the H field at that point in the waveguide.

A measure of the apparent RF power in the waveguide (the sum of the incident and reflected powers) may be obtained by adding the outputs of two thermocouples spaced $\frac{\lambda g}{4}$ apart in the guide as in Fig. 7-21B.

The standing wave ratio, S, may then be used to obtain the true (load) RF power output since:

$$\text{True power output} = \text{Apparent power output} \times \frac{2S}{1 + S^2},$$

where true (load) power = incident power − reflected power.

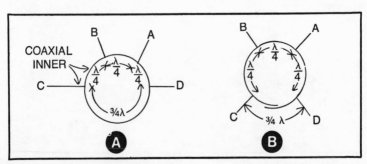

Fig. 7-18. Coaxial hybrid ring coupler.

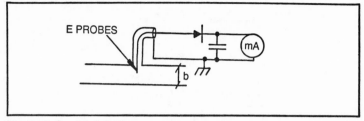

Fig. 7-19. Crystal detector.

Slot Hybrid Power Meter. The two slot hybrid arrangement can provide a more accurate measure of RF power output. In Fig. 7-22 a small fraction of the incident RF power from the source is fed via a slot hybrid to a thermistor probe which has a large negative temperature coefficient of resistance. The thermistor resistance is therefore inversely proportional to the rf power and is made part of a Wheatstone Bridge.

When R is adjusted for balance, it is calibrated to read the incident RF power. Any reflected power passing through the slots is absorbed by a wedge.

The hybrid may be reversed to measure the reflected power in the same way. Then the load power output = incident power − reflected power. The frequency of a microwave signal is commonly measured by a cavity wavemeter.

Cavity Wavemeter. Tunable high Q cavities may be employed in absorption type wavemeters to measure the wavelength or the frequency of a microwave source. The rf signal may be loosely coupled from waveguide to the calibrated cavity (Fig. 7-23). The output of the cavity is detected and passed through dc amplifiers to a meter or an oscilloscope; the cavity is then simply tuned for maximum output.

This device may be employed as a simple spectrum analyser by simultaneously sweeping the tuning and timebase of the display.

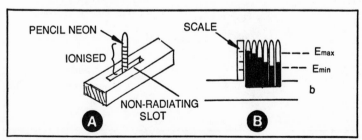

Fig. 7-20. SWR measurement by neon indicators.

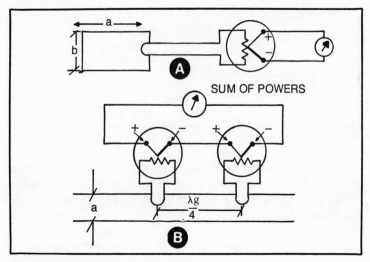

Fig. 7-21. Thermocouple power meters.

CHAPTER SUMMARY

Waveguide Equations.

Cut-off wavelength, $\lambda_c = 2a$

Angle of incidence, $\theta = $ Inv. $\operatorname{Sin} \dfrac{\lambda}{2a} = $ Inv. $\operatorname{Cos} \dfrac{\lambda}{\lambda g}$

Free-space wavelength,
$$\lambda = \frac{\lambda g}{\sqrt{1 + \left(\dfrac{\lambda g}{2a}\right)^2}}$$

Guide wavelength, $\lambda_g = \dfrac{\lambda}{\sqrt{1 - \left(\dfrac{\lambda}{2a}\right)^2}} = \dfrac{\lambda}{\sqrt{-\left(\dfrac{F_c}{F}\right)^2}}$

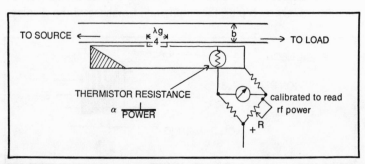

Fig. 7-22. Slot hybrid power meter.

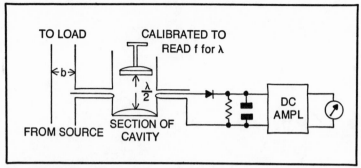

Fig. 7-23. Cavity wavemeter.

Group Velocity, $v_g = c \cos \theta = \dfrac{c \lambda}{\lambda_g}$

Phase Velocity, $v\phi = \dfrac{c}{\cos \theta} = c \dfrac{\lambda_g}{\lambda}$

Group velocity × phase velocity

$$= v_g \times V_\phi = c^2$$

Intrinsic impedance of Free Space
$$= 120 \pi = 377 \ \Omega.$$

Waveguide impedance for TE mode,

$$Z_w = 377 = \frac{\lambda g}{\lambda} \Omega.$$

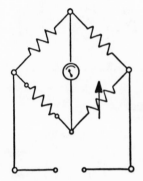

Chapter 8
Introduction to Radar

RADAR stands for *R*adio *A*id to *D*irection-finding *A*nd *R*anging. It uses radio signals which are reflected or re-radiated from such objects as ships and aircraft in order to obtain their ranges and bearings (Fig. 8-1). In some cases the height or elevation of aircraft is also determined. The signals used take the form of very short bursts or pulses of vhf or a much higher radio frequency.

BASIC PRINCIPLES OF RADAR

The range is found by:

☐ Measuring the very short time interval between the start of the transmitted pulse and the start of the reflected signal pulse or echo.

☐ Using the speed of radio waves in the atmosphere which is about 162,000 sea miles/sec or 1 sea mile in 6.1 μs (microseconds).

Because the radar signal covers twice the target range it follows that the time for a radar range of 0.5 sea mile (or 1,000 yds approx.) is 6.1 μs. Consequently the signal pulse must be of very short duration, sometimes less than a microsecond, if echoes from nearby targets are not to overlap. These very short time-intervals are measured by the time-base of a cathode ray tube. One of the commonest and simplest forms of CRT time base is one in which the spot is made to move or sweep uniformly from left to right, obeying a range scale by moving 1000 yds every 6.1 microseconds. The

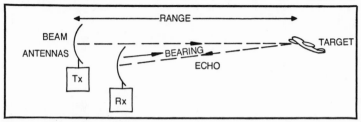

Fig. 8-1. Principle of radar.

start of this sweep from zero range is synchronized with the transmission. At the same time the signal pulses from the receiver are applied to one Y plate causing sharp vertical deflections or "pips" on the trace as shown (Fig. 8-2). The leading edge of the initial pip appears at the start of the trace or zero range, because this signal comes directly from the transmitter. The target range may then be read off opposite the leading edge of the echo pip. By high speed repetition of this procedure the moving spot gives the impression of a steady trace or line. In order to do this the spot flies back or retaces rapidly to the start of the scale and awaits the next transmission and sweep. At the same time it is arranged that the spot is seen or "brightened" during the sweep only; the beam is cut off and the spot "blacked out" for the remaining time.

The Pulse Repetition Frequency (PRF) pulse repetition rate varies in different equipments. If a certain radar set has a PRF of 500 Hz the transmitter and the sweep are triggered 500 times per second. The bearing of the target is obtained by using directional or beam serials for transmission and reception. The target bearing may then be given by training the serial for maximum echo amplitude on the CRT display.

The stages of the block diagram shown in Fig. 8-3A are found in many radar sets; the functions of these various stages may be briefly summarized.

☐ *The Transmitter* is normally in three main units;

    (1) *The Trigger Unit* which produces short pulses at the same repetition frequency as the ac, or astable multivibrator input.

    (2) *The Modulator Unit* which is controlled by the trigger pulses and provides very short pulses of several kilovolts to the oscillator.

    (3) *The Oscillator* which is normally the power output stage of the transmitter and passes radio frequency pulses to the antenna system.

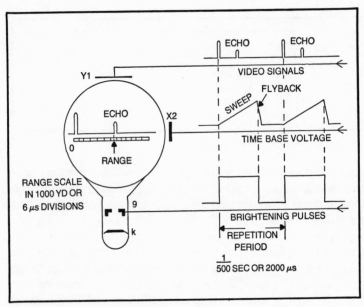

Fig. 8-2. Measurement of range.

□ *The Antenna.* In a few sets separate antennas may be used for transmitter and receiver, but most sets use a duplexing system so that the same antenna is used for transmission and reception so as to reduce top-weight and space. The common Transmit/Receive (T/R) switch effectively connects the antenna to the transmitter while transmitting and to the receiver for the remaining time.

□ *The Receiver* is a sensitive, wideband superhet. The detected output signals take the form of voltage pulses, called video signals, which when applied to one Y plate of the CRT, are seen as 'pips' on the display.

Noise, developed in the first stages of the receiver takes the form of "grass" on the display. The weakest detectable signal should be of greater amplitude than the grass; then the minimum readable signal/noise ratio should be greater than 1 : 1 (OdB).

□ *The Display* (Fig. 8-3B) A synchronizing (sync) pulse from the modulator triggers the multivibrator which produces square waves of length approximating to the time for the maximum range or sweep length. One such square wave switches a time base stage to generate a simultaneous sawtooth voltage which may be amplified and applied to the crt's X plates to provide the sweep and flyback (retrace). One such square wave may be applied to the grid of the crt to brighten the sweep movement only.

204

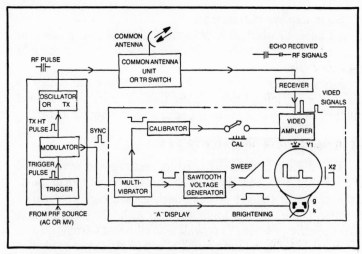

Fig. 8-3A. Block diagram of simple radar set.

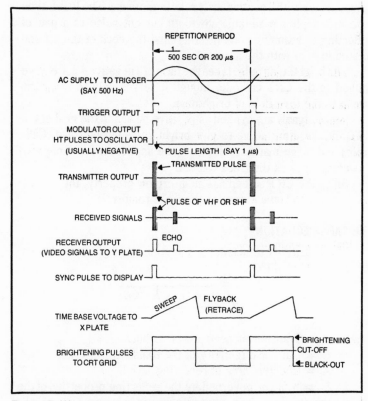

Fig. 8-3B. Waveforms of a simple radar set.

Some displays also include:

A Calibrator which provides a check that the sweep rate conforms with the range scale by producing pips or spots at suitable range intervals.

Range Marker or Strobe in the form of a spot which may be adjusted for any known range on the trace. The strobe is aligned with the leading edge of the target echo when measuring its range.

THE PLAN-POSITION INDICATOR (P.P.I.)

This display is normally used for warning and navigational purposes (Fig. 8-4). Your own ship appears as a bright spot or 'paint' at the center of the crt screen which uses a high persistance phospher. Other ships or aircraft appear as bright spots in their correct relative positions so providing an all-round warning display from which the ranging and bearing of any target can be read off.

The display is given by a semi-bright radial trace which revolves in step with a continuously rotating antenna. The P.P.I. time base unit applies a suitable sawtooth current pulse to a pair of deflecting or scanning coils fitted around the neck of the crt and rotated in step with the antenna.

The brightening pulse takes the form of a negative square wave applied to the CRT cathode, though it serves only to bring the sweep to the threshold of brightness.

Video signals are applied as positive pulses to the grid of the CRT and therefore serve to give bright spots on the trace. Calibrator and range marker pulses may be applied in the same way producing rings as the trace rotates.

Since the CRT screen has an afterglow property, the 'paints' are retained to some extent as the trace rotates.

THE RADAR EQUATION

The sensitivity or maximum detection range of a pulsed radar set is proportional to:

$$4 \sqrt{\frac{P_t \times G_t \times A_r \times \delta}{P_r}}$$

where, P_t = Transmitter peak power output.

G_t = Gain or directivity of the transmitting aerial.

A_r = Effective area of receiving aerial.

δ = A factor governed by the reflecting properties of the target, namely size, conductivity, inclination, etc.

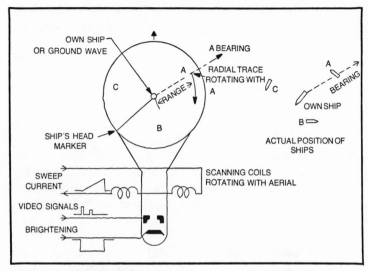

Fig. 8-4. The P.P.I. display.

P_r = The minimum detectable received signal power; this must exceed the receiver noise.

Hence the maximum range of an equipment may be increased by:

☐ Increasing the transmitter power output, bearing in mind that because Range $\alpha\ 4\sqrt{\text{Power}}$ it would be necessary to increase the transmitted power sixteen times in order to double the range.

☐ Reducing the beam width.

☐ Reducing receiver noise, primarily by the design of the first stage.

PARAMETERS OF A PULSE RADAR SET

The main parameters associated with a pulse radar set are:

Pulse Shape

Pulses of various shapes may be used in radar systems but for various practical reasons, the rectangular shape is usually chosen.

Pulse Duration (Width or Length)

This is the duration of the rectangular pulse and is normally measured in microseconds. For most radar sets the pulse duration lies between 0.1 microsecond and 10 microseconds. It is a factor in determining the minimum range obtainable since the echo pulse and the transmitted pulse must not overlap.

Increasing the pulse duration will increase the energy content of the pulse and will increase the maximum range. However, targets whose difference in range corresponds to the pulse duration, cannot be distinguished on the display; for example, a pulse duration of 0.1 microsecond will cover approximately 160 yards of range on the display.

The Pulse Repetition Time (Or Period)

This is the time interval between the leading edges of successive rectangular pulses. It is a factor in determining the maximum range obtainable since the echoes from a particular pulse must be received before the next pulse is transmitted. However for range reliability, the pulse repetition time must be kept sufficiently short to allow a number of pulses to be received from a particular target.

The Pulse Repetition Frequency (Or Rate)

This parameter is also known as the pulse frequency and is the reciprocal of the pulse repetition time. The values of pulse frequency generally lie between 250 Hz and 5000 Hz. The higher the pulse frequency, the greater is the intensity of the echoes on the PPI display. The result will be an improvement in the target definition.

The Peak Power

The peak power is the average power transmitted during the duration of the pulse. This may vary from several kilowatts to a few megawatts. It has been shown that the maximum range available is directly proportional to the fourth root of the peak power so that to triple the range, would require the transmitter power to be increased eighty-one times.

The Average Power

This is the average taken over the pulse repetition period. It follows that:

$$\frac{\text{The average power}}{\text{The peak power}} = \frac{\text{The pulse duration}}{\text{The pulse repetition time}}$$

Equation 8-1

Both of these ratios are equal to *the duty cycle* which has no units. The value of the duty cycle typically ranges from 0.01 to 0.0001.

Power Gain (G) of the Antenna

The maximum range is proportional to $\sqrt{G}$. Increasing the range by increasing the gain reduces the beam width and improves the bearing resolution.

Antenna Rotation Rate

This rate is limited by the number of received pulses required for each target. The higher the antenna rotation rate, the less will be the intensity of the echoes on the PPI display.

The Radio Frequency

The efficiency of surface detection increases with the value of the radio frequency. Moreover, as the radio frequency is increased, the size of the antenna and waveguide elements decreases. The parabola reflectors used with centimeter wavelengths can provide very narrow pencil beams which are especially suitable for accurate bearing measurements. The beam width or beam-angle is proportional to

$$\frac{\text{wavelength}}{\text{width of parabolic reflector}} \qquad \textbf{Equation 8-2}$$

and is defined as the angle between those two directions in which the received signal power falls to half the maximum value which is obtained along the beam axis.

The radio frequencies allocated to marine radar sets are in the Gigahertz range which corresponds to wavelengths which are of the order of centimeters. The relationship between the frequency, f, and the wavelength, λ, in free space is

$$f \text{ in GHz} = \frac{30}{\lambda \text{ in centimeters}} \qquad \textbf{Equation 8-3}$$

and λ in centimeter is

$$\frac{30}{f \text{ in GHz}} \qquad \textbf{Equation 8-4}$$

The following relationships exist between the various parameters

Pulse duration =

$$\frac{\text{average power (watts)} \times \text{pulse repetition time (seconds)}}{\text{peak power}}$$

$$= \frac{\text{average power}}{\text{peak power} \times \text{pulse frequency (Hz)}}$$

$$= \text{duty cycle} \times \text{pulse repetition time}$$

$$= \frac{\text{duty cycle}}{\text{pulse frequency}}$$

Equation 8-5

Pulse repetition time =

$$= \frac{\text{pulse duration} \times \text{peak power}}{\text{average power}}$$

$$= \frac{\text{pulse duration}}{\text{duty cycle}}$$

Equation 8-6

Pulse repetition frequency $= \dfrac{\text{average power}}{\text{pulse duration} \times \text{peak power}}$

$$= \frac{\text{duty cycle}}{\text{pulse duration}}$$

Equation 8-7

Average power $= \dfrac{\text{peak power} \times \text{pulse duration}}{\text{pulse repetition time}}$

$$= \text{peak power} \times \text{pulse duration} \times \text{pulse frequency}$$
$$= \text{peak power} \times \text{duty cycle}$$

Equation 8-8

Peak power $= \dfrac{\text{average power} \times \text{pulse repetition time}}{\text{pulse duration}}$

$$= \frac{\text{average power}}{\text{pulse duration} \times \text{pulse frequency}}$$

$$= \frac{\text{average power}}{\text{duty cycle}}$$

Equation 8-9

Duty cycle $= \text{pulse duration} \times \text{pulse frequency}$

Equation 8-10

Example 8-1

A marine radar set has a peak power of 0.5 MW and a pulse duration of 2 microseconds. If the pulse frequency is 500 Hz, what are the values of the average power and the duty cycle?

Solution

$$\text{Average power} = \text{peak power} \times \text{pulse duration} \times \text{pulse frequency}$$
$$= 0.5 \times 10^6 \times 2 \ 10^{-6} \times 500$$
$$= 500 \text{ W}$$

$$\text{Duty cycle} = \text{pulse duration} \times \text{pulse frequency}$$
$$= 2 \times 10^{-6} \times 500 = 1 \times 10^{-3} = 0.001$$

Note that the duty cycle is also equal to:

$$\frac{\text{average power}}{\text{peak power}} = \frac{500}{0.5 \times 10^6} = 1 \times 10^{-3} = 0.001$$

Example 8-2

A marine radar set has a peak power output of 750 kW and a duty cycle of 0.0005. What is the average power?

Solution

$$\text{Average power} = \text{peak power} \times \text{duty cycle}$$
$$= 750 \times 10^3 \times 0.0005 = 7.5 \times 10^5 \times 5 \times 10^{-4}$$
$$= 375 \text{ W}$$

Example 8-3

The wavelength of a radar transmission in free space is 9.6 centimeters. What is the corresponding radio frequency?

Solution

$$\text{Radio frequency in GHz} = \frac{30}{\text{wavelength in centimeters}}$$
$$= \frac{30}{9.6}$$
$$= 3.125 \text{ GHz}$$

Example 8-4

The peak power of a radar pulse is 1 MW and its average power is 500 W. If the pulse duration is 2 microseconds, what are the values of the pulse repetition time and the pulse frequency?

Solution

$$\text{Pulse repetition time} = \frac{\text{pulse duration} \times \text{peak power}}{\text{average power}}$$
$$= \frac{2 \times 10^{-6} \ 10^6}{500} = \frac{1}{250} \text{ second}$$
$$= 4000 \text{ microseconds}$$
$$\text{pulse frequency} = \frac{1}{\text{pulse repetition time}} = \frac{1}{4000 \times 10^{-6}}$$
$$= 250 \text{ Hz}$$

Example 8-5

The length (duration) of a radar pulse is 5 microseconds, peak power is 800 kW and average power is 2000 W. What is the value of the pulse frequency?

Solution

$$\text{Pulse Frequency} = \frac{\text{average power}}{\text{pulse duration} \times \text{peak power}}$$

$$= \frac{2000}{5 \times 10^{-6} \times 800 \times 10^3}$$

$$= 500 \text{ Hz}$$

Example 8-6

The pulse repetition time of a marine radar set is 2 milliseconds and the duty cycle is 5×10^{-4}. What is the pulse duration?

Solution

Pulse duration = duty cycle × pulse repetition time
$$= 5 \times 10^{-4} \times 2 \times 10^{-3} = 1 \times 10^{-6} \text{ second}$$
$$= 1 \text{ microsecond}$$

Example 8-7

The average power of a radar pulse is 1 kW, the pulse duration is 2 microseconds and the pulse frequency is 400 Hz. What is the pulse's peak power?

Solution

$$\text{Peak Power} = \frac{\text{average power}}{\text{pulse duration} \times \text{pulse frequency}}$$

$$= \frac{1000}{2 \times 10^{-6} \times 400}$$

$$\text{W} = 1.25 \text{ MW}$$

Example 8-8

The peak power of a pulse radar set is increased by 50%. Assuming that all other parameters remain the same, what will be the increase in the maximum range?

Solution

The maximum range is proportional to the fourth root of the transmitter peak power output. The maximum range is therefore multiplied by a factor of $4\sqrt{1.5} = 1.1068$
Therefore, $4\sqrt{1.5}$ is approximately 1.11, and the range is increased by 11%.

RADAR RANGES AND THEIR CORRESPONDING TIME INTERVALS

A radar pulse is an electromagnetic wave which travels with the velocity of light in air. At standard temperature and pressure, this velocity is 2.997×10^8 meters per second or 161700 nautical miles per second where 1 nautical mile $\approx$ 6080 feet $\approx$ 2027 yards.

The time taken for a radar pulse to travel 1 nautical mile is 6.184 microseconds. Therefore the total time interval for a target range of 1 nautical mile is the total time for the pulse to reach the target and the echo to return to the receiver and will be $2 \times 6.184 = 12.368$ microseconds.

The distance traveled by a radar pulse in 1 microsecond = 0.161 711 nautical miles which is approximately 328 yards. Therefore a pulse duration of 1 microsecond will cover a range interval of $328/2 = 164$ yards.

Summarizing:

Radar range in nautical miles

$$= \frac{\text{total round-trip time interval in microseconds}}{12.37}$$

Equation 8-11

and therefore, the total time interval in microseconds for the pulse to travel to the target and back is 12.37 × radar range in nautical miles.

Distance to the target in nautical miles

$$= \frac{\text{time taken by the transmitted pulse to reach the target in microseconds}}{6.18}$$

Equation 8-12

so that the time in microseconds taken by the transmitted pulse to reach the target is 6.18 × distance to the target in nautical miles. The total distance traveled by the pulse to the target and back to the receiver is 2 × radar range.

Example 8-9

The range of a target is 8.7 nautical miles. What is the time in microseconds taken for the transmitted pulse to reach the target?

Solution

The time taken for the transmitted pulse to reach the target is $6.18 \times 8.7 = 53.8$ microseconds, rounded off.

Example 8-10

A radar pulse travels to the target and back to the receiver in a total time interval of 83 microseconds. What is the range of the target in nautical miles?

Solution

Range of the target $= \dfrac{83}{12.37}$

$= 6.7$ nautical miles, rounded off.

Example 8-11

The pulse duration of a marine radar is 2.0 microseconds. What is the maximum separation range between two targets which have the same bearing but which cannot be distinguished on the display?

Solution

A pulse duration of 2.0 microseconds will cover a range interval of $2.0 \times 164 = 328$ yards.

Example 8-12

For calibration purposes, it is required to produce range-marker circles which are separated by range intervals of 1 nautical mile. What is the frequency of the range-marker oscillator?

Solution

The time interval corresponding to a range separation of 1 nautical mile is 12.37 microseconds. This must correspond to the period generated by the range-marker oscillator whose frequency is therefore:

$$\frac{1}{12.37 \times 10^{-6}} \text{ Hz} = 80.8 \text{ kHz, rounded off.}$$

Example 8-13

The range of a radar target is 5.6 nautical miles. What is the total time interval in microseconds for the pulse to travel to the target and back to the receiver?

Solution

The total time interval is $5.6 \times 12.37 = 69.3$ microseconds, rounded off.

PULSE DURATION AND THE DISCHARGE LINE

The pulse duration (length, width) is determined in the Modulator Unit which commonly uses an artificial discharge line consisting of a number of L, C sections. The total discharge time is equal to the duration of the negative pulse applied to the cathode of the magnetron.

Pulse duration $= 2 N \times \sqrt{LC}$ seconds where N = the number of sections and L, C are the inductance (henrys) and the capacitance (farads) of each section.

Example 8-14

A modulator unit uses an artificial discharge line of six sections, each of which contains an inductance of 6.5 μH and a capacitance of 4000 pF. What is the value of the pulse duration?

Solution

The product L $\times$ C = 6.5 $\times$ 10^{-6} $\times$ 4000 $\times$ 10^{-12} = 2.6 $\times$ 10^{-14}
The pulse duration is:

2N $\sqrt{LC}$ = 2 $\times$ 6 $\times$ 2.6 $\times$ 10^{-14} second
= 1.9 microseconds, rounded off.

BANDWIDTH OF RADAR RECEIVER, INTERMEDIATE FREQUENCY (IF) AND VIDEO AMPLIFIER STAGES

To achieve accurate ranging, it is necessary to preserve the shape of the rectangular pulse and, in particular, its leading edge. This requires a wide bandwidth for the radar receiver intermediate and video amplifier stages in order to pass the numerous harmonics associated with a short duration pulse. The bandwidth and the pulse duration are related by

$$\text{Bandwidth in MHz} = \frac{2}{\text{pulse duration (microseconds)}}$$

$$\text{Pulse duration (microseconds)} = \frac{2}{\text{bandwidth in MHz}}$$

Equation 8-14

Since a wide bandwidth is required, the gain of each IF amplifier stage is low and, therefore, the number of such stages in a radar receiver may be five or more.

Example 8-15

A marine radar set uses a pulse duration of 0.5 microsecond. What is the required bandwidth for the receiver IF stages?

Solution

$$\text{Required bandwidth in MHz} = \frac{2}{0.5\ \mu s} = 4\ \text{MHz}.$$

FREQUENCY MODULATED AND CONTINUOUS WAVE RADAR SYSTEMS

Apart from the use of short duration rf pulses there are two other possible radar systems. In FM radar the rf wave is mooulated by a sawtooth; the difference between the instantaneous frequencies being transmitted and received will then be a direct measure of the reflecting objects range. The most common use of this system is in the radio altimeter where the reflecting object is the earth as seen from the aircraft. The instantaneous frequency difference will be an accurate measurement of the vertical distance between the ground and the aircraft.

In a CW Radar system the velocity of a target but not its range may be determined. The principle is based on the Doppler effect in which the frequency of the signal radiated from the reflecting object is shifted when the object is moving relative to the receiver; an example of such a system is a police radar speed trap.

Let the reflecting object (such as a car) be moving with a component of velocity $+ V_s$ in the direction of propagation; the result will be to produce a change in wavelength and hence a shift in frequency at the receiver. If f_s is the wavelength and T is the period ($= 1 f_s$) of the radiation from the source when stationary:—

New wavelength, $\lambda_r = \lambda_s - V_s \times T$ **Equation 8-15**

Velocity of propagation $= C = f_s \lambda_s = f_r (\lambda_s - V_s \times T)$
Equation 8-16

where f_r is the received frequency and C is the velocity of an electromagnetic wave (300,000,000 meters per second or 984,000,000 feet per second). Then:

$$f_r = \frac{C}{\lambda_s - V_s \times T} = \frac{C}{\lambda_s - \dfrac{V_s}{f_s}}$$
$$= f_s \times \left(\frac{C}{C - V_s}\right)$$ **Equation 8-17**

If the source is stationary but the receiver is moving a component of velocity $+ V_r$ in the direction of propagation, there is, as regards the receiver, an apparent change in the velocity of propagation.

Apparent velocity of propagation $= C - V_r = \lambda_s \times f_r$

Therefore, $f_r = \dfrac{C - V_r}{\lambda_s} = f_s \times \dfrac{(C - V_r)}{C}$
Equation 8-18

If the source and the receiver are both moving,

$$f_r = f_s \times \frac{C - V_r}{C - V_s}$$ **Equation 8-19**

The Doppler frequency shift $= f_r - f_s$

216

$$= f_s \times \left(\frac{C - V_r}{C - V_s} - 1 \right)$$

$$= f_s \times \frac{(V_s - V_r)}{(C - V_s)} \longrightarrow f_s \frac{(V_s - V_r)}{C} \qquad \text{Equation 8-20}$$

Since C is very much greater than V_s. The shift therefore depends on the source frequency and the relative velocity between the source and receiver in the direction of propagation. If the relative velocity is 1 mile per hour and f_s = 1 GHz.

$$\text{Doppler Frequency shift} = \frac{10^9 \times 5280}{9.84 \times 10^9 \times 3600} \text{ Hz}$$

$$\approx 0.15 \text{ Hz per mph per GHz}$$

Equation 8-21

For a CW Radar set, the two-way propagation shift is 2×0.15 = 0.3 Hz per mph per GHz.

Example 8-16

A CW Radar set operating on a frequency of 10 GHz. If the target is moving in the direction of propagation with a velocity of 60 mph, calculate the amount of the Doppler shift at the receiver.

Solution

Two-way Doppler shift = $0.3 \times 10 \times 60$
$$= 180 \text{ Hz}$$

CHAPTER SUMMARY

Pulsed Radar

Pulse duration =

$$\frac{\text{average power (watts)} \times \text{pulse repetition time (seconds)}}{\text{peak power (watts)}}$$

$$= \frac{\text{average power}}{\text{peak power} \times \text{pulse frequency (Hz)}}$$

$$= \text{duty cycle} \times \text{pulse repetition time}$$

$$= \frac{\text{duty cycle}}{\text{pulse frequency}}$$

$$\text{Pulse repetition time} = \frac{\text{pulse duration} \times \text{peak power}}{\text{average power}}$$

$$= \frac{\text{pulse duration}}{\text{duty cycle}}$$

$$\text{Pulse repetition frequency} = \frac{\text{average power}}{\text{pulse duration} \times \text{peak power}}$$

$$= \frac{\text{duty cycle}}{\text{pulse duration}}$$

$$\text{Average power} = \frac{\text{average power} \times \text{pulse duration}}{\text{pulse repetition time}}$$

$$= \text{peak power} \times \text{pulse duration} \times \text{pulse frequency}$$
$$= \text{peak power} \times \text{duty cycle}$$

$$\text{Peak power} = \frac{\text{average power} \times \text{pulse repetition time}}{\text{pulse duration}}$$

$$= \frac{\text{average power}}{\text{pulse duration} \times \text{pulse frequency}}$$

$$= \frac{\text{average power}}{\text{duty cycle}}$$

$$\text{Duty cycle} = \text{pulse duration} \times \text{pulse frequency}$$

$$\text{Maximum range is proportional to } 4\sqrt{\frac{P_E \times G_E \times A_r \times \delta}{P_r}}$$

CW Radar

Two-way propagation Doppler shift = 0.3 Hz per mph per GHz.

Chapter 9
Introduction
to Television

Figure 9-1 shows the simplified block diagram of a monochrome (black and white) transmitter.

THE TV CAMERA TUBE

With modern practice the camera tube may be either an image orthicon or a vidicon. The image orthicon (Fig. 9-2) has an electron gun for scanning, an electron multiplier for amplifying the signal and an image section. When light from the scene to be televised is focused onto a photocathode, an electron image is created by photo-emission. The electrons given off are attracted to a thin glass target plate where another image is created by secondary emission effect. A low velocity beam from the electron gun then scans the target and deposits sufficient electrons to cancel the positive charges. The remaining electrons enter the multiplier and are amplified by the system of dynodes. The final video signal appears as the output voltage across a load resistor, which is included in the muplier's anode circuit.

The vidicon tube (Fig. 9-3) has smaller dimensions than the image orthicon and contains only an electron gun with a photoconductive target plate. The output connection is made to the front of the target where there is a conductive section which allows the light to pass through to the rear photoconductive layer: the latter is made from antimony or selenium compounds whose resistance decreases with the amount of incident light. By means of external deflection coils the magnetically focused electron beam is made to scan the photolayer both horizontally and vertically; dark and light picture elements then control the amount of signal current passing through an external load resistor, across which the output video signals voltage is developed. This signal may be regarded as containing frequencies which range from 30 Hz to 4 NHz.

The vidicon tube is at the present time preferred for monochrome and color RV studio cameras. Compared to the image orthicon, the vidicon is simpler in construction, more rugged, smaller in size, weighs less and requires less input power; it is therefore used extensively in closed-circuit TV and for industrial purposes. On the other hand the image orthicon has a better signal-to-noise ratio and a greater light sensitivity so that the scene to be televised requires less illumination.

The output signal from the camera tube is passed through a number of video amplifiers which increase the signal level to the amount required to grid modulate the final rf stage. The wide bandwidth (MHz) required for a TV channel makes control grid modulation more practical than plate modulation, which is commonly used in standard broadcast transmitters.

RF VIDEO SECTION

The crystal oscillator, which initially generates the visual carrier, is operated at low frequency for good stability; the crystal itself is enclosed in a thermostatically controlled oven. The most common form of thermostat is the mercury thermometer type, which is highly sensitive. Cheaper and simpler is the thermocouple variety which uses a bimetal strip.

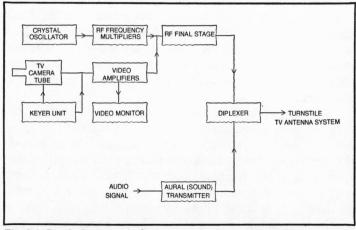

Fig. 9-1. Block diagram of television monochrome transmitter.

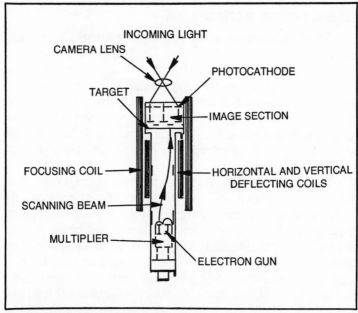

Fig. 9-2. The image orthicon tube.

The oscillator stage is followed by a number of frequency multipliers and RF amplifiers. These increase the frequency up to the value required for the video carrier and at the same time raise the power level to the amount necessary to drive the rf final stage.

KEYER UNIT

The output from the keyer unit contains the following:
- ☐ Vertical serrated synchronizing pulses (60 Hz).
- ☐ Horizontal synchronizing pulses (15750 Hz).
- ☐ Equalizing pulses (31500 Hz).
- ☐ Vertical blanking pulses (60 Hz)
- ☐ Horizontal blanking pulses (15750 Hz)

Before discussing the purpose of these pulses, we must look at the principle of scanning. The scene to be televised is regarded as made up of a number of picture elements that represent the smallest areas capable of being distinguished from their neighbors. For a complete picture the maximum possible number of picture elements is approximately 150,000. Whether an image orthicon or a vidicon tube is used, the scene to be televised is reproduced as an image on the target plate and the picture elements are successively scanned by the narrow focused beam from the electron gun.

221

SCANNING BY THE ELECTRON BEAM

A horizontal deflection coil is mounted externally to the camera tube and the current flowing through this coil has a sawtooth waveform with a frequency of 15750 Hz. During the linear rise of this current the electron beam is deflected across the target face with a constant velocity from left to right. At the end of the linear rise the current falls rapidly so the beam moves quickly back from right to left; this action is called the retrace or flyback. During retrace the horizontal blanking pulse prevents any video information from being transmitted.

While horizontal scanning is taking place, the vertical deflection coil is provided with its sawtooth current whose frequency is 60 Hz. This causes the beam to move downwards from top to bottom at constant speed. The vertical scanning is followed by the retrace which occurs during the interval of the vertical blanking pulse. The combination of horizontal and vertical scanning produces a number of horizontal lines which slope gently downwards from left to right. The complete picture or frame is scanned by a total of 525 lines in a time of 1/30 second (frame frequency = 30 Hz). However in the vertical scanning time of 1/60 second the number of horizontal lines

is only $\dfrac{15750}{60} = 262\frac{1}{2}$ so that it requires two vertical scanning

intervals or fields to scan the complete total of 525 lines (field frequency = 60 Hz). The field frequency is deliberately chosen to equal the commercial line frequency; the video information normally contains some ripple at the line frequency and this causes some faint dark bars to appear on the face of the receiver's kinescope (TV tube). If the field frequency were not equal to the line frequency, the dark bars would move up or down and this would be irritating to the viewer, stationary bars however are barely noticeable.

Summarizing, there are 525 lines to one frame but only 262½ lines in each field. This leads to the principle or interlaced scanning. If the 525 lines were successively scanned in 1/30 second, 30 complete pictures would be transmitted every second. However, with a frequency of only 30 Hz the viewer's eye would notice a certain amount of flicker. A frame of 525 lines is therefore divided into one odd field and one even field, each containing 262½ lines. It then appears to the eye that the pictures are being transmitted at the rate of 60 per second, and this frequency is sufficiently high to avoid flicker effect.

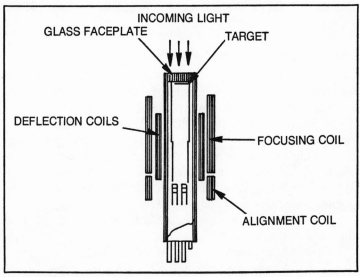

Fig. 9-3. The vidicon tube.

As in Fig. 9-4 the odd field starts at point A and finishes at point B. Vertical retrace then brings the beam back to point C which is the start of the even field. This field ends at point D and the beam is returned to point A for the start of the next odd field. Vertical blanking and retrace removes about 20 horizontal lines so that only 242½ lines per field are visible. The ratio of width to height achieved is called the aspect ratio whose value is set at 4 to 3.

SYNCHRONIZING PULSES

In order to reproduce the picture correctly on the receiver's kinescope, it is necessary to lock the scanning at the transmitter with that of the receiver. This is achieved by transmitting vertical and horizontal synchronizing pulses which are mounted on top of the blanking pulses and trigger the receiver's horizontal and vertical scanning oscillators. Referring to the horizontal pulses, the interval between the start of blanking and the front edge of the porch is the time between the trailing edge and the end of blanking.

The vertical synchronizing pulse is serrated to allow continuous triggering of the receiver's horizontal oscillator during the vertical retrace. This pulse is preceded and followed by six equalizing pulses which have a frequency of 31500 Hz or twice the horizontal scanning frequency. These also have the responsibility for triggering the horizontal oscillator, but their main purpose is to insure that the vertical retrace starts at the same time for both odd and even fields.

VESTIGIAL SIDEBAND TRANSMISSION

To sum up, the composite video signal contains the picture information together with the blanking, synchronizing and equalizing pulses. This signal is viewed by the studio monitor which is the TV equivalent of the audio monitor in AM and FM broadcast stations. When the composite signal amplitude modulates the rf carrier, a white picture element produces minimum percentage modulation while a black element creates maximum modulation. This system is called negative transmission which has the advantages of greater power efficiency and reducing the effects of noise.

The modulation percentages produced by the various parts of the composite signal are:

☐ Synchronizing and equalizing pulses, 100%
☐ Blanking pulses, 75% ± 2.5%
☐ Black, 70% approximately.
☐ White level, 12.5 ± 2.5%

The high video frequencies extending up to 4 MHz represent the fine detail in the picture to be transmitted. If a double sideband system were used, the total bandwidth required would be 8 MHz which would exceed the allocated channel width of 6 MHz. To

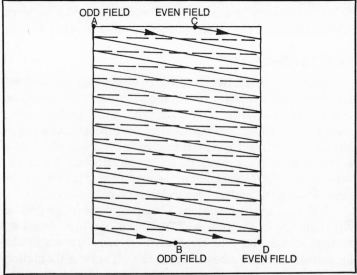

Fig. 9-4. Principle of interlaced scanning.

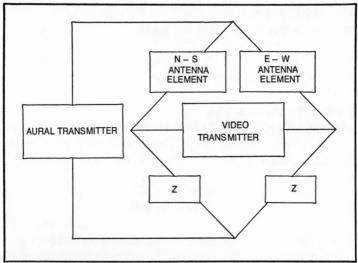

Fig. 9-5. Principle of the diplexer.

reduce the bandwidth the double sideband system is used for video frequencies up to 750 kHz but only the upper sidebands are transmitted for the remaining frequencies. The result is vestigial sideband transmission (emission designation A5C) which is produced by the filter system following the rf power amplifier. The carrier power output from this amplifier is allowed a tolerance of 10% above the authorized value to 20% below.

The modulated signal is finally radiated as a horizontal polarized wave from a vhf/uhf antenna which is generally of the turnstile variety. The use of a horizontal antenna system eliminates some of the effects of noise which is primarily vertically polarized.

THE AURAL TRANSMITTER—THE DIPLEXER

The sound or aural transmitter employs frequency modulation with 100% modulation corresponding to a frequency deviation of 25 kHz. The transmitted audio range is 50 Hz to 15 kHz so that the deviation ratio is $\frac{20 \text{ kHz}}{15 \text{ kHz}} = 1.667$. Preemphasis and corresponding deemphasis are used with a time constant of 75 microseconds. A common antenna system is used for both the AM video signal and the FM aural signal so that it is necessary to avoid interaction between the two transmitters. This is achieved by means of a diplexer (Fig. 9-5) which is essentially a balanced bridge. The north-south and east-west antenna elements are two arms of the bridge which is then balanced by equal impedances in the other arms. The output of the video transmitter is fed to one pair of opposite corners of the bridge while the aural transmitter is connected to the other pair. With the bridge balanced, both transmitters will activate the antenna elements but neither will interact with the other.

FREQUENCIES CONTAINED IN
MONOCHROME AND COLOR TV TRANSMISSIONS

The video carrier frequency, f_V, has a tolerance of ± 1 kHz and is located 1.25 MHz above the channel's lower frequency limit, f_L, so that

$$f_V = (f_L + 1.25) \text{ MHz}$$
$$= (f_U - 4.75) \text{ MHz}$$

Equation 9-1

where f_U is the channel's upper frequency limit. These frequencies are shown in Fig. 9-6 which represent a channel's response curve (not drawn to scale). The aural carrier frequency, f_A also has a frequency tolerance of ± 1 kHz and is positioned 0.25 MHz below the channel's upper frequency limit. Therefore

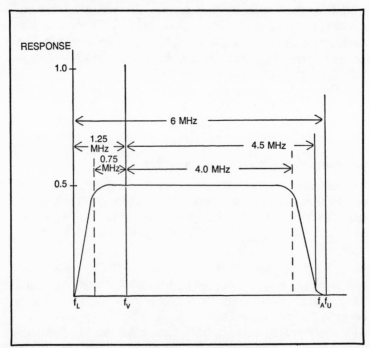

Fig. 9-6. Response curve of monochrome transmission.

226

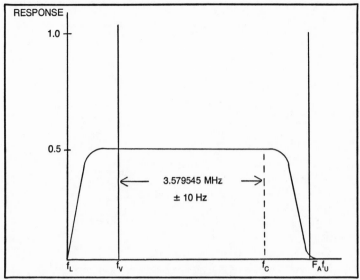

Fig. 9-7. Response curve of color transmission.

$$f_A = (f_U - 0.25) \text{ MHz}$$
$$= (f_L + 5.75) \text{ MHz}$$
$$= (f_V + 4.5) \text{ MHz}$$

Equation 9-2

As a result of the frequency conversion process in the superheterodyne TV receiver, the video and aural intermediate frequencies are respectively 45.75 MHz and 41.25 MHz; their frequency separation is still 4.5 MHz. These values are independent of the channel selected.

Color Television

The ideal response curve for a color transmission is shown in Fig. 9-7. The positioning of the video and aural carriers is the same as in the monochrome transmission but the color information (chrominance signal) is used to amplitude modulate a chrominance subcarrier whose frequency, f_c, is located 3.579545 MHz ± 10 Hz (commonly rounded off to 3.58 MHz) above the video carrier frequency, f_V. Then:

$$f_c = (f_V + 3.579545) \text{ MHz}$$
$$= (f_L + 4.829545) \text{ MHz}$$
$$= (f_U - 1.170455) \text{ MHz}$$
$$= (f_A - 0.920455) \text{ MHz}$$

Equation 9-3

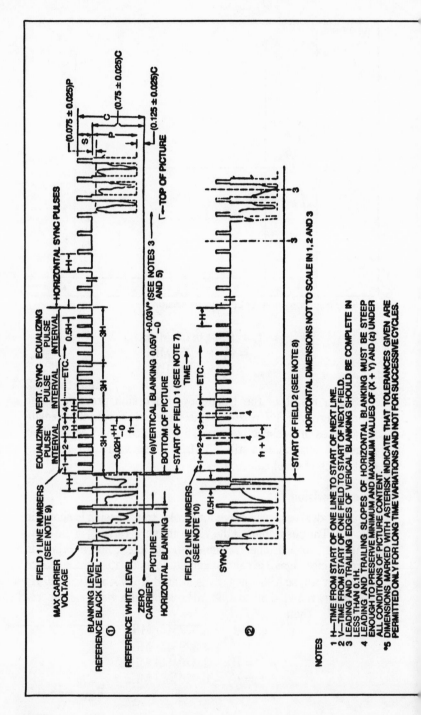

NOTES

1 H—TIME FROM START OF ONE LINE TO START OF NEXT LINE.
2 V—TIME FROM START OF ONE FIELD TO START OF NEXT FIELD.
3 LEADING AND TRAILING EDGES OF VERTICAL BLANKING SHOULD BE COMPLETE IN LESS THAN 0.1H.
4 LEADING AND TRAILING SLOPES OF HORIZONTAL BLANKING MUST BE STEEP ENOUGH TO PRESERVE MINIMUM AND MAXIMUM VALUES OF (X + Y) AND (Z) UNDER ALL CONDITIONS OF PICTURE CONTENT.
*5 DIMENSIONS MARKED WITH ASTERISK INDICATE THAT TOLERANCES GIVEN ARE PERMITTED ONLY FOR LONG TIME VARIATIONS AND NOT FOR SUCCESSIVE CYCLES.

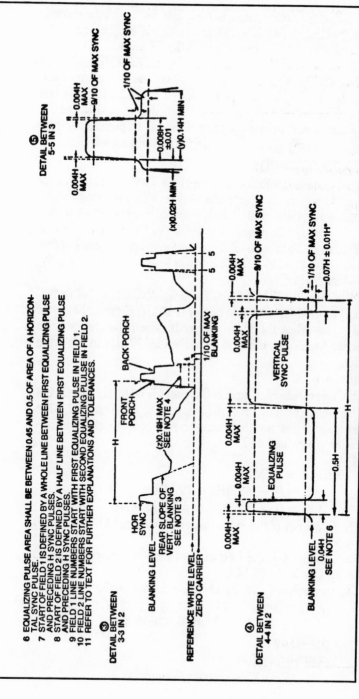

Fig. 9-8. Television synchronizing waveform for color transmission.

Vestigial sideband transmission is also used with the chrominance signal but in this case the sub-carrier is suppressed at the transmitter and must be reinserted at the receiver.

For correct reinsertion it is necessary to synchronize the 3.58 MHz color oscillator in the receiver. This is done by transmitting 8 to 11 cycles of the subcarrier as a "color burst" which is located on the back of porch of the horizontal synchronizing pulse (Fig. 9-8). It is important to realize that the color burst has no picture information since it is only transmitted during the blanking interval.

Offset Carrier Frequencies

In some areas it would be possible for a TV receiver to pick up two separate signals on a particular channel which is being broadcast from two stations located in different cities. The result would be an unacceptable interference pattern (Venetian blind) on the receiver screen. To avoid this effect, the video carrier of one of the stations may be offset by 10 MHz above or below the value normally specified for that channel.

Channels with offset carriers are designated either "+" or "−" according to whether the video carrier is 10 kHz above or below its normal value. When the video carrier is offset, the chrominance sub-carrier frequency will also be shifted by 10 kHz in the same direction.

Example 9-1

The lower frequency limit of Channel 4 is 66 MHz. What is the upper frequency limit and the frequency of the aural carrier? What are the frequencies for the video carrier and the chrominance sub-carrier of Channel 4+?

Solution

Since f_L = 66 MHz.

$f_U = (f_L + 6)$ MHz = 72 MHz.

$f_A = (f_L + 5.75)$ MHz = 71.75 MHz

The frequency of the video carrier for Channel 4 is $(f_L + 1.25)$ MHz = MHz.

For Channel 4+, the frequency of the video carrier is 67.25 MHz + 10 kHz = 67.26 MHz.

The frequency, f_C, of the chrominance subcarrier is:

$$(f_V + 3.579545) \text{ MHz} = 67.26 + 3.579545$$
$$= 70.839545 \text{ MHz.}$$

CHAPTER SUMMARY

Monochrome Television

F_v = Video carrier Frequency

F_A = Aural carrier frequency
F_U = Channel's upper frequency limit
F_L = Channel's lower frequency limit
F_V = $(F_L + 1.25)$ MHz
    = $(F_U - 4.75)$ MHz
F_A = $(F_U - 0.25)$ MHz
    = $(F_L + 5.75)$ MHz
    = $(F_V + 4.5)$ MHz

Frame Frequency = 30 Hz
Field Frequency = 60 Hz
Frequency of vertical synchronizing and blocking pulses = 60 Hz
Frequency of horizontal synchronizing and horizontal pulses = 15750 Hz
Frequency of equalizing pulses = 31500 Hz

Modulation with Negative Transmission

White level = $12.5 \pm 2.5\%$
Blacking level = $75\% \pm 2.5\%$
Synchronzing pulse level = 100%

Color Television

Chrominance sub-carrier frequency, F_C
    = 3.579545 MHz $\pm$ 10 Hz
F_C = $(F_V + 3.579545)$ MHz
    = $(F_L + 4.829545)$ MHz
    = $(F_U - 1.170455)$ MHz
    = $(F_A - 0.920455)$ MHz

Chapter 10
Introduction to Sonar

The first recorded attack by a submarine vessel against a warship took place in 1778 when the American submarine Turtle attacked a British ship during the American war of Independence. There were no established anti-submarine tactics so the British C-in-C ordered that 'when so attacked, ships in harbour were to leave by the nearest exit' - a most practical measure against a submarine capable of only 2 knots and with but a few hours endurance. The use of superior speed provided an effective antisubmarine protection, in World War II, when, for example the liners Queen Elizabeth 1 and Queen Mary survived the whole war, often steaming at high speed across the Atlantic without escort.

HISTORY OF SONAR DEVELOPMENT

No naval ship was sunk by a submarine until the American Civil War when the Confederate submarine Hunley sank a Unionist warship with a single torpedo. By the turn of the century the torpedo had developed into a formidable weapon. Its primary use was in small ships - torpedo boats, which could then attack and damage even a battleship which up to this time had been secure against all smaller craft. A few far sighted Naval Officers foresaw that the submarine launched torpedo would be an even more effec-tive weapon, but the majority regarded the submarine as the weapon of the weaker navy and thought it unlikely that it would greatly effect sea power; consequently we were slow in developing both the submarine and submarine countermeasures.

The first co-ordinated attempt to deal with the destruction of submarines appears in a letter written by the C-in-C British Home

Fleet to the Admiralty dated 29th December 1903 in which he suggested that during the forthcoming maneuvers at Spithead, definite operations should be tried against submarines, the object being to render it possible for the fleet to enter Spithead and anchor without being torpedoed by the submarines stationed in the vicinity.

Such measures to be tried consisted of:

☐ A submarine when its periscope was sighted, was to be approached by a destroyer and a noose thrown over its periscope or dropped over with a boathook, a small hand charge then being slid down the rope and exploded against the periscope.

☐ A towed charge attached to a grapnel with a firing key on board the destroyer. When the grapnel caught up in the periscope the charge was fired.

☐ The indicating net, which was to be laid out in the probable track of a submarine when it was seen to dive. A red flag, attached to a stave on the net's floats gave an indication when the submarine entered the nets.

☐ The lasso net with explosive charges attached, which was thrown over a submarine and drawn tight exploding the charges.

These trials showed:

☐ The Fleet while in submarine waters could never remain stationary for any length of time, thus causing the coal consumption to rise.

☐ The existing antisubmarine methods were ineffective against skillfully handled submarines.

In March 1910 the first submarine committee was formed and carried out trials on:

☐ A double wire sweep.

☐ Bursting shells shortly after they hit the water by means of delayed action fuzes.

☐ Firing the Maxim gun at the periscope.

☐ Torpedoing of submarines by surface craft.

In 1911 the first A/S screens were tried, and in 1912 a report stated "The possibility of obtaining some electric or magnetic apparatus to indicate the presence of submarines was also investigated but did not show any promise of being practical".

The First World War

By 1914 the German Navy possessed 27 seagoing submarines (Underseaboat or U-boats). There was no means of detecting their

233

presence when submerged and even when at periscope depth, they could usually 'see and not be seen'.

For the first two years of the war the U-boats sank many merchant ships in the Atlantic, but usually the crews were given time to take to their boats and the U-boat sank the ship by gunfire rather than use one of their expensive, and sometimes unreliable, torpedoes. Consequently many of the merchant ships were armed and 'Q' ships - heavily armed merchant ships manned by personnel were used as decoys, and sank a number of attacking submarines. The Germans then changed their tactics, adopting unrestricted warfare, attacking without warning from periscope depth with torpedoes. The losses mounted alarmingly so that almost one million tons of Allied shipping were sunk in April 1917 alone; this was almost ten times the building rate and in a few months without improvement, the British nation would have been defeated by lack of supplies.

The existing antisubmarine methods relied on mining near the U-boat bases, surrounding warships with torpedo nets, towing wire sweeps and charges, and small lance bombs for motor boats attacking submarines on the surface. But this did not help much against the patrolling U-boats in the Atlantic. Many bizarre methods of detecting and attacking submarines were suggested and quite a few of them tried:

A Mr. Ashmore claimed to be able to detect a submerged submarine with an 'oil dividing stick' but experiments proved unsuccessful. Another gentleman obtained a grant to train seals and porpoises to indicate the presence of submarines.

The adoption of the convoy system and the development of the hydrophone were the vital factors which turned defeat into victory in the first battle of the Atlantic.

In 1490 Leonardo da Vinci had said "If you cause your ship to stop, place the head of a long tube in the water and place the other extremity to your ear, then you will hear ships at a great distance from you", (and rememer these were sailing ships!) Passive listening methods had been tried from the beginning of the war but detections were limited by the ship's own propeller noise when underway. A further problem was that it was not possible to determine the direction from which the noise came (this was because the wavelength of the sound heard by the operator was long compared to the size of the listening device). This was overcome to some extent by using two listening tubes spaced about 5 ft apart (1 wavelength at 1 kHz) each tube leading to a different ear of the operator who could sense the phase difference when not pointed towards the target. This system continued to be used in American submarines up to World War II.

Active echo ranging were also being investigated. The TITANIC disaster of 1912 had prompted an effort to locate icebergs, and the first recorded detection took place on 27th April 1914 at a range of two miles.

The Allied Submarine Detection Investigation Committee (ASDIC) of 1916 reviewed all existing methods and concentrated on producing practical passive and active sound detection systems. The purely aural methods still suffered from excessive background noise due to the lack of directivity and unrestricted bandwidth. This caused Professor Langevin in France to adopt supersonic frequencies using quartz crystal hydrophones. The received signal was heterodyned in the receiver to give an audio frequency at the headset. By 1918 Professor Langevin had successfully detected and tracked a submerged submarine with an active supersonic asdio set (echo ranging), but the war was over before the equipment could be widely fitted in ships at sea; nevertheless passive directional hydrophones were developed by Captain Ryan and Mr. Nash and widely fitted in 1917 and 1918. The first success with this device after a 7 hour chase of 50 miles which exhausted the U-boats batteries causing it to surface.

Weapons were also greatly improved. The depth charge with hydrostatic fuze was introduced in 1916, but was in such short supply that for months the allowance was only 4 per ship.

The variety of weapons is indicated by the following list:

Number of U-boats sunk by:	
Mines	42
Depth Charges	31
Gun Fire	30
Ramming	19
Torpedo	17
Nets	7
Sweeps	3
Total	149

Not surprisingly when the war ended in 1918 most research and development stopped, so that the second World War started in 1939 with similar (and in many cases the same!) weapons as in 1918. Fortunately there had been progress in the detection field, and we started the second war with a lead over the Germans in asdic equipment comparable to that in radar. The latter is better known as it was a vital factor in the Battle of Britain in 1940, but the former played just as vital a role later in the second Battle of the Atlantic.

Piezo-electric devices were used exclusively until 1927 when the first magnetostriction transducer was tried in the USA. This type gradually replaced the mechanical transmitters in echo sounders but did not supersede quartz steel, piezo-electric asdic transducers until after the second war. The magnetostrictive echo sounder still widely used today is very similar to the echo sounder of 1935.

In the 1930s probably the most significant improvement was the adoption of the retractable 'dome' or hull outfit, which could enable all round training of the transducer and improved streamlining. The first of these was a canvas over a wooden frame, which limited ship speed to 8 knots with the dome down. Then stainless steel became standard for domes soon afterwards.

In 1933 the British Admiralty directed that all small ships were to be equipped with asdics and a series of active sets were fitted. The range recorder and bearing recorder developed into a form which remains today. By 1936 the British Navy were so confident that the asdic was master of the submarine threat that Hitler was able to expand his U-boat fleet without restriction (At the London Conference the relative sizes of the world Navies had been agreed and the Germans were only to have up to half as many submarines as the British).

The Second World War

At the outbreak of war Britain possessed 200 asdic fitted ships and the Germans 57 ocean going submarines. Even though escorts were scattered throughout the world the German Naval Command estimated they needed 300 U-boats to bring about the collapse of Britain. They did not have this number until 1942, when losses to shipping mounted critically as they had done in 1917. The convoy system with existing escorts could not cope.

The main problem the escorts encountered when attacking a U-boat was that the ship had to pass right over the submarine before it fired its depth charges, so that during this final phase of the attack contact was lost. An ahead-firing projectile was necessary so that the submarine could be attacked while contact was maintained. "Hedgehog" met this requirement; 24 small charges were fired to fall in a circle 200 yards ahead of the ship, one bomb making contact with the submarine would explode and detonate the other 23. This was introduced in 1941, one of the design engineers being Neville Shute Norway - perhaps better known as a novelist. Towards the end of 1942 there followed an even more effective weapon - the "Squid" a three-barrelled ahead firing mortar. Each mortar bomb carried a 200 lb. charge compared with only 30 lb. in each hedgehog.

With these three weapons, "depth charge", "hedgehog", and "squid" the Battle of the Atlantic was won, the former being even more effective when dropped from a long range maritime aircraft, which gradually extended their range of operation to cover the whole North Atlantic. These radar-fitted aircraft made life increasingly difficult for the U-boats recharging their batteries on the surface at night, finally forcing them to introduce the Schnorkel or "Snort" mast which enabled the diesel engines to draw in air when at periscope depth. During the war aircraft were also fitted with Magnetic Anomaly Detection (MAD) devices which can detect a submarine when submerged, but these are still a comparatively short range device.

Post War Developments

Asdic ranges had increased from about one to two thousand yards during the war and the weapon range was still limited to a few hundred yards ahead of the attacking ship. There was a threefold requirement for a better weapon system - longer range, more accurate bearing and depth, all round fire capability. These features were introduced in the early 1950s as the combination of an asdic set and a mortar control system. This became the standard 'attack' system in almost all antisubmarine frigates.

The need for a very much longer range asdic set was long recognized, but to achieve a large increase in range a very much more powerful and sophisticated set was required. Asdic equipment was introduced in the late 1950s for this purpose and became the standard 'search' system in most antisubmarine frigates. There was a further development which enabled echoes from any direction to be received at the same time. In 1964 the word SONAR was adopted for NATO purposes. It is derived from *So*und *N*avigation *A*nd *R*anging.

Having developed a considerably longer range sonar set, the next requirement was for a weapon system of comparable range. This is at present provided by the *M*edium range *A*ntisubmarine *T*orpedo *C*arrying *H*elicopter or MATCH. New frigates were equipped to carry helicopters and some of the older ones were converted.

Submarines themselves are also being used as very effective antisubmarine vessels as their passive sonars have even longer ranges than the ship-fitted active sonars.

The helicopter had certain limitations in very rough weather so that an additional vehicle was introduced to carry the homing torpedo to the drop point above the submarine; this vehicle was in the form of a guided missile.

To produce very much longer detection ranges, ways had to be devised of overcoming the problem of the sound beam bending in the sea leaving 'shadow zones' in which the submarine could hide. This was overcome by bouncing the sound pulse off the seabed and up to the surface again; however this required very large sonar sets. In the future a larger and larger part of the ship will be occupied by the sonar equipment and its control, as undoubtedly all the information available from other escorts will be pooled in the computer of each ship. The antisubmarine measures of the past have twice won victories in the Atlantic and since the number of potential enemy submarines is greater today than it has ever been, the antisubmarine role cannot be over emphasized.

THE PROPERTIES OF SOUND

When we hear a sound it means that somewhere or other a moving or vibrating body has transmitted its vibrations to our eardrums. The ear combined with the brain has great powers of classifying sounds and recognizing the kind of source. For example, sounds from a motorcycle, a flute and a dog's bark are easily recognizable. The sound source may be the vibrating column of air in an organ pipe but in all cases the origin of sound is a moving source. Sometimes the vibrations are so slow that they can be seen but usually they are so small and fast that individual vibrations are indistinguishable.

For sound to travel from the source to the receiver (the ear) there must be a medium to carry vibrations. When the first spacemen arrived on the moon, normal speaking from spacesuit to spacesuit was impossible due to the absence of an atmosphere. If the spacesuits however are connected together by some suitable medium, direct communication can take place.

Electromagnetic waves (light, radio waves and radiated heat) are unlike sound waves in this respect as they can be transmitted through empty space.

A particular sound can be defined by its:

Frequency - number of vibrations per second.

Amplitude - "loudness".

Tone - presence of 'harmonics' or multiples
of fundamental frequency.

The ear is sensitive to sounds in the approximate range 30 Hz to 15,000 Hz, which is called the Sonic Region. Vibrations above 15,000 Hz are in the ultrasonic region. Sonar uses waves in both the sonic and ultrasonic regions.

Speed of Sound

Sound travels from the source at a speed which depends on the medium through which it is travelling. For example in air the speed of sound is about 1100 ft/sec at normal temperatures and is less at lower temperatures. In water, sound travels at about 5000 ft/sec and is affected by changes in temperature, salinity and pressure. Light waves and radio waves travel at 186,000 miles/sec and this comparative slowness of sound is one reason why sonar problems can be very different to those of radar.

Transmission of Sound

It has been stated that sound requires a medium through which to travel so let us examine how the medium behaves while the sound is being transmitted.

Suppose a plate is vibrating in water at some frequency, (Fig. 10-1). As the plate moves to the right, the adjacent layers of water on the right are compressed so that the pressure increases. This high pressure water then starts to compress the next layer of water. Similarly when the plate moves to the left, the water on the right is rarified (its pressure is reduced below its static value) and this starts to rarify the adjacent layer.

Consequently a series of pressure and rarification waves move away from the plate at some velocity, which is the "Speed of Sound". If, as is usual, the plate is vibrating sinusoidally, the pressure will vary sinusoidally, so that if a graph is drawn of pressure against distance from source for some fixed time, the result is a sine wave. Moreover if a graph is drawn for pressure against time at some constant distance from the source, once again a sine wave appears. This pressure may be expressed by the formula

$$P_d = P_{max} \, Sin \, (2 \, \pi \, ft + \frac{2\pi \, d}{\lambda})$$ **Equation 10-1**

where P_d = the pressure at distance, d, from the source

P_{max} = maximum pressure created by the sound wave

f = Frequency of vibration in

λ = wavelength of the sound wave.

The formula $P_d = P_{max} \, Sin \, (2 \, \pi \, ft + \frac{2 \, \pi \, d}{\lambda})$ shows that the pressure varies sinusoidally with time and distance and that pressures at positions with a distance λ apart, are in phase.

The pressure associated with a sound wave is one way of describing its "strength" and can be compared to voltage in electricity since both are a measure of the "drive". As in electricity rms values can be used with the relationship: $P_{rms} = \dfrac{P_{max}}{\sqrt{2}} = 0.7 \, P_{max}$

The unit of pressure most commonly used in the microbar (μ bar) where

1 μ bar = 1 dyne/cm^2 = 0.1 newton/m$^2 \approx 10^{-6}$ atmosphere.

Particle Velocity

Instead of using pressure to measure the sound strength we could use the amount of movement that the layers of the medium undergo as they vibrate backwards and forwards under the influence of the varying pressures. The velocity of the particles in the medium gives a measure of this movement and is referred to the "particle velocity". Particle velocity is not generally used in practice to describe acoustic strength but it helps to complete the electrical analogy as it is the movement caused by the pressure. Particle velocity is equivalent in electricity to current and may be measured in cm/sec or m/sec.

Intensity

Since the sound medium such as an ocean is three-dimensional, the acoustic power must be measured as the sound energy is transferred through some specific unit area during a period of unit time. This acoustic power per unit area is called the intensity which is measured in watts/m^2. The equation for intensity is   Intensity = pressure × particle velocity   **Equation 10-2**

The lowest intensity in air the human ear can detect is about 10^{-12} watts/m^2 while the intensity near to the face of a sonar transducer (sound producer) can exceed 10^4 watt/m^2. Intensity is the most usual way of describing the amount of sound present in the sea but pressure could just as easily be used.

Acoustic Impedance

In the analogy with electricity, equivalents have been found for voltage, current and power and there remains only one basic

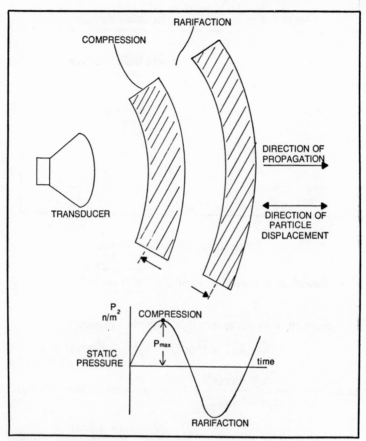

Fig. 10-1. The longitudinal sound wave.

parameter; namely resistance or more generally impedance.

In general Impedance $=\dfrac{\text{Force}}{\text{Motion}}$; for example in electricity

The values of the specific acoustic impedance obtained by

$$\dfrac{\text{Pressure}}{\text{Particle Velocity}}$$

and $\rho \times C$ are precisely the same and although ρC is usually used for acoustic impedance,

$$\dfrac{\text{Pressure}}{\text{Particle Velocity}}$$

has been given here to show that impedance in acoustics has a similar meaning to electrical impedance. The values of the specific acoustic impedance for various media are shown in Table 10-1.

Table 10-1. Acoustical Impedances for Various Materials.

Medium	Specific Acoustic Impedance (Ac Ω)
Nickel	4,350,000
Steel	3,900,000
Quartz	1,650,000
Sea Water	154,000
Rubber	2,900
Air	42

$$\text{In electrics, Power} = \frac{\text{Voltage}^2}{\text{Resistance}}$$

$$\text{Similarly in acoustics, Intensity} = \frac{\text{Pressure}^2}{\rho C}$$

If I = Intensity, P = Pressure, U = Particle Velocity,

$$\rho C = \frac{P}{U} \text{ and } I = P \times U \qquad \textbf{Equation 10-3}$$

impedance is $\dfrac{\text{Voltage (force)}}{\text{Current (motion)}}$. Therefore it would seem logical

to define acoustic impedance as $\dfrac{\text{Pressure (force)}}{\text{Particle Velocity (Motion)}}$ and

in fact this is the case.

When applied to a medium such as air or water the impedance is called the "Specific Acoustic Impedance" and is "the pressure required to produce a particle velocity of 1 cm/sec" (both measured either as rms or peak values). To get an appreciation of what this means, imagine holding a large metal sheet in air and pushing it backwards and forwards as fast as possible. The maximum speed will certainly be greater than 1 cm/sec and the force required will be fairly small resulting in a small specific acoustic impedance. But try and do this in water and the force required to get a reasonable movement will be extremely large; in fact canoe paddles and rowing oars rely on this principle. This indicates that water has a large specific acoustic impedance. The units are Acoustic Ohms when the pressure is in μ bars and the particle velocity is in cm/sec.

Specific Acoustic Impedance

There is another expression for specific acoustic impedance which Newton derived mathematically from the basic wave propagation equations. The relationship is:

Specific Acoustic Impedance = $\rho \times C$ where ρ is the density of the medium and C is the velocity of sound in the medium.
Then:

$$U = \frac{P}{\rho C}$$
Equation 10-4

and,

$$I = \frac{P^2}{\rho C}$$
Equation 10-5

Use of Decibels

The intensities of sounds encountered in underwater acoustics can vary by many orders of magnitude, from 10^4 watts/m^2 to 10^{-5} watts/m^2. Such a large range of numbers unwieldy in calculation and consequently a logarithmic or decibel notation is universally used.

It so happens that the human ear measures intensities on a logarithmic scale quite naturally; if the ear hears a sound that is increasing in strength in a number of steps of apparently equal amounts, it is found that the intensities are *multiplied* by a constant amount to give each step. This effect is illustrated in Table 10-2. The decibel notation gives a method of showing a "ratio of intensities". Decibels are only defined for power ratios (or intensity ratios) and the decibel for voltage or pressure ratios is derived from the power definition.

If it is required to express an intensity I in dB then we must first define a reference intensity I_{ref} to give the comparison or ratio. Then:

$$\text{Intensity, } I = 10 \log_{10} \frac{I}{I_{ref}} \text{ dB} \qquad \textbf{Equation 10-6}$$

Table 10-2. Loudness Judged by Ear and by Acoustical Power.

Loudness as judged by ear	Intensity of sound watt/cm^2
1	1
2	2
3	4
4	8
5	16

Originally the bel was defined as $\log_{10} \dfrac{I}{I_{ref}}$ but these units were found to be too small numerically so that the decibel was born. For sonar the reference intensity is that related to an acoustic pressure of 1 μ bar in seawater.

Attenuation of the Acoustic Wave

If the acoustic source is a pulsating sphere the radiation spreads out as a shell and the inverse square law applies to the intensity (as regards the ocean this is a simplification since top and bottom boundaries exist and there is a channeling effect). The intensity of the received echo is proportional to $\dfrac{1}{(range)^4}$ so that doubling the power output only produces a 16% change in range. Cavitation limits the output intensity to 1 kW/sq ft approximately, and the presence of reverberation may mean that a large increase in power output will not produce a great improvement in detection.

Additional attenuation (converting acoustic energy into heat) is provided by:

☐ Viscous forces which oppose the stresses set up by the acoustic pressure so that energy is drained from the wave. The resultant attenuation factor involves the square of the frequency.

☐ Under adiabatic conditions the pressure variations which occur are accompanied by changes of temperature. There is a heat flow from regions of compression to those of rarification, tending to reduce the pressure differences so that attenuation results.

The long range (20,000 yds) search sets use low frequencies, which are normally less than 10 kHz; however these require very large transducer units to obtain directivity. Higher frequencies of 15 to 30 kHz are therefore employed with short range (3000 yds) sets.

Comparison between Acoustic and E.M. Waves in Water

	Acoustic Wave	E.M. Wave
Speed	5000 ft/sec	186,000 miles/sec
Refraction	Appreciable	Little
Attenuation	Little	Severe

E.M. waves can only be reasonably propagated in water with wavelengths of several kilometers and these are useless for directional purposes.

Doppler Shift

Earlier it was established that

$$\text{Doppler Frequency Shift} = F_s \times \frac{(V_s - V_r)}{C - V_s} \qquad \textbf{Equation 10-7}$$

where,

F_s = Frequency of the sound source when stationary
V_s = velocity of the sound source
V_r = component of the receiver's velocity in the direction of propagation
C = velocity of the sound wave.

If the relative velocity between the source and the receiver is 1 knot (6080 ft/hr), F_s = 1 kHz and $C \approx$ 5000 ft/sec (velocity of sound in seawater).

$$\text{Doppler Shift} = \frac{1000 \text{ Hz} \times 6080 \text{ ft/hr}}{3600 \text{ s/hr} \times 5000 \text{ ft/s}} = 0.34 \text{ Hz}.$$

For two-way propagation,

Doppler Shift = $2 \times 0.34 \approx 0.7$ Hz per knot per kHz.

Sonar Equipment

It is a mistake to consider a sonar set as an "upside down, submerged radar set". The objects of such a system are essentially the same as radar but problems are introduced by the transmission medium and the low information rate; such factors are insignificant in radar.

Briefly, Sonar systems may be divided into two main types:

☐ Passive systems which rely on the detection of a target by listening for self-generated noise such as machinery noise and hull whip. Detections can be made at long ranges.

☐ Active systems which transmit a burst or pulse of sound and which then time the delay between transmission and reception (Fig. 10-2). Because of the low speed of sound in water (5000 ft/sec), only small areas may be scanned at any one time and the received pulse has to be analysed to determine the nature of the echo. For example, clouds of plankton, shoals of fish, rocks etc. can produce echoes which may give false information.

The Doppler effect in Sonar is particularly noticeable so that the simultaneous measure of velocity is possible.

Pulse modulation techniques are the more common although F.M techniques are also used.

Example 10-1

A sonar set on an A/s frigate is operating on a frequency of 9 kHz. If the relative velocity between the frigate and a submarine in the direction of propagation is 18 knots, what is the amount of the two-way propagation Doppler shift?

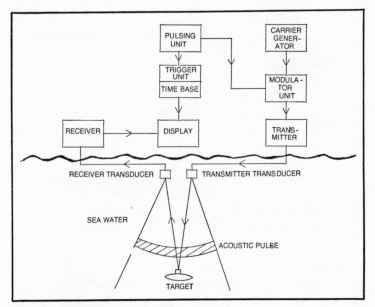

Fig. 10-2. Block diagram of pulsed sonar set.

Solution
    Two-way Doppler shift $= 2 \times 0.34 \times 9 \times 18 = 110$ Hz.

SONAR TRANSDUCERS

    The name transducer is given to devices which convert energy from one form to another; in particular electroacoustic transducers are used for converting acoustical signals into electrical signals suitable for processing. It is common to use electro-acoustic transducers to generate underwater sound and those used solely for this purpose are called *transmitters* while transducers used only for reception are termed *hydrophones*. Usually the same transducer or same type of transducer performs the tasks of both transmission and reception; for this the transducer must possess the characteristics of linearity and reversibility. A transducer is linear if it produces an exact equivalent in electrical terms of the incident acoustic waveform, and it is reversible if it has the ability to convert energy between the electrical and acoustical forms in either direction.

    Sonar tranducers may employ either electric or magnetic fields in their transduction process. Some are inherently linear while others have to be *polarized* to produce linear action. The latter arises if the force producing acceleration of the active mass of the transducer which in turn causes acoustic radiation, is proportional to the square of the applied electrical signal. If the electrical signal is sinusoidal of the form:

$$e = E \sin \omega t,$$

a square-law transducer produces a force proportional to:

$$e^2 = (E \sin \omega t)^2 = \tfrac{1}{2} E^2 (1 - \cos 2 \omega t)$$

This force contains a steady component plus a sinusoidal varying at twice the applied frequency (Fig. 10-3).

If a steady polarizing quantity E_0 is applied together with the sinusoidal signal, the force is then proportional to:

$$E_0 + E \sin \omega t)^2 = E_0^2 + 2E E_0 \sin \omega t + E^2 \sin^2 \omega t$$
$$\approx E_0^2 + 2E E_0 \sin \omega t \text{ if } E_0 >> E$$

The alternating force produced is then proportional to the applied sine wave. If the frequency of the latter is made equal to that of the transducer's mechanical resonance, considerable acoustic energy will be generated.

A square-law transducer, if unpolarized, cannot be used as a receiver. A field either electric or magnetic must first be present for the vibrations within the transducer to alter; only then can an electrical output be produced. Such a transducer must therefore be polarized to make it both linear and reversible.

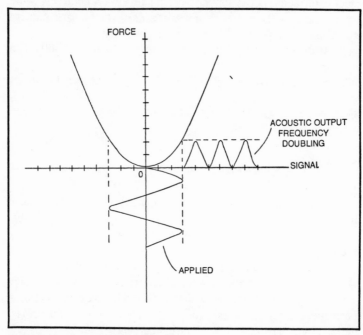

Fig. 10-3. The square-law transducer.

Types of Transducer

Chronologically the types of transducer which have been most commonly employed are the piezo-electric, magnetostrictive and electrostrictive. The properties of these types are:

☐ *Piezoelectric.* Linear. Possible frequency range 5 kHz – 50 MHz. Quartz Crystals mounted between steel plates.

☐ *Magnetostrictive.* Polarized. Up to 200 kHz. Laminated nickel strips.

☐ *Electrostrictive.* Polarized. 5 kHz – 10 MHz. Barium titanate or lead zirconate-titanate discs.

Magnetostrictive Transducers

Magnetostriction occurs in all ferromagnetic materials and is strongly pronounced in nickel, iron and cobalt. In these materials magnetic dipoles are formed spontaneously and these have a preferred orientation within certain localized regions or domains. Ordinarily these domains are randomly disposed but when an external magnetic field is applied, there is an alignment of the domains and depending on the particlar material, a corresponding expansion or contraction takes place (Fig. 10-4). The strain produced is independent of the sense of the applied field (nickel always contracts whilst iron expands in the presence of weak fields) so that polarization has to be used to ensure linearity and reversibility.

At the operating point, P, the magnetizing force is 400 AT/m and $\dfrac{-\Delta 1}{1} = 7.5 \times 10^{-6}$. Since Young's Modulus for nickel $= 2 \times 10^{11}$ newton/m², the longitudinal stress
$= 7.5 \times 10^{-6} \times 2 \times 10^{11}$
$= 1.5 \times 10^{6}$ n/m².

The polarizing magnetic field can be provided in one of four ways:

☐ By incorporating a permanent magnet in the transducer housing in contact with the magnetostrictive element (Fig. 10-5).

☐ By winding a separate coil (carrying a direct current) round the element.

☐ By superimposing the signal on a dc current level.

☐ By heating the element and allowing it to cool while subjecting it to a high intensity magnetic field, thereby creating a permanent magnet. Alternatively the element may be remagnetized by means of a short duration current pulse.

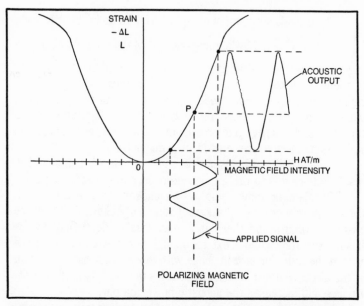

Fig. 10-4. Relationship between strain and magnetic field intensity for nickel.

The element itself consists of nickel strips with the lamination used to reduce eddy current losses. The nickel is commonly annealed which provides an oxide layer on the surface of each lamination thereby insulating one strip from another (this also reduces the area of the hysteresis loop and hence the losses). The magnetizing coil consists of a small number of thick turns and carries a current of a few amperes; it is provided with heavy insulation so that this type of transducer needs no further protection and is completely immersed in water.

It is important that there is an appreciable length/width ratio since there are transverse as well as longitudinal vibrations. By making the natural transverse frequency widely different from the longitudinal, there is little coupling between the two sets of vibrations. However, if the dimensions at the end of the bar are small in comparison with the wavelength of the sound in the water, little acoustic radiation will occur and there is a danger of cavitation; the flaring is therefore introduced to improve the acoustic power output and hence the efficiency. Flaring does moreover lower the mechanical Q (about 20 in water when unflared, down to 5 if flared). Although there is of course a certain mismatch between nickel and water, the transducer element permits adequate acoustic coupling.

The transducer element of Fig. 10-5 operates in the $\frac{\lambda}{2}$ mode ($\frac{\lambda}{4}$ mode is achieved by keeping one end of the element rigid); as regards actual dimensions it must be remembered that the velocity of sound in nickel is much greater than in water. The element is supported at a vibration mode and since this is the position of maximum mechanical strain, the magnetizing coil should be concentrated around this region to provide maximum linkage with the flux which is most effective in producing magnetostriction.

A single coil may be used to excite a number of elements. The result of flaring is to bring the node nearer to the radiating end.

The element shown employs air-backed resonance in which the sponge rubber is non-porous but contains pockets of air. Severe mismatch occurs and there is almost total reflection of waves arising from the region of excitation. These reflected waves arrive back at the radiating face in phase with those which have travelled by the direct route, this virtually doubles the velocity of the radiating face and increases the acoustic power output.

The equivalent electrical circuit of an excited transducer element shown in Fig. 10-6.

To improve efficiency it is common to tune out the inductance by a capacitor and then match the remaining resistance to the output impedance of the sonar set.

The efficiency of a magnetostrictive transducer depends on the degree of the electromechanical coupling together with the eddy current and hysteresis losses, which increase rapidly as the fre-

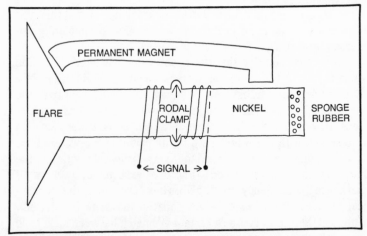

Fig. 10-5. Magnetostrictive transducer element.

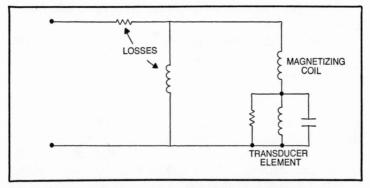

Fig. 10-6. Equivalent circuit of magnetostrictive transducer element.

quency is raised. Overall efficiency for a typical sonar set is approximately 40%, for example, 2 kW electrical power input for 800 W acoustic power output as measured by a calibrated hydrophone.

Piezo-Electric Transducer

The effect is linear and reversible (strain is directly proportional to the electric field applied across the crystal) and therefore no polarization is necessary (Fig. 10-7).

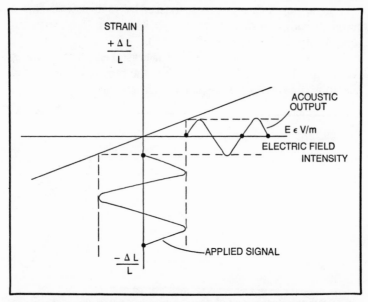

Fig. 10-7. Relationship between strain and electric field intensity for quartz.

The piezo-electric strain coefficient for quartz is 2.3×10^{-12} meters/volt.

In order to apply the electric field it is either necessary to coat the crystal surfaces with a metal film or enclose the crystal between conducting plates. Sea water must therefore not be allowed access to a piezo-electric element for two reasons; firstly it might corrode the metallic surfaces and secondly it would provide an alternative path for current to flow between the plates, thereby shorting out the element. The equivalent electrical circuit is shown in Fig. 10-8.

It is common practice to tune out the capacitance with an inductor and match the remaining resistance to the output impedance of the sonar set's final stage.

The Q of the crystal in air may well be several thousand but the loading effect on the crystal of producing acoustic radiation into water reduces the Q to about 5-10.

Where crystal transducers with a large radiating surface area are needed, it is usual to build the required unit in a mosaic of smaller elements. A typical mosaic construction consists of a number of similar elements mounted side by side and bonded to a back plate of steel.

At low frequencies the crystal elements required are very thick and need excessive driving voltages (order of kV). It is then desirable to operate a thin element in such a way that it resonates at a frequency lower than that characterized by its thickness. This is accomplished by bonding metal plates to its opposite faces to form a sandwich type of transducer (Fig. 10-9).

The simplest form consists of a crystal element which is bonded to a block of metal $\lambda/4$ thick at the required frequency of operation; this acts as an acoustic transformer and only imposes a

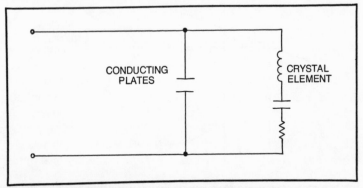

Fig. 10-8. Equivalent circuit of quartz transducer element.

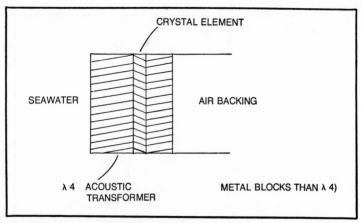

Fig. 10-9. Sandwich crystal element.

resistive load on the element. The element itself will be operated far below its normal resonance and will appear to present capacitive reactance. If an airbacked block of metal less than $\lambda/4$ in thickness is bonded to its other force, the loading it imposes on the element is inductive. By a suitable choice of dimensions the inductance of the load plate can be made to resonate with the capacitance of the element at the design frequency.

Quartz possesses many of the desirable properties of a transducer. It has a high Curie Temperature (573°C) and is stable both chemically and physically. It has a low temperature coefficient and can be easily worked. However, it has a high electrical impedance and low strain coefficient and therefore is not suitable for high power radiation. Typical overall efficiency for a quartz transducer is 80-90%.

Electrostrictive Transducers

All dielectric materials exhibit the phenomenon of electrostriction but in the class of dielectrics known as ferroelectrics, the effect is very pronounced. Within these materials electric dipoles are formed spontaneously which have a preferred orientation within certain localized regions of domains. Ordinarily these domains are randomly disposed and the overall electric moment of the material is zero. Application of an electric field, however, causes the domains to become aligned with the field and the physical dimensions of the material alter. The mechanical strain is proportional to the square of the applied field and is independent of the field's sense (Fig. 10-10).

253

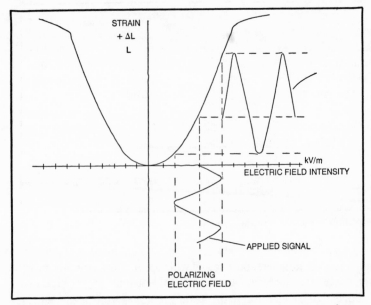

Fig. 10-10. Relationship between strain and electric field intensity for an electrostrictive transducer.

Since electrostrictive materials are inherently nonlinear, they must be polarized to give true transducer action and reversibility. This can be done by heating the material to a temperature at which the electrostrictive properties disappear (the Curie Temperature) and then allowing it to cool slowly while subjecting it to a high intensity electric field; however the degree of polarization tends to deteriorate with time.

Materials commonly employed for electrostrictive elements are barium titanate (combination of barium carbonate and titanium dioxide), and lead zirconate to which has been added a small amount of lead titanate.

For barium titanate the strain coefficient over the region of the applied signal is of the order of 100×10^{-12} meters/volt which is many times greater than the value for quartz. Therefore electrostrictive transducers are capable of producing acoustic powers of the order of kW (similar to magnetostrictive transducers); they have the advantages of being lighter and simpler in construction. However the Curie temperatures for barium titanate and lead zirconate are 120°C and 320°C and hence these transducers must be operated at lower temperatures than either quartz or nickel (Curie Temperatures of 573°C and 360°C respectively).

254

The electrostrictive transducer element is commonly in the form of a disc whose polarization causes to expand along its thickness and contract along its radius. Before polarization, conducting surfaces are included to produce the finished transducer elements. The equivalent circuit is as for the piezo-electric element except that the electrical impedance is much lower.

As with the piezo-electric effect it is important that sea-water is denied access to the element. The element with its chosen backing is mounted in an insulating liquid, usually caster oil, and coupled into the water by a thin aluminum diaphragm or by a "ρ c-rubber" membrane whose acoustic impedance matches that of sea-water. The latter method is gaining in popularity since it is possible to streamline the flow of water past the transducer.

More complex forms of sandwich construction are often used. In some the area of the radiating face is different from that of the rest of the sandwich and a conical matching section is then employed. In addition the sandwich construction may be multi-layered to increase the acoustic power radiated (ceramic elements driven in parallel).

With high power outputs the large amplitude vibrations may shatter the element; to prevent this a bolt is passed along the axis so that the transducer is prestressed (Fig. 10-11).

THE EFFECT OF OCEANOGRAPHY ON SONAR PERFORMANCE

Oceanography (the science of the sea) is a very extensive field of study involving both pure and applied science. Our concern is the

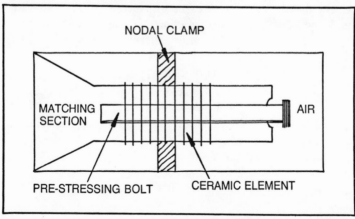

Fig. 10-11. Electrostrictive transducer element with sandwich construction.

propagation of acoustic energy, and the extent to which conditions in the sea affect the performance of sonar equipment.

Acoustic paths in the sea are never straight lines. The problem is the variation in acoustic velocity which occurs with charges in depth, temperature and salinity; variation in velocity causes refraction—bending—of the paths, and bending of the paths determines how much of the surrounding sea is under sonar surveillance for a given design of sonar equipment.

Velocity of Sound in the Sea

The velocity of sound is:

$$C = \sqrt{\frac{E}{\rho}}$$
Equation 10-8

where, C = velocity of sound
      E = elasticity of sea water
      ρ = density of sea water

Elasticity and density vary with
☐ temperature
☐ pressure or depth below the surface, and
☐ salinity

An empirical but more useful formula for the velocity of sound is

$$C = 4422 + 11.25T - 0.045T^2 + 0.018D + 4.3 (S - 34),$$
Equation 10-9

where C is the velocity of sound in feet per second. T is the temperature in degrees Fahrenheit, D is the depth in feet and S is the salinity in parts per thousand by weight. From this formula it can be seen that the velocity increases with increases in temperature, depth and salinity. The relative effect of changes in temperature, depth and salinity can be seen by differentiating equation (10-9) with respect to each variable in turn to give:

$$\Delta C = (11.25 - 0.9T) \Delta T$$
$$= 0.018 \Delta D$$
$$= 4.3 \Delta S.$$
Equation 10-10

Equation 10-10 shows a change in velocity of approximately 2 feet per second is produced by a
   1. change in temperature of:
        ¼° at 37°F
        ⅓° at 60°F
        ½° at 90°F
or 2. change in depth of 100 feet
or 3. change in salinity of half part per 1000.

Practical Considerations

Changes in velocity in the horizontal plane are insignificant compared to those in the vertical plane and are therefore ignored.

Vertical salinity gradients (changes in salinity with depth) are very small compared to vertical temperature gradients and may therefore be ignored.

From the figures quoted following the equation above it can be seen that the effect of change of depth on speed of sound is insignificant except when temperature changes are isothermal (zero) or near isothermal.

Refraction

Refraction—a change in the direction of the acoustic path (acoustic ray)—occurs when the path crosses the boundary between two regions of differing acoustic velocity.

In Fig. 10-12 C_1 = velocity of sound in the region above the boundary and C_2 = velocity of sound in the region below the boundary. If the acoustic path is from the region of C_1 to the region of C_2 and C_1 is greater than C_2, the acoustic path is refracted in the direction of the normal to the boundary on crossing the boundary as indicated. Conversely for a path from the region of C_2 to the region of C_1 it is refracted away from the normal on crossing the boundary. A useful way of remembering the direction of refraction is that the path will be refracted towards a lower velocity and away from a high velocity.

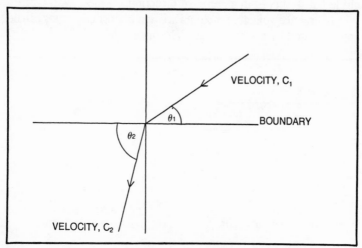

Fig. 10-12. Refraction of the acoustic path (velocity C_1 is greater than velocity C_2).

Snell's Law states $\dfrac{C_1}{C_2} = \dfrac{\cos\theta_1}{\cos\theta_2}$. An important point can be deduced from this: the more nearly the acoustic path approaches the normal to the boundary between the regions of differing velocity, the less it will be refracted on crossing the boundary.

Velocity Gradients

In practice, clearly defined boundaries between regions of differing velocity do not occur.

Figures 10-13A and B show a number of thin layers in which the acoustic velocity changes by a small identical amount from layer to layer (from the top downwards). For an acoustic path starting in the region of velocity C_1 as shown, refraction towards the normal occurs at each boundary. As the layers are made thinner and the change in acoustic velocity between successive layers is made smaller and smaller, the acoustic path approximates more and more closely to the arc of a circle. In the limit, the layers become vanishingly thin and the change in acoustic velocity from layer to layer becomes vanishingly small and the acoustic path becomes an arc of a circle. This then, is the acoustic path followed in a negative velocity gradient (the acoustic velocity decreases with increasing depth).

By following a similar argument, it can be shown that for a positive velocity gradient, the acoustic path is still the arc of the circle but is curved in an upward direction.

In practice velocity gradients are non-uniform, but they can be approximated by a series of straight lines.

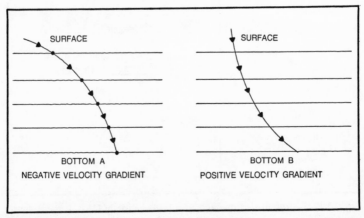

Fig. 10-13. Refraction of acoustic path in seawater.

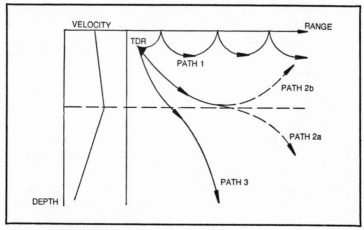

Fig. 10-14. The effect of the velocity maximum.

Velocity Maximum

After a velocity gradient has been approximated by a series of straight lines, it is frequently found that a point of velocity maximum (break-point) occurs. An acoustic path which is tangential to the break point level splits into two as shown in Fig. 10-14. An acoustic path which starts off at a relatively shallow angle such as path 1, is refracted as shown in an upward direction. Path 2a starts off as a relatively steep angle such that it becomes just tangential to the break point level; regarded as a limiting case of path 1, it too is reflected in an upward direction. Path 3 starts off at even steeper angle; it too is refracted in an upward direction but reaches the break point level at such an angle that it crosses the break point level and continues in a general downward direction. Path 2b starts off at the same angle as path 2a; regarded as a limiting case of path 3 and although tangenial at the break point level, it too crosses the break point level and continues in a general downward direction. The combination of paths 2a and 2b, i.e. a path which splits at the break point level is therefore the limiting case for both path 1 and path 3.

Temperature Gradients

The temperature of sea water in general decreases from the surface downwards. Practically all the change occurs in the top 3000 feet, and is most marked in the top 1000 feet; at 3000 feet the sea temperature becomes isothermal at 37°F which is the temperature of maximum density for seawater. As the surface temperature in temperate zones is 50 - 60°F and in the tropics is 85° - 90°F, quite considerable changes in sound velocity occur in going from the sea surface down to 3000 feet.

The Bathythermograph

The Bathythermograph is an instrument which is lowered over the stern of a ship and which produces a graph of temperature against depth on a smoked slide. The graph is approximated by a series of straight lines; from this, and taking into account the effect of pressure in isothermal regions, a velocity gradient as series of straight line approximations can be produced (Fig. 10-15). Some care and experience is necessary in order that important features on the Bathythermograph slides are not lost as a result of the straight line approximations.

Ray Diagrams

Ray diagrams show acoustic paths (acoustic rays) plotted as a graph of range depth. The acoustic paths occur in the vertical plane of the sea. It is important to remember that, conventionally, range is plotted to a much smaller scale than depth; consequently acoustic paths appear much more curved than they are in practice; for example, the radius of curvature of a path in an isothermal layer is of the order of 50 miles.

Certain simplifications are made in plotting ray diagrams:

1. The sea surface is assumed to be plane.

2. The beamwidth is assumed to be finite and the acoustic intensity is assumed to be uniform across the beam.

3. The break point level is assumed to be a plane.

Normally only the ray which marks the limit of range the critical ray—is plotted, but other rays may be added as required.

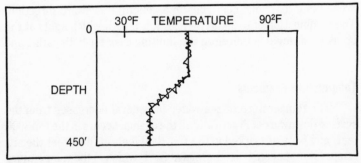

Fig. 10-15. The bathythermograph slide.

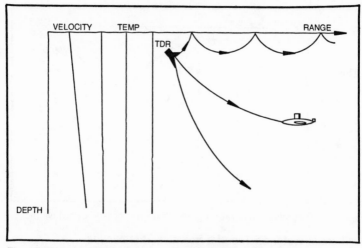

Fig. 10-16. Acoustic ray diagram for isothermal water.

It is assumed that all the parameters involved such as the depth of ocean, size of target etc, are very much greater than the acoustic wavelength. If this were not so, it would be necessary to use diffraction theory.

Isothermal Water

Neglecting any salinity variations, there will be a positive velocity gradient of 2 ft/sec per 100 ft due to the change of the pressure with the depth.

Acoustic rays will be refracted towards the surface so that the whole of the surrounding water may be insonified (Fig. 10-16). Reflections will occur at the surface of the sea and these will involve a certain energy loss governed by the sea state. Interference between direct and reflected rays will not normally be important since the acoustic radiation is pulsed.

Negative Gradient on Top of Isothermal Water

Due to the negative temperature gradient or thermocline, rays leaving the transducer will be bent towards the bottom (Fig. 10-17). There will be a limiting ray which just touches the surface and governs the maximum range available. Although a sonar set may be designed to cover up to 20,000 yds, its range may in fact be reduced to below 1000 yds. These bad conditions may be improved and the shadow zone reduced, by lowering the transducer; such is the case with the Variable Depth Sonar (V.D.S.) set.

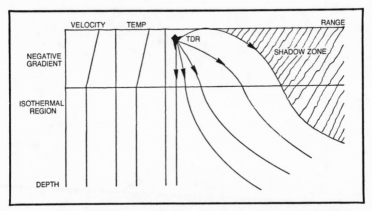

Fig. 10-17. Negative temperature gradient on top of isothermal water.

Isothermal Water on Top of a Negative Thermocline

These are the most common conditions encountered. In the top isothermal region rays will be refracted towards the surface; reflections will occur and there will be a surface duct formed with a range governed by the performance of the particular set, the frequency used and the loss per reflection (Fig. 10-18).

The limiting ray, which splits, will be tangential to the boundary between the top layer and the region of the negative thermocline. The upper split will give the maximum range along the surface duct since it will involve the least number of reflections. The onset of the shadow zone will be determined by the lower split so that below the surface layer, the range may only be a few thousand yards or less. Beneath the thermocline the rays are again bent towards the surface and there is a certain degree of focusing. Typically a region a few miles across and some 20 - 30 miles away may be insonified to give strong target echoes (convergent sonar).

The size of the shadow zone may be reduced by using the V.D.S. and lowering the transducer beneath the surface layer (Fig. 10-19).

One result is to form a sound channel in which the divergence is cylindrical and the intensity is therefore only inversely proportional to the range (as opposed to (range)^2 with spherical spreading). Hence by using such a channel, low frequency signals can be propagated over very long distances. This principle is used in Sound Fixing And Ranging in which a charge is exploded in a channel and the position fixed from the transit times involved with various listening stations (means of locating splash down point of ballistic missiles).

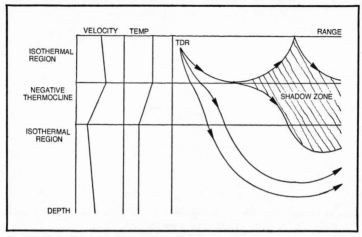

Fig. 10-18. Isothermal water on top of a negative thermocline.

During calm tropical afternoons there can be a severe negative thermocline at the surface; this may amount to a change of 50°F in the first 100 ft. This condition may be followed by an isothermal region and subsequently by a further negative thermocline (Fig. 10-20). With the transducer near the surface, the range available may possibly be limited to a few hundred yards. Again the V.D.S. will provide a considerable improvement provided the transducer is lowered beneath the isothermal region.

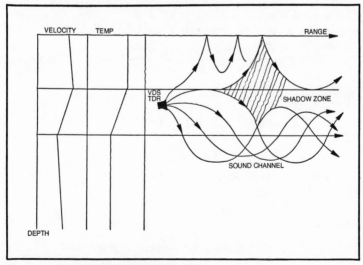

Fig. 10-19. The use of the variable depth sonar.

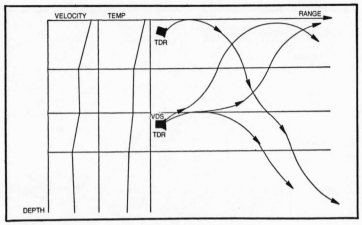

Fig. 10-20. Acoustic ray diagram for tropical conditions.

Bottom Bounce

It is possible to insonify the shadow zones by "bouncing" the acoustic pulse off the bottom. However such reflections can involve considerable losses dependent on the nature of the bottom, which may be absorbent mud, reflecting sand or scattering rocks.

A system using "bottom-bounce" requires an extremely large transducer which operates at low frequencies with a peak output power of the order of hundreds of kW.

CHAPTER SUMMARY

The Sound Wave

Intensity, I = Acoustic Pressure, P × Particle Velocity, V

$$= \frac{(\text{Acoustic Pressure, } P)^2}{\text{Specific Acoustic Impedance, } \rho C}$$

$$\frac{\text{Pressure, } P}{\text{Particle Velocity, } V} = \text{Specific Acoustic Impedance, } \rho C \; A\Omega$$

$$\text{Intensity, } I = 10 \log \frac{I}{I_{ref}} \; dB$$

$I_{ref} = 1 \; \mu$ bar in seawater.

Intensity of received echo is inversely proportional to $(\text{range})^4$.

Doppler Frequency Shaft

$$= F_s \times \frac{(V_s - V_T)}{C - V_s}$$

$$= 0.34 \; Hz/kHz/knot \text{ (one-way propagation)}$$

$$\approx 0.7 \; Hz/kHz/knot \text{ (two-way propagation)}$$

264

Velocity of Sound

Velocity of sound, $C = \sqrt{\dfrac{E}{\rho}}$ 5000 ft/sec in seawater

$C = 4422 + 11.25T - 0.045T^2 + 0.018\,D + 4.3\,(s - 34)$ ft/sec.

$C = (11.35 - 0.9T)\,\Delta T$

$\quad = 0.018\,\Delta D$

$\quad = 4.3\,\Delta S.$

Snell's Law: $\dfrac{C_1}{C_2} = \dfrac{\cos\theta_1}{\cos\theta_2}$

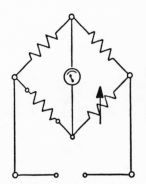

Chapter 11
Miscellaneous Topics

This chapter covers various items relating to electronic communications.

AC MACHINES

Alternator Frequency. The frequency generated by an alternator is directly proportional to the rotor speed and the number of pairs of poles which the rotor possesses. In equation form:

$$f = \frac{P}{2} \times \frac{N}{60} = \frac{PN}{120} \text{ or } N = \frac{120f}{P} \qquad \textbf{Equation 11-1}$$

where, f = generated frequency in Hz.

P = *total* number of poles

N = rotor speed in revolutions per minute (rpm)

Note that the frequency is independent of the number of phases.

Polyphase Induction Motor—Polyphase Synchronous Motor. When a polyphase supply is connected to a stator with P poles, a rotating magnetic field is created; the speed of rotation, N_s, is given by:

$$\text{Synchronous speed, } N_s = \frac{120f \text{ rpm}}{P} \qquad \textbf{Equation 11-2}$$

where f is the frequency of the polyphase supply. In the operation of an induction motor, it is necessary that the rotor speed N, shall be less than the synchronous speed, N_s. The difference between the speeds, $N_s - N$, is called the slip although it is more common to refer to the percentage slip, S, defined by:

$$\text{Percentage slip, } S = \frac{N_s - N}{N_s} \times 100\% \quad \textbf{Equation 11-3}$$

It follows that:

$$N = N_s \times (1 - \frac{S}{100}) \ , \ N_s = \frac{N}{1 - \frac{S}{100}} \quad \textbf{Equation 11-4}$$

The value of S depends on the load applied to the meter. On no-load conditions the slip may be as low as 0.1% but under loaded conditions, the slip increases although it rarely exceeds 10%. The polyphase *synchronous* motor also uses the principle of the rotating magnetic field but, in this case, the rotor must operate at the synchronous speed, N_s, given by

$$N_s = \frac{120f}{P} \quad \textbf{Equation 11-5}$$

The full rated load of an ac motor is measured in horsepower (hp) where 1 horsepower is equal to 746 watts. The motor efficiency is given by

$$\text{Percentage efficiency, } \eta = \frac{\text{Power output, } P_{out}}{\text{Power input, } P_{in}} \times 100\%$$

Equation 11-6

Since an ac motor will have a power factor, the power input, P_{in}, is:

$$P_{in} = E \times I \times \text{pf.}$$

It follows that the motor power output is

$$P_{out} = \frac{E \times I \times \text{pf} \times \eta}{100 \times 746} \text{ hp} \quad \textbf{Equation 11-7}$$

where, E = line voltage, I = line current.
For a dc motor, the percentage efficiency is again

$$\eta = \frac{P_{out}}{P_{in}} \times 100\%$$

but, $P_{in} = E \times I$ and therefore:

$$P_{out} = \frac{E \times I \times \eta}{100 \times 746} \text{ hp} \quad \textbf{Equation 11-8}$$

Example 11-1

The rotor of a three phase alternator has six poles and the speed is 1200 rpm. What is generated frequency?

Solution

$$\text{Generated frequency, } f = \frac{PN}{120} = \frac{6 \times 1200}{120} = 60 \text{ Hz.}$$

Example 11-2

A four-pole induction motor is connected to a three phase, 60 Hz supply. Under load the rotor speed is 1750 rpm. What is the value of the percentage slip?

Solution

$$\text{Synchronous speed, } N_s = \frac{120f}{P} \text{ rpm} = \frac{120 \times 60}{4} \text{ rpm}$$

$$= 1800 \text{ rpm}$$

$$\text{Percentage slip, } S = \frac{(1800 - 1750)}{1800} \times 100 = \frac{50}{18}$$

$$= 2.8\%, \text{ rounded off.}$$

Example 11-3

A six-pole synchronous motor is connected to a three phase, 60 Hz supply. What is the full load motor speed?

Solution

The synchronous motor can only operate at the synchronous speed, N_s.

$$N_s = \frac{120f}{P} = \frac{120 \times 60}{6} = 1200 \text{ rpm.}$$

Example 11-4

A 5 hp single phase induction motor is operated from a 110 V, 60 Hz supply. If the motor is 90% efficient and has a lagging power factor of 0.8, calculate the line current at the full rated load.

Solution

$$\text{Motor power output, } P_{out} = 5 \times 746 = 3730 \text{ W}$$

$$\text{Power input, } P_{in} = \frac{P_{out}}{\text{Percentage efficiency}} \times 100$$

$$= 3730 \times 100 \text{ W}$$

$$\text{Line current, } I = \frac{P_{in}}{E \times pf} = \frac{3730 \times 100}{90 \times 110 \times 0.8}$$

$$A = 47 \text{ A, rounded off.}$$

Example 11-5

A 4 hp dc motor is operated from a 120 V supply. If the motor is 85% efficient, what is the line current at the full rated load?

Solution

Motor power output, $P_{out} = 4 \times 746 = 3084$ W

Power input, $P_{in} = \dfrac{P_{out} \times 100}{\text{Percentage efficiency}} = \dfrac{3084}{85} \times 100$

Line current $= \dfrac{P_{in}}{E} = \dfrac{3084 \times 100}{85 \times 120}$

$A = 30$ A rounded off.

Example 11-6

A synchronous motor is operated from 220 V, 60 Hz, single-phase supply. The motor has a leading power factor of 0.75 and an efficiency of 70%. If the line current is 35 A, calculate the motor power output.

Solution

$$\text{Motor power output} = \frac{E \times I \times pf \times \eta}{100 \times 746}$$

$$= \frac{200 \times 35 \times 0.75 \times 70}{100 \times 746}$$

$$= 5.4 \text{ hp, rounded off.}$$

THE CRYSTAL

The Crystal. When a crystal such as quartz vibrates, an alternating voltage appears between a pair of opposite faces; this is called the piezoelectric effect. The fundamental frequency of vibration for a particular crystal is inversely proportional to the crystal's thickness and also depends on the type of cut. The crystal may be compared with a series LCR circuit with the inductance, capacitance and resistance related to equivalent physical properties of the crystal. The crystal itself is placed between metal surfaces (the holder) to which the positive feedback voltage is applied. Electrically the holder may be regarded as a capacitance (typically a few pFs) in parallel with the LCR circuit of the crystal; this equivalent circuit of the crystal and its holder is shown in Fig. 11-1.

Although a crystal's fundamental frequency is primarily determined by the thickness and the cut, the frequency may be varied slightly by connecting a small trimmer capacitor across the crystal and its holder. In addition the vibration of the crystal is complex and contains overtone frequencies; these are virtually harmonics of the fundamental frequency and it is mainly the odd overtones which are produced. The upper limit of the fundamental frequency is about 20 to 25 MHz and is determined by the minimum thickness to which a crystal may be cut without the danger of fracturing.

The Q of a crystal is normally several thousand (compared with 300 or less for a conventional LCR circuit) and this is one important reason for the high degree of frequency stability obtainable from a crystal oscillator. Another reason is the crystal's low temperature coefficient.

Temperature Coefficient. A change in temperature can cause a change in a crystal's resonant frequency. The crystal's temperature coefficient may be used to calculate the amount of frequency shift which can be expected from a given change in temperature. This coefficient is measured in Hz per MHz per degree Centigrade (parts per million per degree Centigrade) and may be either positive or negative. For example, if a crystal is marked as $-30/10^6/°G$, it means that if the temperature *increases* by one degree Centigrade, the *decrease* (because of the negative coefficient) will be 30 Hz for every megahertz of the crystal's operating frequency. Therefore the change in the crystal's operating frequency, Δf = value of the temperature coefficient (either positive or negative) × crystal frequency × temperature charge which is positive if the temperature is increasing and negative if the temperature is decreasing. Note that if the temperature coefficient is negative and the temperature is decreasing, the result will be an increase in frequency.

Since the frequency change, Δf, occurs at the crystal oscillator stage, the change in the output of the final rf stage will be Δf × the total produce factor of the frequency multiplier stages (if any).

To improve the frequency stability, the crystal may be enclosed in a thermostatically controlled oven. For broadcast stations the FCC has specified certain temperature tolerances at the crystal

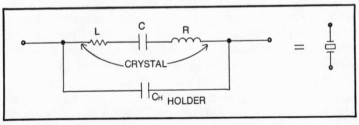

Fig. 11·1. The equivalent circuit of a crystal and its holder.

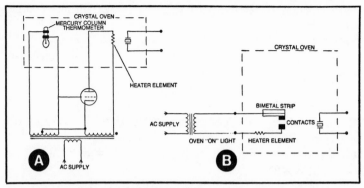

Fig. 11-2. Thermostats for Crystal ovens

position within the oven. If an X-cut or Y-cut crystal is used, the permitted tolerance is only ± 0.1° C, but with a low temperature coefficient crystal, the tolerance is ± 1.0°C. The form of thermostat may either be the mercury thermometer type or the less sensitive, but simpler and cheaper thermocouple variety (Figs. 11-2A and 11-2B). In Fig. 11-2A any increase of temperature above the tolerance limit will cause the triode to be permanently cut off so that the heater element will carry no current. If the temperature in Fig. 11-2B falls below the tolerance limit, the bimetal strip will cause the contacts to close and complete the circuit for the heater element. In the caring of crystals, precautions must be taken to insure that excessive voltage is not developed across the crystal since this may cause the crystal to fracture. If the crystal becomes dirty, it must be removed from its holder, held by the edges (not the faces) and then washed in either carbon tetrachloride, alcohol or soap and water.

Example 11-7

A Y-cut crystal has an operating frequency of 3750 kHz at a temperature of 20° C. If the crystal temperature coefficient is $-15/10^6/°C$, calculate the operating frequency at 25°C.

Solution

Since 3750 kHz = 3.75 MHz, $\Delta f = -15 \times 3.75 \times (25 - 20) = -281.25$ Hz. The operating frequency at 25°C = 3750 kHz -281.25 Hz = 3749.719 kHz, rounded off.

Example 11-8

A transmitter has an operating frequency of 22 MHz and uses a 2725 kHz crystal which is enclosed in an oven with the temperature at 65°C. If the crystal temperature coefficient is $+5/10^6/°C$ and the oven temperature decreases to 63°C, what is the transmitter output frequency?

Solution

The total product factor of the frequency multiplier stages is:

$$\frac{22 \text{ MHz}}{2725 \text{ kHz}} = 8$$

Change in the crystal operating frequency, $\Delta f = +5 \times 2.725 \times (63 - 65) = -27.25$ Hz.

Change in the transmitter output frequency $= 8 \times \Delta f = 8 \times (-27.25) = -218$ Hz

Transmitter output frequency $= 22$ MHz -218 Hz
$$= 21999.782 \text{ kHz.}$$

THE AUDIO SYSTEM OF A BROADCAST STATION

The units making up the audio system of a broadcast station may include:

Microphones. Every microphone consists basically of a diaphragm which vibrates in the presence of a sound wave and some form of transducer which is capable of converting the mechanical vibration into an electrical signal. Some microphones may have their diaphragms stretched in order to improve the frequency response; this is achieved by making the diaphragm's natural resonant frequency higher than the upper limit of the audio range.

Dynamic or moving coil microphone (Fig. 11-3). Joined with the diaphragm is a circular coil whose turns pass between the poles of a permanent magnet. When the diaphragm vibrates, the coil cuts the magnetic flux so that there is an induced voltage which is the electrical equivalent of the sound wave. This type of microphone is commonly used in broadcast studios.

Features:

(a) Low output impedance.

(b) Wide frequency response.

(c) No power supply necessary.

(d) Relatively low level of output.

(e) Relatively unaffected by humidity and temperature.

(f) Low hum.

(g) Light weight but strong construction.

Carbon Microphone (Fig. 11-4). Attached to the diaphragm is a "button" which contains fine carbon granules. Vibration of the diaphragm varies the pressure on the granules and alters the resistance of the button. A low voltage (6 V) battery is connected in

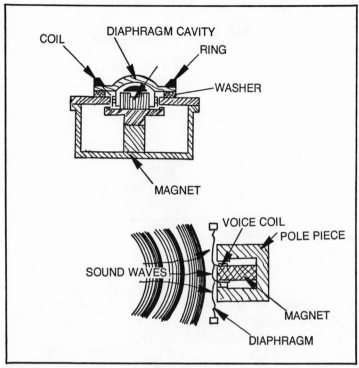

Fig. 11-3. The dynamic microphone.

series with the button and the primary of an audio transformer. The primary current and therefore the secondary voltage will then correspond to the movement of the diaphragm created by the sound wave.

Features:

(a) Very high sensitivity associated with a high level of output.

(b) Poor frequency response which is the main reason why the carbon microphone is no longer widely used.

(c) Background hissing present in the microphone's output.

(d) Carbon granules subject to "packing" with excessive moisture (the microphone must not be allowed to get wet).

(e) Low output impedance (100Ω or less).

(f) Inexpensive.

Crystal Microphone (Fig. 11-5). In this type the transducer is commonly a series of Rochelle salt crystals which display the piezoelectric effect and are wax-impregnated in an airtight container.

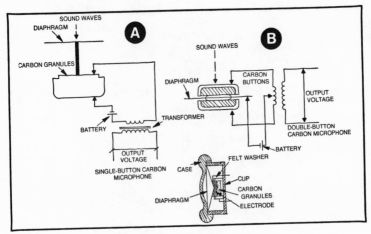

Fig. 11-4. The carbon microphone.

Features:

(a) Adversely affected by excessive heat (the microphone must be protected from hot sunlight), shock and humidity (Rochelle salt dissolves in water).

(b) Good frequency response.

(c) Absence of background noise.

(d) High impedance output which may allow hum pickup.

(e) No power supply required.

Ceramic Microphone. Principle and construction are similar to the crystal microphones except for the use of certain ceramic materials as opposed to Rochelle salt. The ceramic materials act as transducers in the same way as the crystals but are less affected by extremes of temperature, humidity and shock.

Velocity (Ribbon) Microphone (Fig. 11-6). This type is commonly used in a broadcast studio. The diaphragm is a very light aluminum ribbon which is allowed to move freely in a magnetic field. When the sound wave causes a pressure difference on opposite sides of the ribbon, it causes the ribbon to vibrate. The corresponding audio electrical signal is then induced into the ribbon.

However, the output impedance of this type of microphone is extremely low and therefore the signal is fed to a step-up transformer which not only raises the output level to a practical value but also matches the low microphone impedance to the impedance of a standard audio line.

Features:

(a) Blasting or wind may effect the ribbon which is delicate: its use is confined to an indoor studio.

274

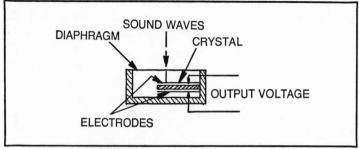

Fig. 11-5. The crystal microphone.

(b) No power supply required.
(c) Low level of background noise.
(d) Good frequency response.
(e) High level of output.
(f) Not affected by temperature and humidity.

The microphones as described may be omnidirectional in which case sound is picked up equally from all directions. A good example is a round table discussion where the microphone with its circular pickup pattern is positioned at the center of the table. However microphones may also be designed for bi-directional or unidirectional purposes. A bi-directional microphone has equal pickup from *two* horizontal directions which are normally 180° apart; this would be used for a dialogue in which the two speakers

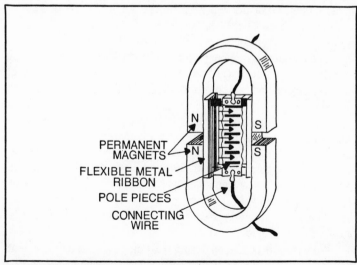

Fig. 11-6. The velocity (ribbon) microphone.

275

are sitting at opposite sides of a table. However a singer facing a large audience would require a unidirectional (one direction) microphone where there would be maximum pickup from the singer's direction but virtually no pickup from the audience. Yet other microphones use a "heart-shaped" or cardiod pattern which is suitable when the sound source covers a wide area, for example a large orchestra. This type of pattern then allows only minimum pickup from the position of the audience which is to the rear of the microphone.

When two microphones feed into a particular mixer, it is important that both outputs are phased so that the two voltages are instantaneously additive and do not oppose or cancel each other. This would be the situation when microphones are symmetrically placed with respect to a singer; without correct phasing there would be a reduction in the total audio output together with varying degrees of distortion.

Tape Recorders. This is a brief description about some of the problems associated with tape recorders. For example, if the playback head is oxidized or dirty, the audio output and the high frequency response are reduced. Distortion known as flutter or wow is the result and there is also an increase in the noise level. To prevent the dirt from causing wear on the playback head, cleaning may be carried out by using carbon tetrachloride or alcohol. Apart from dirt or oxide, there are a number of other possible reasons for high frequency loss. These include

(a) Excessive or uneven wear on the surface of the head.

(b) Poor contact between the tape and head.

(c) Misalignment between the tape and the head.

The frequency response of a tape recorder may be measured by using an accurately calibrated audio generator. Sine waves of various frequencies but constant amplitude are recorded and then played back.

The overall response curve is then obtained by reading the audio output for each frequency on a VU meter.

Turntables. Common forms of turntable distortion are referred to as rumble and wow. Rumble is the result of turntable vibration and is a low frequency which may either be constant or may vary randomly in a series of pulses. It can be caused by defective shock mountings or a turntable which is not correctly balanced and leveled.

Wow may be produced during recording but at the turntable it is caused by changes in velocity between the groove on the record and the stylus (in a broadcast station a diamond stylus is normally used since this type provides high-quality reproduction with minimum wear and distortion). The effect occurs once for each revolution of the record and consists of a low frequency modulation which is caused either by an eccentric record/ turntable or defects in the motor and its drive mechanism.

To check turntable speed a stroboscopic disc is illuminated by a neon light operated from the 60 Hz line supply. The disc displays groups of bars in the form of circles for each standard speed. When checking a particular speed, the corresponding group of circles is observed; the bars will then appear to be stationary if the speed is correct.

When determining the frequency response of the turntable pickup, a standard test record is used. This contains a number of constant amplitude tones which are played in sequence. The output of the pickup's amplifier is measured for each tone and the overall frequency response can then be plotted.

Figure 11-7 shows part of the audio system of a broadcast station. The output of each microphone, tape recorder or turntable is fed into that particular channel's pre-amplifier which is a high gain audio stage used to improve the signal-to-noise ratio at the mixer. This unit contains individual attenuators for each channel and is responsible for creating the program signal. Following the mixer stage is another variable attenuator, the master gain control, which determines the level of the composite signal before it enters the program amplifier.

The output of the program amplifier is monitored by the VU meter which may be desensitized by an attenuator T-pad, and is

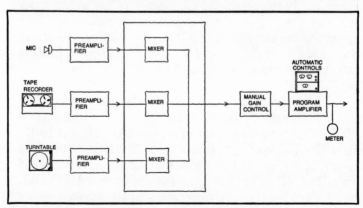

Fig. 11-7. The audio system of a broadcast station.

then fed to further amplifier stages which climax in the modulator. Such audio stages contain automatic controls which are known by many names such as automatic gain control (agc) limiter, compression amplifier or loudness controller. All these basically serve two purposes; to raise the average audio level and at the same time limit the audio peaks to prevent excessive modulation. Every operator must know how to adjust both manual and automatic controls in the event such action is necessary to keep the modulation level below the prescribed limits.

If the studio is located at a distance from the transmitter, the program (line) amplifier can be fed into a 600 ohm program transmission line which will link the transmitter to the studio. Throughout the audio system the lines may contain equalizers to avoid frequency distortion.

The gains of the pre-amplifier and the program amplifier, the attenuations of the mixer stage and the master gain control are all normally expressed in dBs. Since these units are cascaded, the overall gain of the system may be obtained by taking the algebraic sum of the individual gains and losses.

Line Equalizers. An audio transmission line of appreciable length will act as a low pass filter because of its distributed inductance and capacitance. The high frequency of a signal such as music will be attenuated and the result will be distortion. The purpose of a line equalizer is therefore to eliminate the distortion and achieve a response which is virtually constant over the required audio range, typically 50 to 15000 Hz.

A line equalizer is a high pass filter which will attenuate the low frequencies by the same amount as the line attenuates the high frequencies. By this means the combination of line and equalizer will reduce the frequency distortion to a minimum level. With program transmission lines the equalizers are inserted at the studio and are adjusted for the required flat response. Common forms of equalizer circuit are shown in Fig. 11-8.

Example 11-9

In a studio broadcast system, a particular microphone has an output capability of −60 VU and feeds a pre-amplifier with a gain of 40dB. The following stage is the mixer which has a loss of 16 dB. What is the signal input to the program amplifier? If the output of the program amplifier is +7VU, calculate the output of the amplifier and its gain. If the VU meter circuit uses a desensitizing pad of −10 dB, what is the reading of the VU meter and what is the voltage across its terminals?

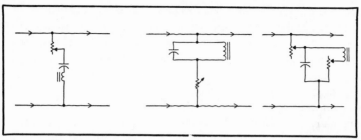

Fig. 11-8. Line equalizer circuits.

Solution

The signal input to the program amplifier $= -60 + 40 - 16 = -36$ VU.

Since the input to the program amplifier is -36 VU, the gain of the amplifier is $36 + 7 = 43$ dB. A level of $+7$ VU is equivalent to a power of 7dB above a reference level of 1mW. The power output of the program amplifier is antilog$_{10}$ 7 mW $= 5$ mW, rounded off.

A power level of $+7$ VU is applied to the VU meter circuit and the attenuator pad has a value of -10 dB. The power level indicated on the VU meter $= +7 - 10 = -3$ VU.

A level of -3 VU is equivalent to a power of 0.5 mW which is developed across a 600 Ω line. The voltage is $\sqrt{0.5 \times 10^{-3} \times 600}$ V $= \sqrt{3 \times 10^5}$ mV $= 548$ mV, rounded off.

Example 11-10

The power output of a pre-amplifier is -25 dBm, and the following mixer stage and the master gain control have a total loss of 12 dB. It is required to feed $+10$ dBm to the program transmission line. Assuming that the input and output resistances of the program amplifier are equal, what is the voltage gain of the program amplifier?

Solution

Power input to the program amplifier $= -25 - 12 = -37$ dB. The power gain of the program amplifier $= +10 - (-37) = 47$ dB. Voltage gain of the amplifier is:

$$\text{Antilog}_{10}\left(\frac{17}{20}\right) = \text{antilog}_{10}\,(2.35) = 224.$$

THE SUPERHETERODYNE RECEIVER

Frequency Conversion to the IF. Figure 11-9 represents a block diagram of the initial stages in either an AM or an FM superheterodyne broadcast receiver. The purpose of the mixer and the local oscillator is to achieve frequency conversion; in this

279

process, the receiver is tuned to a particular signal and the carrier frequency is then converted to a fixed intermediate frequency (IF) which is 455 kHz in the AM broadcast. Therefore, for all incoming carrier frequencies, the IF stages always operate on the same fixed intermediate frequency and consequently may be designed to provide high selectivity and sensitivity.

As indicated in Fig. 11-9 the rf tuned circuits of the initial amplifier, the mixer and the local oscillator, are mechanically ganged so that as the rf amplifier and the input circuit to the mixer are tuned to the desired signal frequency, f_s, the local oscillator stage generates a frequency, f_{LO}, and produces a continuous rf output, which differs in frequency from the incoming carrier by the value of the IF (f_{IF}).

The output of the local oscillator and the incoming signal are both fed to the mixer stage which contains a non-linear device. In general, when two signals of frequencies f_s and f_{LO} are mixed together (this mixing process is sometimes called "heterodyning" or "beating"), the result contains components at the frequencies f_s, f_{LO}, $f_s + f_{LO}$ and $f_{LO} - f_s$ (or $f_s - f_{LO}$).

The difference frequency, $f_{LO} - f_s$ (or $f_s - f_{LO}$), will be equal to the IF; the mixer output circuit may therefore be tuned to the intermediate frequency and this will automatically eliminate the three unwanted frequencies (f_s, f_{LO}, $f_s + f_{LO}$) as well as other components created by the mixing process. During the frequency conversion, the modulation originally carried by the signal, f_s, is transferred to the IF component in the mixer output. However, if the local oscillator frequency is greater than the incoming signal frequency (known as "tracking above"), the upper sidebands carried by f_s will become the lower sidebands in the IF stages and vice-versa.

If the local oscillator frequency tracks above the incoming signal frequency,

$$f_{LO} = f_s + f_{IF} \text{ and } f_s = f_{LO} - f_{IF}, \, f_{IF} = f_{LO} - f_s$$

If the local oscillator frequency tracks below the incoming signal frequency.

$$f_{LO} = f_s - f_{IF} \text{ and } f_s = f_{LO} + f_{IF}, \, f_{IF} = f_s - f_{LO}$$

If an AM broadcast receiver, the local oscillator always tracks above in order to reduce the required size of the local oscillator tuning capacitor. However, in TV and FM broadcast receivers, which operate in the vhf and uhf bands, the local oscillator may track either above or below.

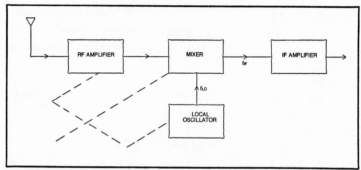

Fig. 11-9. Frequency conversion in the superheterodyne receiver.

For the reception of continuous wave (CW) signals, the receiver will contain a beat frequency oscillator (BFO). The output of this oscillator and the IF signal are heterodyned in the receiver's second detector stage. The resulting difference frequency is an audio note (typically 1000 Hz) which is heard on the loudspeaker for Morse code reception.

Image Channel. Consider that a superheterodyne receiver is tuned to a carrier frequency of 640 kHz in the AM broadcast band. Since the IF is 455 kHz, the local oscillator will generate $640 + 455 = 1095$ kHz. Assume that there exists an unwanted signal whose carrier frequency is $1095 + 455 = 1550$ kHz (which also lies within the AM broadcast band of 535 kHz to 1605 kHz). If this signal is sufficiently strong to reach the mixer stage, it will beat with the local oscillator output, and its carrier frequency will also be converted to the IF. Once this has occurred, the IF stages will be unable to separate the wanted and the unwanted signals; both will be detected and both will be heard on the loudspeaker. The unwanted signal of 1550 kHz is an example of an image channel since its frequency is the image of the wanted signal in the "mirror" of the local oscillator frequency (the frequency of the wanted signal is the same amount below the local oscillator frequency as the image channel is above). The frequency of an image channel therefore differs from the wanted carrier frequency by an amount equal to twice the IF. The frequency of the image channel is

$$f_s + (2 \times f_{IF}) = f_{LO} + f_{IF}$$

Equation 11-9

if the local oscillator is tracking above, or is

$$f_s - (2 \times f_{IF}) = f_{LO} - f_{IF}$$

Equation 11-10

for tracking below.

Example 11-11

A superheterodyne AM broadcast receiver whose IF is 455 kHz, is tuned to a station operating on 980 kHz. What is the frequency generated by the local oscillator?

Solution

Since the receiver is used for AM broadcast, the local oscillator frequency must be tracking above the signal frequency. Therefore the local oscillator frequency is:

$$f_{LO} = f_s + f_{IF} = 980 + 455 = 1435 \text{ kHz.}$$

Example 11-12

When a superheterodyne receiver is tuned to 3.12 MHz, its local oscillator generates 3.77 MHz. If the receiver is now retuned to 4.36 MHz, calculate the new frequency of the local oscillator?

Solution

The local oscillator is tracking above and the value of the IF is 3.77 − 3.12 = 0.65 MHz = 650 kHz. When the receiver is retuned to 4.36 MHz, the new frequency of the local oscillator is 4.36 + 0.65 = 5.01 MHz.

Example 11-13

A superheterodyne AM broadcast receiver with an IF of 455 kHz is tuned to receive a station operating on 670 kHz. Under these conditions, what is the frequency of the image channel?

Solution

In an AM broadcast receiver the frequency of the local oscillator is tracking above the signal frequency and the frequency of the image channel is

$$f_s + (2 \times f_{IF}) = 670 + 910 = 1580 \text{ kHz.}$$

Example 11-14

When a superheterodyne receiver is tuned to 4.68 MHz, interference is experienced from an image channel operating on 5.78 MHz. What is the value of the intermediate frequency?

Solution

The frequency of the image channel differs from the frequency of the desired signal by twice the value of the IF. The value of the intermediate frequency is therefore:

$$\frac{5.78 - 4.68}{2} = \frac{1.1}{2} = 0.55 \text{ MHz} = 550 \text{ kHz.}$$

Example 11-15

When an FM receiver is tuned to 104.9 MHz, its local oscillator is generating 94.2 MHz. If the receiver is retuned to 99.8 MHz, calculate the frequency of the image channel.

Solution

The local oscillator is tracking below and the value of the intermediate frequency is $104.9 - 94.2 = 10.7$ MHz. When the receiver is retuned to 99.8 MHz, the frequency of the image channel is $f_s - (2 \times f_{IF}) = 99.8 - (2 \times 10.7) = 78.4$ MHz.

FREQUENCY AND POWER TOLERANCES

A radio station is assigned a particular carrier frequency at which the station must be operated within a certain tolerance. Such tolerances may be expressed either as a percentage of the assigned frequency or as a particular number of Hz.

Tolerance in Hz = ± Assigned carrier frequency ×

$$\frac{\text{Percentage tolerance}}{100} \qquad \textbf{Equation 11-11}$$

$$\text{Percentage tolerance} = \pm \frac{\text{Tolerance in Hz}}{\text{Assigned carrier frequency}} \times 100\%$$

$$\textbf{Equation 11-12}$$

In addition to a frequency tolerance, the radio station must also maintain its rf operating power within certain limits. The power tolerance for AM and FM broadcast stations is $+5\%$ to -10% while that of a TV broadcast stations is $+10\%$ to -20%.

Example 11-16

A particular radio station is assigned a carrier frequency of 29.75 MHz and is allowed a frequency tolerance of $\pm 0.002\%$. What is this tolerance expressed in Hz?

Solution

$$\text{Tolerance} = \pm 29.75 \times 10^6 \times \frac{0.002}{100} = \pm \underline{595} \text{ Hz.}$$

Example 11-17

A radio station has an assigned frequency of 45.5 MHz and a frequency tolerance of ± 2275 Hz. What is this tolerance expressed as a percentage?

Solution

$$\text{Percentage tolerance} = \pm \frac{2275}{45.5 \times 10^6} \times 100$$

$$= \pm 50 \times 100 \times 10^{-6} = \pm \underline{0.005\%}$$

Example 11-18

A AM transmitter operating on 32 MHz is permitted a frequency tolerance of $\pm 0.005\%$. If the multiplier stages following the master oscillator consist of 3 doublers, what is the maximum frequency variation allowed in the oscillator stage?

Solution

The carrier has a maximum permitted frequency variation of $\pm$ $\frac{0.005}{100} \times 32 \times 10^6$ Hz $= \pm 1600$ Hz. The total product factor of the frequency multiplier stages is equal to $2 \times 2 \times 2 = 8$. The maximum frequency variation allowed in the oscillator is therefore:

$$\pm \frac{1600}{8} = \pm 200 \text{ Hz}$$

Example 11-19

A standard AM broadcast station is assigned an operating power of 25 kW. While keeping within the required tolerance limits, what is the power range permitted?

Solution

A standard AM broadcast station is allowed to transmit its power output from 10% below,

$$25 - \frac{10 \times 25}{100} = 22.5 \text{ kW.}$$

to 5% above,

$$25 + \frac{5 \times 25}{100} = 26.25 \text{ kW}$$

Note that the same percentage power tolerances apply to FM broadcast stations.

Example 11-20

The visual transmitter of a TV broadcast station is assigned an operating power of 25 kW. While keeping within the required tolerance limits, what is the power range permitted?

Solution

Both the visual and aural transmitters of a TV broadcast station are required to transmit their power outputs from 20% below,

$$25 - \frac{20 \times 25}{100} = 20 \text{ kW}$$

to 10% above,

$$25 + \frac{10 \times 25}{100} = 27.5 \text{ kW}$$

Example 11-21

What is the permitted power range of a 10 watt noncommercial education FM broadcast station?

Solution

The operating power of a 10 watt (or less) noncommercial educational FM broadcast station must not exceed 105% of the authorized value; no lower limit is specified. The upper limit is therefore

$$\frac{105}{100} \times 10 = 10.5 \text{ watts.}$$

THE FREQUENCY MONITOR

The frequency tolerance of an AM broadcast station is ± 20 Hz. The FCC requires that every broadcast station has a means of determining the number of Hz by which the actual radiated carrier frequency differs from the assigned value. Such a device has to be approved by the FCC and is known as a frequency monitor; this auxiliary unit contains a crystal-controlled oscillator which is entirely separate from the AM transmitter. The amount by which the carrier frequency is too high or too low is shown on a frequency deviation indicator which must be checked at intervals during the broadcast day and the reading entered in the transmitter log.

Periodically the accuracy of the frequency monitor is measured. An external check is made of the radiated carrier frequency and the result is compared with the simultaneous reading of the frequency monitor. The error in the frequency monitor can then be corrected by adjusting the monitor oscillator frequency (although the oscillator is crystal-controlled, the frequency can be varied a few Hz by adjusting the value of a trimmer capacitor across the crystal). The error in the frequency monitor = (the deviation (positive for "high", negative for "low") from the assigned frequency as recorded by the frequency monitor) minus (the deviation (positive for "high", negative for "low") as indicated by the external frequency check).

Example 11-21

An external frequency check of an AM broadcast station carrier reveals that at a particular time the carrier frequency was 8 Hz low. The transmitter log showed for the same time, the carrier frequency was 10 Hz high. What was the error in the station frequency monitor?

Solution

Error in the frequency monitor = + 10 Hz − (−8 Hz)

= + 18 Hz or 18 Hz high

Example 11-22

At a particular time the log of an AM broadcast station showed that the carrier frequency was 10 Hz low. An external frequency check made at the same time, indicated that the carrier frequency was 7 Hz low. What was the frequency monitor reading?

Solution

The error in the frequency monitor was $- 10\,Hz - (-7\,Hz) = -3\,Hz$ or the frequency monitor was reading 3 Hz low.

HETERODYNE FREQUENCY METER

This method of measuring an unknown frequency (kHz to a few hundred MHz) uses a combination of a variable frequency calibrated oscillator and a mixer detector stage (Fig. 11-10). The unknown frequency, f_u, and the output of the variable frequency oscillator, f_o, are fed to the mixer/detector stage. The heterodyne process then creates a component at the difference frequency, $f_o - f_u$ or $f_u - f_o$ and, provided this difference frequency is within the audio range, the output of the mixer/detector stage can be heard with a suitable loud-speaker or a set of headphones. If the tuning capacitor of the variable frequency oscillator (vfo) is now adjusted so that the pitch of the difference or beat frequency becomes lower and lower, a null or zero beat condition will eventually occur and the difference between f_o and f_u is then less than 20 Hz (the lower limit of frequencies which can be detected by the human ear). For greater accuracy, the VFO may be amplitude modulated by a 400 Hz tone. When the two frequencies f_o and f_u are very close, the amplitude of the tone will wax and wane at a rate equal to their difference frequency so that, by adjusting the tuning capacitor until the volume of the tone is constant, f_o will be made exactly equal to f_u. Since the frequency output of the VFO has been calibrated as a function of the dial setting of the tuning capacitor, the value of f_u may be determined.

Calibration of the VFO is achieved with the aid of the stable harmonies from a 1.0 MHz crystal oscillator incorporated within the frequency meter. Moreover, if a suitable HF receiver is available, certain harmonics of the crystal oscillator may be checked against the primary frequency standard station WWV which radiates signals on 5, 10, 15, 20, 25 and 30 MHz and is maintained by the National Bureau of Standards in Boulder, Colorado. The frequency of the crystal oscillator may then be corrected by adjusting a trimmer capacitor across the crystal. The calibration information is finally presented in the form of a chart in which certain dial settings are shown to correspond to particular listed frequencies. As an example, the spacing between adjacent frequencies may be constant at 100 Hz, but when the unknown frequency falls between

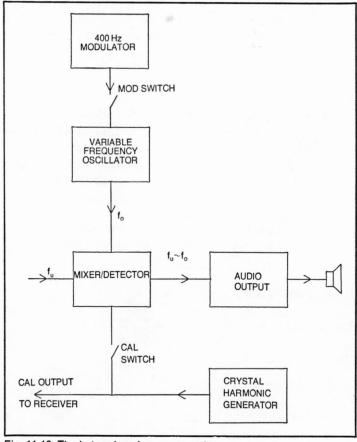

Fig. 11-10. The heterodyne frequency meter.

two adjacent listed frequencies, its value may be determined by the method of interpolation.

If dial settings of d_1 and d_2 correspond to the listed frequencies of f_1 and f_2, then a dial reading, d_3, which is intermediate between d_1 and d_2, will correspond to a frequency, f_3, given by

$$f_3 = f_1 + \frac{(d_3 - d_1)}{(d_2 - d_1)} \times (f_2 - f_1) \quad \textbf{Equation 11-13}$$

or,

$$f_3 = f_2 - \frac{(d_2 - d_3) \times (f_2 - f_1)}{(d_2 - d_1)} = \frac{d_2 f_1 + d_3 f_2 - d_3 f_1 - d_1 f_2}{(d_2 - d_1)}$$

Equation 11-14

Example 11-23

In the calibration chart of a heterodyne frequency meter, the dial settings of 153.4 and 154.6 correspond to listed frequencies of 12439.6 kHz and 12439.7 kHz. The frequency to be measured produces a zero beat at a dial reading of 153.9. What is the value of this frequency?

Solution

A change in the dial setting of $154.6 - 153.4 = 1.2$ corresponds to a frequency change of $12439.7 - 12439.6 = 0.1$ kHz $= 100$ Hz. Assuming a linear relationship between the changes in dial setting and frequency (the principle behind interpolation), a change of 1.0 in dial setting is equivalent to a frequency change of:

$$\frac{100 \text{ Hz}}{1.2}$$

Between 153.4 and 153.9 there is a dial reading difference of $153.9 - 153.4 = 0.5$ which will represent a change in frequency of:

$$\frac{100 \times 0.5}{1.2} = 42 \text{ Hz}$$

The measured frequency is therefore,

$$12439.6 \text{ kHz} + 42 \text{ Hz} = 12439.642 \text{ kHz}$$

Alternatively, $f_1 = 12439.6$ kHz, $f_2 = 12439.7$ kHz, $d_1 = 153.4$, $d_2 = 154.6$ and $d_3 = 153.9$.
Then the measured frequency is:

$$f_3 = 12439.6 + \frac{(153.9 - 153.4) \times (12439.7 - 12439.6)}{(154.6 - 153.4)}$$

$$= 12439.6 + \frac{0.5 \times 0.1}{1.2}$$

$$= 12439.6 + 0.042$$

$$= 12439.642 \text{ kHz}$$

Example 11-24

The calibration chart of a heterodyne frequency meter should show the following:

Listed Frequency	Dial Setting
2971 kHz	753.4
2972 kHz	759.8

What is the frequency corresponding to a dial reading of 757.7?

Solution

The frequency corresponding to 757.7 is

$$2972 - \frac{(759.8 - 757.7)(1 \text{ kHz})}{(759.8 - 753.4)} = 2972 - \frac{2.1}{6.4} = 2971.672 \text{ kHz}$$

Example 11-25

The second harmonic of a transmitter output frequency produces a zero beat on a heterodyne frequency meter when the dial reading is 1703.8. When the meter is calibrated against a secondary frequency standard, dial settings of 1701.6 and 1705.9 are equivalent to frequencies of 4735 kHz and 4736 kHz respectively. What is the transmitter output frequency?

Solution

The frequency of the second harmonic is:

$$4735 + \frac{(1703.8 - 1701.6)\,(1\text{ kHz})}{1705.9 - 1701.6} = 4735 + \frac{2.2}{4.3}$$

$$= 4735.512 \text{ kHz, rounded off.}$$

The transmitter output frequency is:

$$\frac{4735.512}{2} = 2367.756 \text{ kHz}$$

CHAPTER SUMMARY

AC Machines

$$\text{Alternator frequency, } f = \frac{PN}{120}$$

$$\text{Synchronous speed of ac motors} = \frac{120\,f}{P}\,\text{rpm}$$

$$\text{Percentage slip of induction motor, } S = \frac{N_s - N}{N_s} \times 100\%$$

$$\text{Percentage efficiency, } \eta = \frac{P_{out}}{P_{in}} \times 100\%$$

$$\text{Output power} = \frac{E \times I \times pf \times \eta}{100 \times 746}\,\text{hp.}$$

Crystal

Crystal Oscillator Frequency Shift
= Temperature Coefficient × Frequency is
MHz × Temperature Change in °C
Output Frequency Shift
= Oscillator Frequency Shift × Total Product Factor of the Frequency Multiplier Stages.

Superheterodyne Receiver

$$F_0 = F \pm F_{IF}$$

Frequency of the Image Channel $= F_s \pm (2 \times F)$

$$= F_{LO} \pm F_{IF}$$

Frequency Tolerance

Tolerance is Hz $= \pm$ Assigned Carrier Frequency $\times \dfrac{\text{percentage tolerance}}{100}$

Percentage Tolerance $= \pm \dfrac{\text{Tolerance in Hz}}{\text{Assigned Carrier Frequency}} \times 100\%$

Frequency Monitor

Frequency Monitor Error

= (deviation from the assigned Frequency as recorded by the Frequency Monitor) − (deviation as indicated by the external frequency check)

Heterodyne Frequency Meter

Measured Frequency, $F3 = F1 + \dfrac{(d_3 - d_1)\,(F_2 - F1)}{(d_2 - d_1)}$

$$= F2 - \dfrac{(d_2 - d_3)\,(F_2 - F_1)}{d_2 - d_1}$$

$$= \dfrac{d_2 F_1 + d_3 F_2 - d_3 F_1 - d_1 F_2}{d_2 - d_1}$$

Appendix A
Semiconductor
Letter Symbols

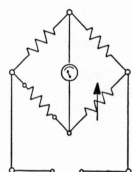

Letter symbols used in solid state circuits are those proposed as standard for industry, or are special symbols not included as standard. Semiconductor symbols consists of a basic letter with subscripts, either alphabetical or numerical, or both, in accordance with the following rules:

☐ A capital (upper case) letter designates external circuit parameters and components, large-signal device parameters, and maximum (peak), average (dc), or root-mean-square values of current, voltage, and power (I, V, P, etc.)

☐ Instantaneous values of current, voltage, and power, which vary with time, and small-signal values are represented by the lower case (small) letter of the proper symbol (i, v, p, i_e, v_{eb}, etc.).

☐ DC values, instantaneous total values, and large signal values, are indicated by capital subscripts i_C, I_C, v_{EB}, V_{EB}, P_C, etc.).

☐ Alternating component values are indicated by using lower case subscripts: note the examples i_c, I_c, v_{eb}, V_{eb}, P_c, p_c.

☐ When it is necessary to distinguish between maximum, average, or root-mean-square values, maximum or average values may be represented by the addition of a subscript m or av; example are i_{cm}, I_{CM}, I_{cav}, i_{CAV}.

☐ For electrical quantities, the first subscript designates the electrode at which the measurement is made.

☐ For device parameters, the first subscript designates the element of the four-pole matrix; examples are I or i for input, O or o for output, F or f for forward transfer, and R or r for reverse transfer.

☐ The second subscript normally designates the reference electrode.

☐ Supply voltages are indicated by repeating the associated device electrode subscript, it which case, the reference terminal is then designated by the third subscript; note the cases V_{EE}, V_{CC}, V_{EEB}, V_{CCB}.

☐ In devices having more than one terminal of the same type (say two bases), the terminal subscripts are modified by adding a number following the subscript and placed on the same line, for example, V_{B1-B2}.

☐ In multiple-unit devices the terminal subscripts are modified by a number preceding the electrode subscript; note the example V_{1B-2B}.

Signal And Rectifier Diodes

PRV	Peak Reverse Voltage
I_o	Average Rectifier Forward Current
I_r	Average Reverse Current
I_{surge}	Peak Surge Current
V_F	Average Forward Voltage Drop
V_R	DC Blocking Voltage

Zener Diodes

I_F	Forward current
I_Z	Zener current
I_{ZK}	Zener current near breakdown knee
I_{ZM}	Maximum dc zener current (limited by power dissipation)
I_{ZT}	Zener test current
V_f	Forward voltage
V_Z	Nominal zener voltage
Z_Z	Zener impedance
Z_{ZK}	Zener impedance near breakdown knee
Z_{ZT}	Zener impedance at zener test current
I_R	Reverse current
V_R	Reverse test voltage

Transistors

A_G	Available gain
A_P	Power gain

A_I	Current gain
B or b	Base electrode
BV_{BCO}	DC base-to-collector breakdown voltage, base reverse-biased with respect to collector, emitter open.
BV_{BEO}	DC base-to-emitter breakdown voltage, base reverse-biased with respect to emitter, collector open.
BV_{CBO}	DC collector-to-base breakdown voltage, collector reverse-biased with respect to base, emitter open.
BV_{CEO}	DC collector-to-emitter breakdown voltage, collector reverse-biased with respect to emitter, base open.
BV_{EBO}	DC emitter-to-base breakdown voltage, emitter reverse-biased with respect to base, collector open.
BV_{ECO}	DC emitter-to-collector breakdown voltage, emitter reverse-biased with respect to collector, base open.
C or c	Collector electrode
C_c	Collector junction capacitance
C_e	Emitter junction capacitance
C_{ib}, C_{ic}, C_{ie}.	Input capacitance for common base, collector, and emitter respectively.
C_{ob}, C_{oc}, C_{oe}.	Output terminal capacitance, ac input open, for common base, collector and emitter, respectively.
D	Distortion
E or e	Emitter electrode
f_{ab}, f_{ac}, f_{ae}.	Alpha cutoff frequency for common base, collector, and emitter, respectively.
f_{co}	Cutoff frequency
f_{max}	Maximum frequency of oscillation
GC(CB), GC(CC), GE(CE).	Grounded (or common) base, collector, and emitter, respectively.
G_b, G_c, G_e	Power gain for common base, collector, and emitter, respectively.
h	Hybrid parameter

h_{fe}, h_{fb}, h_{fc}.	Small signal forward current transfer ratio, ac output shorted, common emitter, common base, common collector, respectively.
h_{ib}	Small-signal input impedance, ac output shorted, common base.
h_{ob}	Small-signal output admittance, ac input open, common base.
I	Direct current (dc).
I_B, I_C I_E	DC current for base, collector, and emitter, respectively.
I_{CBO}	DC collector current, collector reverse-biased with respect to base, emitter-to-base open.
I_{CES}	DC collector current, collector reverse-biased with respect to emitter, base shorted to emitter.
I_{EBO}	DC emitter current, emitter reverse-biased with respect to base, collector-to-base open.
NF	Noise Figure
P_D	Total average power dissipation of all electrodes of a semiconductor device.
P_G	Power gain
P_{Go}	Over-all power gain
P_{in}	Input power
P_{out}	Output power
$r'b$	Equivalent base resistance, high frequencies
T_j	Junction temperature
T_{stg}	Storage temperature
t_f	Fall time, from 90 percent to 10 percent of pulse (switching applications).
t_r	Rise time, from 10 percent to 90 percent pulse (switching applications).
t_s	Storage time (switching applications).
V_{EB}	Base-to-emitter dc voltage
V_{CE}	Collector-to-base dc voltage
V_{CE}	Collector-to-emitter dc voltage
V_{CEO}	DC collector-to-emitter voltage with collector junction reverse-biased, zero base current.
V_{CER}	Similar to V_{CEO}, except with a resistor (of value R) between base and emitter.
V_{CES}	Similar to V_{CEO}, except with base shorted to emitter.

V_{CEV}	DC collector-to-emitter voltage, used when only voltage bias is used.
V_{CEX}	DC collector-to-emitter voltage, base-emitter back biased.
V_{EB}	Emitter-to-base dc voltage.
V_{pt}	Punch-through voltage

Field Effect Transistors

I_D	Drain current
I_{DGO}	Maximum leakage from drain to gate with source open
I_{DSS}	Drain current with gate connected to source
I_G	Gate current
I_{GSS}	Maximum gate current (leakage) with drain connected to source
$V_{(BR)DGO}$	Drain to gate, source open
V_D	DC drain voltage
$V_{(BR)DGS}$	Drain to gate, source connected to drain
$V_{(BR)DS}$	Drain to source, gate connection not specified
$V_{BR)DSX}$	Drain to source, gate biased to cutoff or beyond
$V_{(BR)GS}$	Gate to source, drain connection not specified
$V_{(BR)GSS}$	Gate to source, drain connected to source
$V_{(BR)GD}$	Gate to drain, source connection not specified
$V_{(BR)GDS}$	Gate to drain, source connected to drain
V_G	DC gate voltage
$V_{G1S(OFF)}$	Gate 1-source cutoff voltage (with gate 2 connected to source)
$V_{G2S(OFF)}$	Gate 2-source cutoff voltage (with gate 1 connected to source)
$V_{GS(OFF)}$	Cutoff.

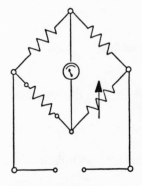

Appendix B
Electron Tube
Letter Symbols

A number of letter symbols which are used as a form of shorthand notation in technical literature when designating electron-tube operating conditions are explained and listed below.

☐ Maximum, average, and root-mean-square values are represented by capital (upper case) letters, for example: I, E, P.

☐ Where needed to distinguish between values in item 1 above, the maximum value may be represented by the subscript "m", for example: E_m, I_m, P_m.

☐ Average values may be represented by the subscript "av", for example: E_{av}, I_{av}, P_{av}. (When items 2 and 3 above are used, then item 1 indicates r-m-s, or effective, values).

☐ Instantaneous values of current, voltage, and power which vary with time are represented by the small (lower case) letter of the proper symbol, for example: i, e, p.

☐ External resistance, impedance, etc. in the circuit external to an electron tube electrode may be represented by the upper case symbol with the proper electrode subscript, for example: R_g, R_{sc}, Z_g, Z_{sc}.

☐ Values of resistance, impedance, etc. inherent within the electron tube are represented by the lower case symbol with the proper electrode subscript, for example: r_g, Z_g, r_p, Z_p, C_{gp}.

☐ The symbols "g" and "p" are used as subscripts to identify ac values of electrode currents and voltages, for example: e_g, e_p, i_g, i_p.

☐ The total instantaneous values of electrode currents and voltages (dc plus ac components) are indicated by the lower case symbol and the subscripts "b" for plate and "c" for grid, for example: i_b, e_c, i_c, e_b.

☐ No-signal or static currents and voltages are indicated by upper case symbol and lower case subscripts "b" for plate and "c" for grid, for example: E_c, I_b, E_b, I_c.

☐ R.m.s. and maximum values of a varying component are indicated by the upper case letter and the subscripts "g" and "p", for example: E_g, I_p, E_p, I_g.

☐ Average values of current and voltage for the with-signal condition are indicated by adding the subscript "s" to the proper symbol and subscript, for example: I_{bs}, E_{bs}.

☐ Supply voltages are indicated by the upper case symbol and double subscript "bb" for plate, "cc" for grid, "ff" for filament, for example: E_{ff}, E_{cc}, E_{bb}.

An alphabetical list of electron tube symbols follows for easy reference.

C_{gk}	Grid-cathode capacitance
C_{gp}	Grid-plate capacitance
C_{pk}	Plate-cathode capacitance
E_b	Plate voltage, dc value
E_c	Grid voltage, dc value
E_{cc}	Grid bias supply voltage
E_{co}	Negative tube cutoff voltage
E_f	Filament voltage
E_{ff}	Filament supply voltage
E_k	dc cathode voltage
e_b	Instantaneous plate voltage
e_c	Instantaneous grid voltage
e_g	ac component of grid voltage
e_p	ac component of plate voltage
I_b, I_o	dc plate current
I_c	dc grid current
I_f	Filament current
I_k	Cathode current
i_b	Instantaneous plate current
i_c	Instantaneous grid current
i_g	ac component of grid current
i_p	ac component of plate current
P_g	Grid dissipation power
P_o	Output power

P_p	Plate dissipation power
R_g	Grid resistance
R_L	Load resistance
R_k	Cathode resistance
R_p	Plate resistance, dc
R_{sc}	Screen resistance
r_L	ac load resistance
r_p	Plate resistance, ac
t_k	Cathode heating time

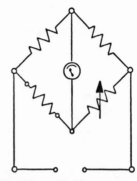

Appendix C
FCC Information

ELEMENTS OF A REMOTE-CONTROL AM STATION

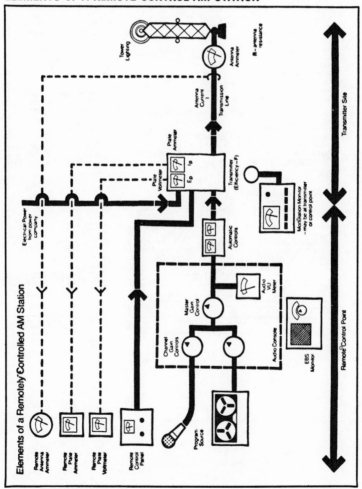

AM STATION LICENSE

FCC Form 352

UNITED STATES OF AMERICA
FEDERAL COMMUNICATIONS COMMISSION

File No.: BL-13,040

Call Sign: W S L W

STANDARD BROADCAST STATION LICENSE

Subject to the provisions of the Communications Act of 1934, subsequent Acts, and Treaties, and Commission Rules made thereunder, and further subject to conditions set forth in this license, the LICENSEE

REGIONAL RADIO, INC.

is hereby authorized to use and operate the radio transmitting apparatus hereinafter described for the purpose of broadcasting for the term ending 3 a.m. Local Time **October 1, 1972**

The licensee shall use and operate said apparatus only in accordance with the following terms:

1. On a frequency of **1310** kHz.

2. With nominal power of **—** watts nighttime and **5 kilo** watts daytime,

with antenna input power of **—** watts — directional
antenna nighttime .... [current — amperes / resistance — ohms]

and antenna input power of **5 kilo** watts non-directional
antenna daytime .... antenna [current 8.90 amperes / resistance 63.0 ohms]

3. Hours of operation: **Daytime as follows:**
Jan. 7:30am to 5:30pm; Feb. 7:15am to 6:00pm;
Mar. 6:30am to 6:30pm; Apr. 5:45am to 7:00pm;
May 5:15am to 7:30pm; June 5:00am to 7:45pm;
July 5:15am to 7:45pm; Aug. 5:30am to 7:15pm;
Sep. 6:00am to 6:30pm; Oct. 6:30am to 5:45pm;
Nov. 7:00am to 5:15pm; Dec. 7:30am to 5:00pm;
Eastern Standard Time (non-advanced)

Transmitter may be operated by remote control from 73 East Main Street, White Sulphur Springs, West Virginia

4. With the station located at: **White Sulphur Springs, West Virginia**

5. With the main studio located at:
73 East Main Street
White Sulphur Springs, West Virginia

6. The apparatus herein authorized to be used and operated is located at:
Rural area 0.75 mi. North of
White Sulphur Springs, West Virginia

North Latitude: 37° 48' 34.5"
West Longitude: 80° 17' 59"

7. Transmitter(s): **BAUER, FB-5V**

(or other transmitter currently listed in the Commission's "Radio Equipment List, Part B, Aural Broadcast Equipment" for the power herein authorized). **

8. Obstruction marking specifications in accordance with the following paragraphs of FCC Form 715: **1, 3, 11, and 21**

9. Conditions:
ANTENNA: 190' (193' overall height) uniform cross section, guyed, series excited vertical radiator. Ground system consists of 120 equally spaced, buried copper radials 106 to 190 feet in length plus 120 interspaced radials 50 to 106 feet in length.

The Commission reserves the right during said license period of terminating this license or making effective any changes or modification of this license which may be necessary to comply with any decision of the Commission rendered as a result of any hearing held under the rules of the Commission prior to the commencement of this license period or any decision rendered as a result of any such hearing which has been designated but not held, prior to the commencement of this license period.

This license is issued on the licensee's representation that the statements contained in licensee's application are true and that the undertakings therein contained so far as they are consistent herewith, will be carried out in good faith. The licensee shall, during the term of this license, render such broadcasting service as will serve public interest, convenience, or necessity to the full extent of the privileges herein conferred.

This license shall not vest in the licensee any right to operate the station nor any right in the use of the frequency designated in the license beyond the term hereof, nor in any other manner than authorized herein. Neither the license nor the right granted hereunder shall be assigned or otherwise transferred in violation of the Communications Act of 1934. This license is subject to the right of use or control by the Government of the United States conferred by Section 606 of the Communications Act of 1934.

1/ This license consists of this page and pages **—**

Dated: **NOVEMBER 4, 1971**

FEDERAL
COMMUNICATIONS
COMMISSION

300

ELEMENTS OF DIRECTIONAL AM STATION

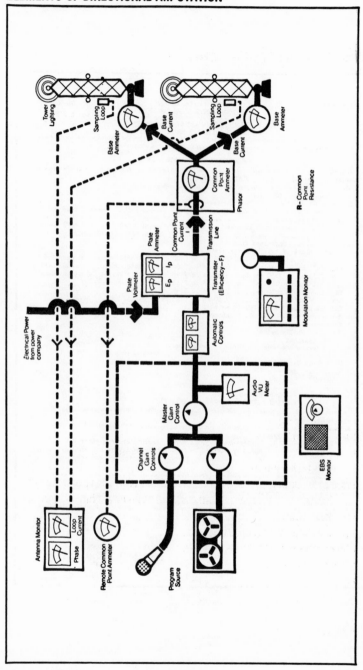

DIRECTIONAL AM STATION LICENSE

FCC Form 352

UNITED STATES OF AMERICA
FEDERAL COMMUNICATIONS COMMISSION

File No.: BR-989

Call Sign: K X X O

STANDARD BROADCAST STATION LICENSE
MAIN AND AUXILIARY TRANSMITTERS

Subject to the provisions of the Communications Act of 1934, subsequent Acts, and Treaties, and Commission Rules made thereunder, and further subject to conditions set forth in this license, the LICENSEE

SAN ANTONIO BROADCASTING, INC.

is hereby authorized to use and operate the radio transmitting apparatus hereinafter described for the purpose of broadcasting for the term ending 5 a.m. Local Time **JUNE 1, 1977**

The licensee shall use and operate said apparatus only in accordance with the following terms:

1. On a frequency of **1300** kHz.

2. With nominal power of **1 kilo** watts nighttime and **5 kilo** watts daytime,
   with antenna input power of **1.08 kilo** watts — directional [Common Point   current   **3.93** amperes
   antenna nighttime .... [Common Point   resistance **70**   ohms,
   and antenna input power of **5.4 kilo** watts — directional [Common Point   current   **8.79** amperes
   antenna daytime .... [Common Point   resistance **70** ohms

3. Hours of operation: **Unlimited Time.**
   Average hours of sunrise and sunset:
   Jan. 7:30 am to 5:30 pm; Feb. 7:15 am to 6:00 pm;   Transmitters may be operated by
   Mar. 6:30 am to 6:30 pm; Apr. 6:00 am to 7:00 pm;   remote control from 2805 East
   May 5:15 am to 7:30 pm; June 5:00 am to 7:45 pm;   Skelly Drive, Tulsa, Oklahoma.
   July 5:15 am to 7:45 pm; Aug. 5:45 am to 7:15 pm;
   Sep. 6:00 am to 6:30 pm; Oct. 6:30 am to 5:45 pm;
   Nov. 7:00 am to 5:15 pm; Dec. 7:30 am to 5:15 pm;
   Central Standard Time (Non-Advanced).

4. With the station located at: **Tulsa, Oklahoma**

5. With the main studio located at:
   2805 East Skelly Drive
   Tulsa, Oklahoma

6. The apparatus herein authorized to be used and operated is located at: North Latitude: **36° 02' 19"**
   West Longitude: **95° 56' 07"**

   8601 South Harvard
   Tulsa Oklahoma

7. Transmitter(s): COLLINS, 820E-1 (Main)
   WESTERN ELECTRIC, 405-B2 (Auxiliary)
   (or other transmitter currently listed in the Commission's "Radio Equipment List, Part B, Aural Broadcast Equipment" for the power herein authorized).

8. Obstruction marking specifications in accordance with the following paragraphs of FCC Form 715: **

9. Conditions: (See Page 1A.)
   **Towers 1, 2, & 4:   Paragraphs 1, 3, 12 & 21.   Beacons and all obstruction lights
         shall be flashed, with flashing of towers synchronized so that
         at any instant two towers are lighted and one tower is not.
      Tower 3:   Paragraph 1.

The Commission reserves the right during said license period of terminating this license or making effective any changes or modifications of this license which may be necessary to comply with any decision of the Commission rendered as a result of any hearing held under the rules of the Commission prior to the commencement of this license period or any decision rendered as a result of any such hearing which has been designated but not held, prior to the commencement of this license period.

This license is issued on the licensee's representation that the statements contained in licensee's application are true and that the undertakings therein contained so far as they are consistent herewith, will be carried out in good faith. The licensee shall, during the term of this license, render such broadcasting service as will serve public interest, convenience, or necessity to the full extent of the privileges herein conferred.

This license shall not vest in the licensee any right to operate the station nor any right in the use of the frequency designated in the license beyond the term hereof, nor in any other manner than authorized herein. Neither the license nor the right granted hereunder shall be assigned or otherwise transferred in violation of the Communications Act of 1934. This license is subject to the right of use or control by the Government of the United States conferred by Section 606 of the Communications Act of 1934.

1/ This license consists of this page and pages **1a, 2, 3, & 4.**

Dated: **DECEMBER 17, 1975**

FEDERAL
COMMUNICATIONS
COMMISSION

File No. BR-989   Call Sign: K X X O

Date: 12-17-75
DA- 2

1. DESCRIPTION OF DIRECTIONAL ANTENNA SYSTEM

No. and Type of Elements: Four, triangular cross-section, guyed, series-excited vertical towers. Two towers used daytime, three used nighttime. A communications type antenna is side-mounted near the top of the W (No. 4) tower.

Height above Insulators: 284' (135°)

Overall Height: 288' (Towers 1 and 3); 290' (Tower 4); 289' (Tower 2)

Spacing Orientation: West to West Center Tower, 273.5' (130°) - Day;
West to East Center Tower, 547' (26C°)
East Center to East Tower, 547' (260°) - Night
Line of towers bears 72° true.

Non-Directional Antenna: None used.

Ground System consists of   240 - 43' buried copper wire radials equally spaced about each tower; 120 - 43' to 284' buried copper wire radials alternately spaced. All radials bonded together by a copper wire at a radius of 43' from each tower. Copper strap between transmitter ground and bond straps at each tower.

2. THEORETICAL SPECIFICATIONS

		E(No.1)	EC(No.2)	WC(No.3)	W(No.4)
Phasing:	Night	0°	-9.44°	-	C°
	Day	-	-	0°	-52°
Field Ratio:	Night	0.85	1.36	-	0.65
	Day	-	-	1.0	C.80

3. OPERATING SPECIFICATIONS

		E(No.1)	EC(No.2)	WC(No.3)	W(No.4)
Phase Indication:*	Night	17°	0°	-	8°
	Day	-	-	0°	57°
Antenna Base Current Ratio:	Night	0.608	1.0	-	0.473
	Day	-	-	1.0	0.818
Antenna Monitor Sample Current Ratio:	Night	56	1C0	-	40
	Day	-	-	100	80

*As indicated by Potomac Instruments Antenna Monitor.   PM-112

ELEMENTS OF AN FM STATION

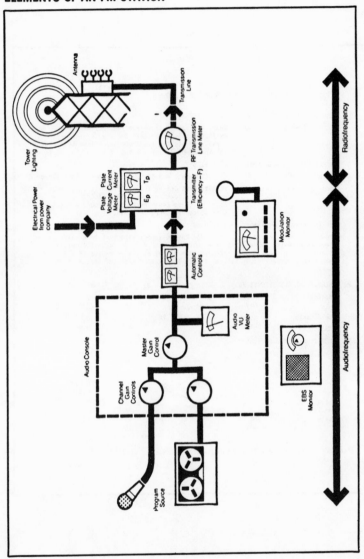

FM STATION LICENSE

FCC Form 352-A

United States of America
FEDERAL COMMUNICATIONS COMMISSION

File No. **BRH-2019**

Call Sign: **W F Y N-FM**

FM BROADCAST STATION LICENSE

Subject to the provisions of the Communications Act of 1934, as amended, treaties, and Commission Rules, and further subject to conditions set forth in this license, the LICENSEE

FLORIDA KEYS BROADCASTING CORPORATION

is hereby authorized to use and operate the radio transmitting apparatus hereinafter described for the purpose of broadcasting for the term ending 3 a.m. Local Time: **FEBRUARY 1, 1979**

The licensee shall use and operate said apparatus only in accordance with the following terms:

1. Frequency (MHz) . . . . : 92.5
2. Transmitter output power . . . . : 10 kilowatts
3. Effective radiated power . . . . : 25 kilowatts (Horiz.) & 23.5 kilowatts (Vert.)
4. Antenna height above
   average terrain (feet) . . . . : 135' (Horiz.) & 130' (Vert.)
5. Hours of operation . . . . : Unlimited
6. Station location . . . . : Key West, Florida
7. Main studio location . . . . . . :
   Fifth Avenue Stock Island
   Key West, Florida
8. Remote Control point . . . . . . :

9. Antenna & supporting structure: North Latitude: 24° 34' 01"
   West Longitude: 81° 44' 54"
   ANTENNA: COLLINS, 37M-5/300-C-5, Five-sections (Horiz. & Vert.), FM antenna side-mounted near the top of the north tower of WKIZ(AM) directional array. Overall height above ground 155 feet.
10. Transmitter location . . . . . . :
    Fifth Avenue Stock Island
    Key West, Florida

11. Transmitter(s) . . . . : COLLINS, 830-F-1A

12. Obstruction markings specifications in accordance with the following paragraphs of FCC Form 715: 1, 3, 11 & 21.
13. Conditions:

The Commission reserves the right during said license period of terminating this license or making effective any changes or modification of this license which may be necessary to comply with any decision of the Commission rendered as a result of any hearing held under the rules of the Commission prior to the commencement of this license period or any decision rendered as a result of any such hearing which has been designated but not held, prior to the commencement of this license period.

This license is issued on the licensee's representation that the statements contained in licensee's application are true and that the undertakings therein contained so far as they are consistent herewith, will be carried out in good faith. The licensee shall, during the term of this license, render such broadcasting service as will serve public interest, convenience, or necessity to the full extent of the privileges herein conferred.

This license shall not vest in the licensee any right to operate the station nor any right in the use of the frequency designated in the license beyond the term hereof, nor in any other manner than authorized herein. Neither the license nor the right granted hereunder shall be assigned or otherwise transferred in violation of the Communications Act of 1934. This license is subject to the right of use or control by the Government of the United States conferred by section 606 of the Communications Act of 1934.

This license consists of this page and pages —

Dated: **JANUARY 28, 1976**

FEDERAL
COMMUNICATIONS
COMMISSION

FCC EMISSION DESIGNATIONS

The first symbol of each emission designation indicates the type of modulation, the second symbol shows the type of transmisison, and the third symbol (if any) reveals the supplementary characteristics. For example, A3H means:

    A—amplitude modulation (type of modulation)
    3—telephony (type of transmission)
    H—single sideband, full carrier (supplementary characteristics)

Symbols for types of modulation

Amplitude	A
Frequency (or phase)	F
Pulse	P

Symbols for types of transmission

Absence of any modulation intended to carry information	0
Telegraphy without the use of modulating AF tone	1
Telegraphy by on-off keying of a modulating AF, or by the on-off keying of the modulated emission	2
Telephony (including sound broadcasting)	3
Facsimile (with modulation of main carrier either directly or by a frequency modulated sub-carrier)	4
Television (visual only)	5
Double sideband	(None)

Single sideband

Reduced carrier	A
Full carrier	H
Suppressed carrier	J
Two independent sidebands	B
Vestigial sideband	C

Pulse:

Amplitude modulated	D
Width (or duration) modulated	E
Phase (or position) modulated	F
Code modulated	G

FCC TOLERANCES AND STANDARDS
Carrier frequency

Standard AM broadcast stations ....±20 Hz
Commercial FM broadcast stations..±2 kHz
Television broadcast stations—aural and visual transmitters.......±1 kHz
Non-commercial educational FM broadcast stations:
    (1) Licensed for power of more than 10 watts..................±2 kHz
    (2) Licensed for power of 10 watts or less......................±3 kHz
Studio transmitter link (STL) 0.005%
International broadcast stations 0.0015%

Public Safety Radio Services
Frequency range

MHz	All fixed and base stations	All mobile stations	
		Over 3 W	3 W or less
	Percent	Percent	Percent
Below 25	0.01	0.01	0.02
25 to 50	.002	.002	.005
50 to 450[1]	.0005	.0005	.005
450 to 470[2,3]	.00025	.0005	.0005
470 to 512	.00025	.0005	.0005
806 to 820	.00015	.00025	.00025
351 to 888	.00015	.00025	.00025
250 to 1,427[2]			
1,427 to 1,435[4]	.03	.03	.03
Above 1,435[2]			

307

(1)Stations authorized for operation on or before Dec. 1, 1961, in the frequency band 73.0 – 74.6 MHz may operate with a frequency tolerance of 0.005 percent.

(2)Radiolocation equipment using pulse modulation shall meet the following frequency tolerance: the frequency at which maximum emission occurs shall be within the authorized frequency band and shall not be closer than $1.5/T$ MHz to the upper and lower limits of the authorized frequency band where T is the pulse duration in microseconds. For other radiolocation equipment, tolerances will be specified in the station authorization.

(3)Operational fixed stations controlling mobile relay stations, through use of the associated mobile frequency, may operate with a frequency tolerance of 0.0005 percent.

(4)For fixed stations with power above 200 watts, the frequency tolerance is 0.01 percent if the necessary bandwidth of the emission does not exceed 3 kHz. For fixed station transmitters with a power of 200 watts or less and using time division multiplex, the frequency tolerance can be increased to 0.05 percent.

Power

Transmitters of standard AM and FM commercial broadcast stations..10% below and
5% above

Aural and visual transmitters of TV broadcast stations..20% below and
10% above

Current

All currents..5%

Modulation—Standard AM Broadcast

Minimum modulation on *average modulation peaks* 85%
Maximum modulation on *positive modulation peaks* 125%
Maximum modulation on *negative modulation peaks* 100%
Maximum carrier shift allowed 5%

Temperature for Master-Oscillator Crystals

X-cut and Y-cut crystals... ±0.1° C
Low temperature-coefficient crystals .... ±1.0° C

Final RF stage: Plate Voltage and Plate Current Meters

Accuracy at full-scale reading..2%
Maximum permissible full-scale reading: 5 times minimum normal reading

Meters: Recording Antenna Current

Accuracy at full-scale reading...**2%**

Maximum permissible full-scale reading for the scale of current-squared meters ....3 times minimum normal reading

Portion of scale used for accuracy with current-squared meters ....Upper two-thirds

FCC STANDARDS

Standard AM Broadcast

Band ....535–1605 kHz

Channel width...10 kHz

FM Commercial Broadcast

Band ....88–108 MHz

Channel width ....200 kHz

Transmitted AF range (main channel)..........................50 to 15000 Hz

100% modulation (deviation ratio = 5).........................±75 kHz swing

Time constant for pre-emphasis and de-emphasis..........75 microseconds

Television Broadcast

Bands

     Channels 2 through 4..54 to 72 MHZ

     Channels 5 and 6 ....76 to 88 MHz

     Channels 7 through 13 ....174 to 216 MHz

     Channels 14 through 83.......................................470 to 890 MHz

Channel width..6 MHz

Field frequency...60 Hz

Frame frequency..30 Hz

Lines per frame...525

Horizontal scanning frequency...15750 Hz

Aspect ratio...4 to 3

Visual bandwidth ....4.9 MHz

Frequency separation between aural carrier frequency and channel upper limit...0.25 MHz

Frequency separation between visual carrier frequency (below) and aural carrier frequency...4.5 MHz

Frequency separation between visual carrier frequency (below) and chrominance sub-carrier frequency ....3.579545 MHz ±10 Hz

Reference white level...................12.5% of peak carrier level (±2.5%)

Reference black level................................70% of peak carrier level

Blanking level in a monochrome TV signal........................75% of peak carrier level (±2.5%)

100% modulation for the aural FM transmission............±25 kHz swing

Transmitted AF range (main channel) ....50 Hz to 15 kHz
Deviation ratio..1.667

Public Safety Radio Services

Maximum audio frequency..3 kHz
A1 emission—maximum bandwifth.....................................0.25 kHz
A3 emission—maximum bandwidth ....8 kHz
Minimum modulation on average modulation peaks 70%
Maximum modulation on negative modulation peaks....................100%

F3 emission

Frequency band (MHz)	Authorized bandwidth (kHz)	Frequency deviation (kHz)
25 to 50	20	5
50 to 150	*20	*5
150 to 450	20	5
450 to 470	20	5
470 to 512	20	5
806 to 821	20	5
831 to 866	20	5

In each frequency band the deviation ratio is 1.667

*Stations authorized for operation on or before Dec. 1, 1961, in the frequency band 73.0–74.6 MHz may continue to operate with a bandwidth of 40 kHz and a deviation of 15 kHz.

Harmonic Attenuation

The mean power of emissions shall be attenuated below the mean power output of the transmitter in accordance with the following schedule:

(1) On any frequency removed from the assigned frequency by more than 50% up to and including 100% of the authorized bandwidth: at least 25 decibels.

(2) On any frequency removed from the assigned frequency by more than 250% of the authorized bandwidth: at least 35 decibels.

(3) On any frequency removed from the assigned frequency by more than 250 percent of the authorized bandwidth: at least 43 plus 10 log (mean output power in watts) decibels or 80 decibels, whichever is the lesser attenuation.

Index

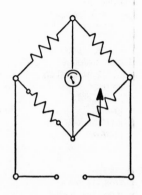

Index

313

Edited by Roland Phelps